THE
JUNIOR CLASSICS

SELECTED AND ARRANGED BY
WILLIAM PATTEN
MANAGING EDITOR OF THE HARVARD CLASSICS

INTRODUCTION BY
CHARLES W. ELIOT, LL.D.
PRESIDENT EMERITUS OF HARVARD UNIVERSITY

WITH A READING GUIDE BY
WILLIAM ALLAN NEILSON, Ph.D.
PROFESSOR OF ENGLISH, HARVARD UNIVERSITY
PRESIDENT SMITH COLLEGE, NORTHAMPTON, MASS., SINCE 1917

VOLUME SEVEN

Stories of Courage and Heroism

P. F. COLLIER & SON CORPORATION
NEW YORK

CONTENTS

CONTENTS

CONTENTS

CONTENTS

5

ILLUSTRATIONS

ILLUSTRATIONS

8

PREFACE

PREFACE

The stories in this volume are true stories, and
have been arranged in chronological order, an
arrangement that will aid the reader to remember
the times to which the stories relate.

Almost any encyclopedia can be consulted for
general details of the life stories of the interesting
people whose names crowd the volume except perhaps in the cases of Peter Williamson and John
Tanner, "The True Story of a Kidnapped Boy,"
and "A White Boy Among the Indians." Peter
Williamson was kidnapped in Glascow, Scotland,
when he was eight years old, was captured by the
Cherokee Indians in 1745, and (though the story
does not tell this) he returned to England and became a prominent citizen. He first made the British Government pay damages for his kidnapping,
gave the first exhibition in England of Indian war
dances, and was the first Englishman to publish a
street directory. He was finally pensioned by the
Government for his services in establishing a penny
post.

John Tanner, the son of a clergyman, was stolen
by the Indians some years later. His mother died
when he was very young, his father treated him
harshly, and so when the Indians kidnapped him
he made no effort to escape. John remained among
them until he was an old man, and the story of his

PREFACE

life, which he was obliged to dictate to others as he could neither read nor write, was first published about 1830. The stories of these boys are considered to be two of the most reliable early accounts we possess of life among the Indians.

Acknowledgment for permission to include several stories included in this volume is made in Volume X.

WILLIAM PATTEN.

HOW PHIDIAS HELPED THE IMAGE-MAKER

By Beatrice Harraden

DURING the time when Pericles was at the head of the state at Athens he spared no pains and no money to make the city beautiful. He himself was a lover and patron of the arts, and he was determined that Athens should become the very center of art and refinement, and that she should have splendid public buildings and splendid sculptures and paintings. So he gathered round him all the great sculptors and painters, and set them to work to carry out his ambitious plans; and some of you know that the "Age of Pericles" is still spoken of as an age in which art advanced towards and attained to a marvellous perfection.

On the Acropolis, or Citadel of Athens, rose the magnificent Temple of Athena, called the Parthenon, built under the direction of Phidias, the most celebrated sculptor of that time, who adorned it with many of his works, and especially with the huge statue of Athena in ivory, forty-seven feet in height. The Acropolis was also enriched with another figure of Athena in bronze—also the work of Phidias.

The statue was called the "Athena Promachus"; that is "The Defender." If you turn to your Grecian History you will find a full description of the

11

PHIDIAS

Parthenon and the other temples of the gods and heroes and guardian deities of the city. But I want to tell you something about Phidias himself, and little Iris, an image-maker's daughter.

It was in the year 450 B.C., in the early summer, and Phidias, who had been working all the day, strolled quietly along the streets of Athens.

As he passed by the Agora (or market-place), he chanced to look up, and he saw a young girl of about thirteen years sitting near him. Her face was of the purest beauty; her head was gracefully poised on her shoulders; her expression was sadness itself. She looked poor and in distress. She came forward and begged for help; and there was something in her manner, as well as in her face, which made Phidias pause and listen to her.

"My father lies ill," she said plaintively, "and he cannot do his work, and so we can get no food: nothing to make him well and strong again. If I could only do his work for him I should not mind; and then I should not beg. He does not know I came out to beg—he would never forgive me; but I could not bear to see him lying there without food."

"And who is your father?" asked Phidias kindly.

"His name is Aristæus," she said, "and he is a maker of images—little clay figures of gods and goddesses and heroes. Indeed, he is clever; and I am sure you would praise the 'Hercules' he finished before he was taken ill."

"Take me to your home," Phidias said to the girl; as they passed on together he asked her many questions about the image-maker. She was proud

12

of her father; and Phidias smiled to himself when he heard her speak of this father as though he were the greatest sculptor in Athens. He liked to hear her speak so enthusiastically.

"Is it not wonderful," she said, "to take the clay and work it into forms? Not everyone could do that—could you do it?"

Phidias laughed.

"Perhaps not so well as your father," he answered kindly. "Still, I can do it."

A sudden thought struck Iris.

"Perhaps you would help father?" she said eagerly. "Ah! but I ought not to have said that."

"Perhaps I can help him," replied Phidias good-naturedly. "Anyway, take me to him."

She led him through some side streets into the poorest parts of the city, and stopped before a little window, where a few roughly-wrought images and vases were exposed to view. She beckoned to him to follow her, and opening the door, crept gently into a room which served as their workshop and dwelling-place. Phidias saw a man stretched out on a couch at the farther end of the room, near a bench where many images and pots of all sorts lay unfinished.

"This is our home," whispered Iris proudly, "and that is my father yonder."

The image-maker looked up and called for Iris.

"I am so faint, child," he murmured. "If I could only become strong again I could get back to my work. It is so hard to lie here and die."

Phidias bent over him.

"You shall not die," he said, "if money can do

13

you any good. I met your little daughter, and she told me that you were an image-maker; and that interested me, because, I, too, can make images, though perhaps not as well as you. Still, I thought I should like to come and see you and help you; and if you will let me, I will try and make a few images for you, so that your daughter may go out and sell them, and bring you home money. And meanwhile, she shall fetch you some food to nourish you."

Then he turned to Iris, and putting some coins into her hands bade her go out and bring what she thought fit. She did not know how to thank him, but hurried away on her glad errand, and Phidias talked kindly to his fellow-worker, and then, throwing aside his cloak, sat down at the bench and busied himself with modelling the clay.

It was so different from his ordinary work that he could not help smiling.

"This is rather easier," he thought to himself, "than carving from the marble a statue of Athena. What a strange occupation!" Nevertheless, he was so interested in modelling the quaint little images that he did not perceive that Iris had returned, until he looked up, and saw her standing near him, watching him with wonder, which she could not conceal.

"Oh, how clever!" she cried. "Father, if you could only see what he is doing!"

"Nay, child," said the sculptor, laughing; "get your father his food, and leave me to my work. I am going to model a little image of the goddess Athena, for I think the folk will like to buy that,

14

since that rogue Phidias has set up his statue of her in the Parthenon."

"Phidias, the prince of sculptors!" said the image-maker. "May the gods preserve his life; for he is the greatest glory of all Athens."

"Ay," said Iris, as she prepared her father's food, "that is what we call him—the greatest glory of all Athens."

"We think of him," said Aristæus, feebly, "and that helps us in our work. Yes, it helps even us poor image-makers. When I saw the beautiful Athena I came home cheered and encouraged. May Phidias be watched over and blessed all his life!"

The tears came into the eyes of Phidias as he bent over his work; it was a pleasure to him to think that his fame gained for him a resting-place of love and gratitude in the hearts of the poorest citizens of Athens. He valued this tribute of the image-maker far more than the praises of the rich and great. Before he left, he saw that both father and daughter were much refreshed by the food which his bounty had given to them, and he bade Aristæus be of good cheer, because he would surely regain his health and strength.

"And because you love your art," he said, "I shall be a friend to you and help you. And I shall come again to-morrow and do some work for you—that is to say, if you approve of what I have already done, and then Iris will be able to go out and sell the figures."

He hastened away before they were able to thank him, and he left them wondering who this new friend could be. They talked of him for a long time, of his kindness and his skill; and Aristæus dreamt that night about the stranger who had come to work for him.

The next day Phidias came again, and took his place at the image-maker's bench, just as if he were always accustomed to sit there. Aristæus, who was better, watched him curiously, but asked no questions.

But Iris said to him: "My father and I talk of you, and wonder who you are."

Phidias laughed.

"Perhaps I shall tell you some day," he answered. "There, child, what do you think of that little vase? When it is baked it will be a pretty thing."

As the days went on, the image-maker recovered his strength; and meanwhile Phidias had filled the little shop with dainty-wrought images and graceful vases, such as had never been seen there before.

One evening, when Aristæus was leaning against Iris, and admiring the stranger's work, the door opened and Phidias came in.

"What, friend," he said cheerily, "you are better to-night I see!"

"Last night," said Aristæus, "I dreamt that the friend who held out a brother's hand to me and helped me in my trouble was the great Phidias himself. It did not seem wonderful to me, for only the great do such things as you have done for me. You must be great."

"I do not know about that," said the sculptor, smiling, "and after all, I have not done so much for you. I have only helped a brother-workman;

for I am an image-maker too—and my name is Phidias."

Then Aristæus bent down and reverently kissed the great sculptor's hands.

"I cannot find words with which to thank you," he murmured, "but I shall pray to the gods night and day that they will for ever bless Phidias, and keep his fame pure, and his hands strong to fashion forms of beauty. And this I know well: that he will always have a resting-place of love and gratitude in the poor image-maker's heart."

And Phidias went on his way, tenfold richer and happier for the image-maker's words. For there is something lovelier than fame and wealth, my children; it is the opportunity of giving the best of one's self and the best of one's powers to aid those of our fellow-workers who need our active help.

THE FIGHT AT THE PASS OF THERMOPYLÆ

By Charlotte M. Yonge

THERE was trembling in Greece. "The Great King," as the Greeks called Xerxes, the chief ruler of the East, was marshaling his forces against the little free states that nestled amid the rocks and gulfs of the Eastern Mediterranean—the whole of which together would hardly equal one province of the huge Asiatic realm! Moreover, it was a war not only on the men but on their gods. The Persians were zealous adorers of the sun and the fire, they

17

abhorred the idol-worship of the Greeks, and defiled and plundered every temple that fell in their way. Death and desolation were almost the best that could be looked for at such hands—slavery and torture from cruelly barbarous masters would only too surely be the lot of numbers, should their land fall a prey to the conquerors.

The muster place was at Sardis, and there Greek spies had seen the multitudes assembling and the state and magnificence of the king's attendants. Envoys had come from him to demand earth and water from each state in Greece, as emblems that land and sea were his, but each state was resolved to be free, and only Thessaly, that which lay first in his path, consented to yield the token of subjugation. A council was held at the Isthmus of Corinth, and attended by deputies from all the states of Greece to consider of the best means of defense. The ships of the enemy would coast round the shores of the Ægean Sea, the land army would cross the Hellespont on a bridge of boats lashed together, and march southwards into Greece. The only hope of averting the danger lay in defending such passages as, from the nature of the ground, were so narrow that only a few persons could fight hand to hand at once, so that courage would be of more avail than numbers.

The first of these passes was called Tempe, and a body of troops was sent to guard it; but they found that this was useless and impossible, and came back again. The next was at Thermopylæ. Look in your map of the Archipelago, or Ægean Sea, as it was then called, for the great island of

Negropont, or by its old name, Eubœa. It looks like a piece broken off from the coast, and to the north is shaped like the head of a bird, with the beak running into a gulf, that would fit over it, upon the main land, and between the island and the coast is an exceedingly narrow strait. The Persian army would have to march round the edge of the gulf. They could not cut straight across the country, because the ridge of mountains called Œta rose up and barred their way. Indeed, the woods, rocks, and precipices came down so near the sea-shore, that in two places there was only room for one single wheel track between the steeps and the impassable morass that formed the border of the gulf on its south side. These two very narrow places were called the gates of the pass, and were about a mile apart. There was a little more width left in the intervening space; but in this there were a number of springs of warm mineral water, salt and sulphurous, which were used for the sick to bathe in, and thus the place was called Thermopylæ, or the Hot Gates. A wall had once been built across the westernmost of these narrow places, when the Thessalians and Phocians, who lived on either side of it, had been at war with one another; but it had been allowed to go to decay, since the Phocians had found out that there was a very steep narrow mountain path along the bed of a torrent, by which it was possible to cross from one territory to the other without going round this marshy coast road.

This was, therefore, an excellent place to defend. The Greek ships were all drawn up on the further side of Eubœa to prevent the Persian vessels from getting into the strait and landing men beyond the pass, and a division of the army was sent off to guard the Hot Gates. The council at the Isthmus did not know of the mountain pathway, and thought that all would be safe as long as the Persians were kept out of the coast path.

The troops sent for this purpose were from different cities, and amounted to about 4,000 who were to keep the pass against two millions. The leader of them was Leonidas, who had newly become one of the two kings of Sparta, the city that above all in Greece trained its sons to be hardy soldiers, dreading death infinitely less than shame. Leonidas had already made up his mind that the expedition would probably be his death, perhaps because a prophecy had been given at the Temple at Delphi that Sparta should be saved by the death of one of her kings of the race of Hercules. He was allowed by law to take with him 300 men, and these he chose most carefully, not merely for their strength and courage, but selecting those who had sons, so that no family might be altogether destroyed. These Spartans, with their helots or slaves, made up his own share of the numbers, but all the army was under his generalship. It is even said that the 300 celebrated their own funeral rites before they set out lest they should be deprived of them by the enemy, since, as we have already seen, it was the Greek belief that the spirits of the dead found no rest till their obsequies had been performed. Such preparations did not daunt the spirits of Leonidas and his men, and his wife, Gorgo, was not a woman to be faint-hearted or hold him back. Long before, when she was a very little girl, a word of hers had saved her father from listening to a traitorous message from the King of Persia; and every Spartan lady was bred up to be able to say to those she best loved that they must come home from battle "with the shield or on it"—either carrying it victoriously or borne upon it as a corpse.

When Leonidas came to Thermopylæ, the Phocians told him of the mountain path through the chestnut woods of Mount Œta, and begged to have the privilege of guarding it on a spot high up on the mountain side, assuring him that it was very hard to find at the other end, and that there was every probability that the enemy would never discover it. He consented, and encamping around the warm springs, caused the broken wall to be repaired, and made ready to meet the foe.

The Persian army were seen covering the whole country like locusts, and the hearts of some of the southern Greeks in the pass began to sink. Their homes in the Peloponnesus were comparatively secure—had they not better fall back and reserve themselves to defend the Isthmus of Corinth? But Leonidas, though Sparta was safe below the Isthmus, had no intention of abandoning his northern allies, and kept the other Peloponnesians to their posts, only sending messengers for further help.

Presently a Persian on horseback rode up to reconnoiter the pass. He could not see over the wall, but in front of it and on the ramparts, he saw the Spartans, some of them engaged in active sports, and others in combing their long hair. He rode back to the king, and told him what he had seen.

Now Xerxes had in his camp an exiled Spartan prince, named Demaratus, who had become a traitor to his country, and was serving as counselor to the enemy. Xerxes sent for him, and asked whether his countrymen were mad to be thus employed instead of fleeing away; but Demaratus made answer that a hard fight was no doubt in preparation, and that it was the custom of the Spartans to array their hair with especial care when they were about to enter upon any great peril. Xerxes would, however, not believe that so petty a force could intend to resist him, and waited four days, probably expecting his fleet to assist him, but as it did not appear, the attack was made.

The Greeks, stronger men and more heavily armed, were far better able to fight to advantage than the Persians with their short spears and wicker shields, and beat them off with great ease. It is said that Xerxes three times leapt off his throne in despair at the sight of his troops being driven backwards; and thus for two days it seemed as easy to force a way through the Spartans as through the rocks themselves. Nay, how could slavish troops, dragged from home to spread the victories of an ambitious king, fight like freemen who felt that their strokes were to defend their homes and children?

That evening a wretched man, named Ephialtes, crept into the Persian camp, and offered, for a great sum of money, to show the mountain path that would enable the enemy to take the brave defenders in the rear! A Persian general, named Hydarnes, was sent off at nightfall with a detachment to secure this passage, and was guided through the thick forests that clothed the hill-side. In the stillness of the air, at daybreak, the Phocian guards of the path were startled by the crackling of the chestnut leaves under the tread of many feet. They started up, but a shower of arrows was discharged on them, and forgetting all save the present alarm, they fled to a higher part of the mountain, and the enemy, without waiting to pursue them, began to descend.

As day dawned, morning light showed the watchers of the Grecian camp below a glittering and shimmering in the torrent bed where the shaggy forests opened; but it was not the sparkle of water, but the shine of gilded helmets and the gleaming of silvered spears. Moreover, a man crept over to the wall from the Persian camp with tidings that the path had been betrayed, that the enemy were climbing it, and would come down beyond the Eastern Gate. Still, the way was rugged and circuitous, the Persians would hardly descend before midday, and there was ample time for the Greeks to escape before they could thus be shut in by the enemy.

There was a short council held over the morning sacrifice. Megistias, the seer, on inspecting the entrails of the slain victim, declared that their appearance boded disaster. Leonidas ordered him to retire, but he refused, though he sent home his only son.

There was no disgrace in leaving a post that could not be held, and Leonidas recommended all the allied troops under his command to march away while yet the way was open. As to himself and his Spartans, they had made up their minds to die at their post, and there could be no doubt that the example of such a resolution would do more to save Greece than their best efforts could ever do if they were careful to reserve themselves for another occasion.

All the allies consented to retreat, except the eighty men who came from Mycenæ and the 700 Thespians, who declared that they would not desert Leonidas. There were also 400 Thebans who remained; and thus the whole number that stayed with Leonidas to confront two million of enemies were fourteen hundred warriors, besides the helots or attendants on the 300 Spartans, whose number is not known, but there was probably at least one to each.

Leonidas had two kinsmen in the camp, like himself, claiming the blood of Hercules, and he tried to save them by giving them letters and messages to Sparta; but one answered that "he had come to fight, not to carry letters;" and the other, that "his deeds would tell all that Sparta wished to know." Another Spartan, named Dienices, when told that the enemy's archers were so numerous that their arrows darkened the sun, replied, "So much the better, we shall fight in the shade." Two of the 300 had been sent to a neighboring village, suffering severely from a complaint in the eyes. One of them called Eurytus, put on his armor, and commanded his helot to lead him to his place in the ranks; the other, called Aristodemus, was so overpowered with illness that he allowed himself to be carried away with the retreating allies. It was still early in the day when all were gone, and Leonidas gave the word to his men to take their last meal. "To-night," he said, "we shall sup with Pluto."

Hitherto, he had stood on the defensive, and had husbanded the lives of his men; but he now desired to make as great a slaughter as possible, so as to inspire the enemy with dread of the Grecian name. He therefore marched out beyond the wall, without waiting to be attacked, and the battle began. The Persian captains went behind their wretched troops and scourged them on to the fight with whips! Poor wretches, they were driven on to be slaughtered, pierced with the Greek spears, hurled into the sea, or trampled into the mud of the morass; but their inexhaustible numbers told at length. The spears of the Greeks broke under hard service, and their swords alone remained; they began to fall, and Leonidas himself was among the first of the slain. Hotter than ever was the fight over his body, and two Persian princes, brothers of Xerxes, were there killed; but at length word was brought that Hydarnes was over the pass, and that the few remaining men were thus enclosed on all sides. The Spartans and Thespians made their way to a little hillock within the wall, resolved to let this be the place of their last stand; but the hearts of the Thebans failed them, and they came towards the Persians holding out their hands in entreaty for mercy. Quarter was given to them, but they were all branded with the king's mark as untrustworthy deserters. The helots probably at this time escaped into the mountains; while the small desperate band stood side by side on the hill still fighting to the last, some with swords, others with daggers, others even with their hands and teeth, till not one living man remained amongst them when the sun went down. There was only a mound of slain, bristled over with arrows.

Twenty thousand Persians had died before that handful of men! Xerxes asked Demaratus if there were many more at Sparta like these, and was told there were 8,000. The body of the brave king was buried where it fell, as were those of the other dead. Much envied were they by the unhappy Aristodemus, who found himself called by no name but the "Coward," and was shunned by all his fellow-citizens. No one would give him fire or water, and after a year of misery, he redeemed his honor by perishing in the fore-front of the battle of Platæa, which was the last blow that drove the Persians ingloriously from Greece.

The Greeks then united in doing honor to the brave warriors who, had they been better supported, might have saved the whole country from invasion. The poet Simonides wrote the inscriptions that were engraved upon the pillars that were set up in the pass to commemorate this great action. One was outside the wall, where most of the fighting had been. It seems to have been in honor of the whole number who had for two days resisted—

> "Here did four thousand men from Pelops' land
> Against three hundred myriads[1] bravely stand."

In honor of the Spartans was another column—

> "Go, traveller, to Sparta tell
> That here, obeying her, we fell."

[1] A myriad consisted of ten thousand.

BRAVERY OF REGULUS

On the little hillock of the last resistance was placed the figure of a stone lion, in memory of Leonidas, so fitly named the lion-like, and the names of the 300 were likewise engraven on a pillar at Sparta.

Lion, pillars, and inscriptions have all long since passed away, even the very spot itself has changed; new soil has been formed, and there are miles of solid ground between Mount Œta and the gulf, so that the Hot Gates no longer exist. But more enduring than stone or brass—nay, than the very battle-field itself—has been the name of Leonidas. Two thousand three hundred years have sped since he braced himself to perish for his country's sake in that narrow, marshy coast road, under the brow of the wooded crags, with the sea by his side. Since that time how many hearts have glowed, how many arms have been nerved at the remembrance of the Pass of Thermopylæ, and the defeat that was worth so much more than a victory!

BRAVERY OF REGULUS

By Charlotte M. Yonge

THE first wars that the Romans engaged in beyond the bounds of Italy were with the Carthaginians.

The first dispute between Rome and Carthage was about their possession in the island of Sicily; and the war thus begun had lasted eight years, when it was resolved to send an army to fight the Cartha-

ginians on their own shores. The army and fleet
were placed under the command of the two consuls,
Lucius Manlius and Marcus Attilius Regulus. On
the way, there was a great sea-fight with the
Carthaginian fleet, and this was the first naval battle that the Romans ever gained. It made the way
to Africa free; but the soldiers, who had never been
so far from home before, murmured, for they expected to meet not only human enemies, but monstrous serpents, lions, elephants, asses with horns,
and dog-headed monsters, to have a scorching sun
overhead, and a noisome marsh under their feet.
However, Regulus sternly put a stop to all murmurs, by making it known that disaffection would
be punished by death, and the army safely landed,
and set up a fortification at Clypea, and plundered
the whole country round. Orders here came from
Rome that Manlius should return thither, but that
Regulus should remain to carry on the war. This
was a great grief to him. He was a very poor
man, with nothing of his own but a little farm of
seven acres, and the person whom he had employed
to cultivate it had died in his absence; a hired laborer
had undertaken the care of it, but had been unfaith-
ful, and had run away with his tools and his cattle,
so that he was afraid that, unless he could return
quickly, his wife and children would starve. However, the Senate engaged to provide for his family,
and he remained, making expeditions into the country round, in the course of which the Romans really
did fall in with a serpent, as monstrous as their
imagination had depicted. It was said to be 120
feet long, and dwelt upon the banks of the river

Bagrada, where it used to devour the Roman soldiers as they went to fetch water. It had such tough scales that they were obliged to attack it with their engines meant for battering city walls; and only succeeded with much difficulty in destroying it.

The country was most beautiful, covered with fertile corn-fields and full of rich fruit-trees, and all the rich Carthaginians had country-houses and gardens, which were made delicious with fountains, trees, and flowers. The Roman soldiers, plain, hardy, fierce, and pitiless, did, it must be feared, cruel damage among these peaceful scenes; they boasted of having sacked 300 villages, and mercy was not yet known to them. The Carthaginian army, though strong in horsemen and in elephants, kept upon the hills and did nothing to save the country, and the wild desert tribes of Numidians came rushing in to plunder what the Romans had left. The Carthaginians sent to offer terms of peace; but Regulus, who had become uplifted by his conquests, made such demands that the messengers remonstrated. He answered, "Men who are good for anything should either conquer or submit to their betters;" and he sent them rudely away, like a stern old Roman as he was.

His merit was that he had no more mercy on himself than on others.

The Carthaginians were driven to extremity, and made horrible offerings to Moloch, giving the little children of the noblest families to be dropped into the fire between the brazen hands of his statue, and grown-up people of the noblest families rushed in of their own accord, hoping thus to propitiate their gods, and obtain safety for their country. Their time was not yet fully come, and a respite was granted to them. They had sent, in their distress, to hire soldiers in Greece, and among these came a Spartan, named Xanthippus, who at once took the command, and led the army out to battle, with a long line of elephants ranged in front of them, and with clouds of horsemen hovering on the wings. The Romans had not yet learnt the best mode of fighting with elephants, namely, to leave lanes in their columns where these huge beasts might advance harmlessly; instead of which, the ranks were thrust and trampled down by the creatures' bulk, and they suffered a terrible defeat; Regulus himself was seized by the horsemen, and dragged into Carthage, where the victors feasted and rejoiced through half the night, and testified their thanks to Moloch by offering in his fires the bravest of their captives.

Regulus himself was not, however, one of these victims. He was kept a close prisoner for two years, pining and sickening in his loneliness, while in the meantime the war continued, and at last a victory so decisive was gained by the Romans, that the people of Carthage were discouraged, and resolved to ask terms of peace. They thought that no one would be so readily listened to at Rome as Regulus, and they therefore sent him there with their envoys, having first made him swear that he would come back to his prison if there should neither be peace nor an exchange of prisoners. They little knew how much more a true-hearted Roman cared for his city than for himself—for his word than for his life.

Worn and dejected, the captive warrior came to the outside of the gates of his own city, and there paused, refusing to enter. "I am no longer a Roman citizen," he said; "I am but the barbarians' slave, and the Senate may not give audience to strangers within the walls."

His wife Marcia ran out to greet him, with his two sons, but he did not look up, and received their caresses as one beneath their notice, as a mere slave, and he continued, in spite of all entreaty, to remain outside the city, and would not even go to the little farm he had loved so well.

The Roman Senate, as he would not come in to them, came out to hold their meeting in the Campagna.

The ambassadors spoke first, then Regulus, standing up, said, as one repeating a task, "Conscript fathers, being a slave to the Carthaginians, I come on the part of my masters to treat with you concerning peace, and an exchange of prisoners." He then turned to go away with the ambassadors, as a stranger might not be present at the deliberations of the Senate. His old friends pressed him to stay and give his opinion as a senator who had twice been consul; but he refused to degrade that dignity by claiming it, slave as he was. But, at the command of his Carthaginian masters, he remained, though not taking his seat.

Then he spoke. He told the senators to persevere in the war. He said he had seen the distress of Carthage, and that a peace would be only to her advantage, not to that of Rome, and therefore he strongly advised that the war should continue. Then, as to the exchange of prisoners, the Carthaginian generals, who were in the hands of the Romans, were in full health and strength, whilst he himself was too much broken down to be fit for service again, and indeed he believed that his enemies had given him a slow poison, and that he could not live long. Thus he insisted that no exchange of prisoners should be made.

It was wonderful, even to Romans, to hear a man thus pleading against himself, and their chief priest came forward, and declared that, as his oath had been wrested from him by force, he was not bound by it to return to his captivity. But Regulus was too noble to listen to this for a moment. "Have you resolved to dishonor me?" he said. "I am not ignorant that death and the extremest tortures are preparing for me; but what are these to the shame of an infamous action, or the wounds of a guilty mind? Slave as I am to Carthage, I have still the spirit of a Roman. I have sworn to return. It is my duty to go; let the gods take care of the rest."

The Senate decided to follow the advice of Regulus, though they bitterly regretted his sacrifice. His wife wept and entreated in vain that they would detain him; they could merely repeat their permission to him to remain; but nothing could prevail with him to break his word, and he turned back to the chains and death he expected as calmly as if he had been returning to his home. This was in the year B.C. 249.

"Let the gods take care of the rest," said the

Roman; the gods whom alone he knew, and through
whom he ignorantly worshiped the true God, whose
Light was shining out even in this heathen's truth
and constancy. How his trust was fulfilled is not
known. The Senate, after the next victory, gave
two Carthaginian generals to his wife and sons to
hold as pledges for his good treatment; but when
tidings arrived that Regulus was dead, Marcia began to treat them both with savage cruelty, though
one of them assured her that he had been careful
to have her husband well used. Horrible stories
were told that Regulus had been put out in the sun
with his eyelids cut off, rolled down a hill in a
barrel with spikes, killed by being constantly kept
awake, or else crucified. Marcia seems to have
heard, and perhaps believed in these horrors, and
avenged them on her unhappy captives till one had
died, and the Senate sent for her sons and severely
reprimanded them. They declared it was their
mother's doing, not theirs, and thenceforth were
careful of the comfort of the remaining prisoner.

It may thus be hoped that the frightful tale of
Regulus' sufferings was but formed by report
acting on the fancy of a vindictive woman, and that
Regulus was permitted to die in peace of the disease
brought on far more probably by the climate and
imprisonment, than by the poison to which he
ascribed it. It is not the tortures he may have
endured that make him one of the noblest characters
of history, but the resolution that would neither let
him save himself at the risk of his country's pros-
perity, nor forfeit the word that he had pledged.

THE RABBI WHO FOUND THE DIADEM

Translated from the Talmud by Dr. A. S. Isaacs

GREAT was the alarm in the palace of Rome, which soon spread throughout the entire city. The empress had lost her costly diadem, and it could not be found. They searched in every direction, but all in vain. Half distracted, for the mishap boded no good to her or her house, the empress redoubled her exertions to regain her precious possession, but without result. As a last resource it was proclaimed in the public streets: "The empress has lost a precious diadem. Whoever restores it within thirty days shall receive a princely reward. But he who delays, and brings it after thirty days, shall lose his head."

In those times all nationalities flocked toward Rome; all classes and creeds could be met in its stately halls and crowded thoroughfares. Among the rest was a rabbi, a learned sage from the East, who loved goodness, and lived a righteous life in the stir and turmoil of the Western world. It chanced one night as he was strolling up and down, in busy meditation, beneath the clear, moonlit sky, he saw the diadem sparkling at his feet. He seized it quickly, brought it to his dwelling, where he guarded it carefully until the thirty days had expired, when he resolved to return it to the owner.

He proceeded to the palace, and, undismayed at sight of long lines of soldiery and officials, asked for an audience with the empress.

"What dost thou mean by this?" she inquired, when he told her his story and gave her the diadem. "Why didst thou delay until this hour? Dost thou know the penalty? Thy head must be forfeited."

"I delayed until now," the rabbi answered calmly, "so that thou mightst know that I return thy diadem, not for the sake of the reward, still less out of fear of punishment; but solely to comply with the Divine command not to withhold from another the property which belongs to him."

"Blessed be thy God!" the empress answered, and dismissed the rabbi without further reproof; for had he not done right for right's sake?

HOW LIVIA WON THE BROOCH

By Beatrice Harraden

IT was the day before the public games in Rome, in the year 123 B.C., and a tall man of magnificent appearance and strength was standing outside the Temple of Hercules, talking to a young girl whose face bore some resemblance to his own. The people passing by looked at them, and said, half aloud, "There stands the gladiator Naevus. I wonder how he will bear himself in the Public Games on the morrow?"

And another man, who was talking eagerly with his companion, stopped when he caught sight of the gladiator (who was a well-known figure in Rome), and said, in a loud voice, "That is the man I told you about, Fabricius. A fine fellow, is he not?

To-morrow he will fight with the new hero, Lucius. And, of course, he will be victorious, as usual. If he disappoints my hopes, I shall lose a great deal of money."

"You have plenty to spare!" laughed his friend, as they passed on together.

The gladiator did not take the slightest notice of any remarks which were made about him; indeed, it was doubtful whether he heard them, being engaged in earnest conversation with the young girl, his daughter.

"Do not be anxious about me, Marcella," he said, seeing that the tears were falling from her eyes. "I shall be victorious, as I have always been, and then, child, I shall buy your freedom, together with my own, and we shall leave Rome, and return to Sicily."

"Nay, father," she answered, between her sobs, "I never doubted your strength, but my heart is full of fears for you; and yet I am proud when I hear every one praising you. Last night my master Claudius gave a great banquet, and when I came to hand round the ewer of rose-water, I heard the guests say that Naevus was the strongest and finest gladiator that Rome had ever known. My master Claudius and two of the guests praised the new man Lucius, but the others would not hear a word in his favor."

The gladiator smiled.

"You shall be proud of me to-morrow, Marcella," he said. "I have just been offering up my prayers to the god Hercules; and in the name of Hercules I promise you, child, that I shall conquer the new man Lucius, and that to-morrow's combat shall be my last fight. So you may go home in peace. You look tired, child. Ah! it is a bitter thing to be a slave! But courage, Marcella; a few days more of slavery, and then we shall be free. For this end I have fought in the arena; and this hope has given me strength and skill."

She took from her neck a piece of fine cord, to which was attached a tiny stone. She put it in his great hand.

"Father," she said pleadingly, "the Greek physician gave this to me. He told me it was an Eastern charm to keep the lives of those who wore it. Will you wear it on the morrow?"

He laughingly assented, and the two walked together as far as the Forum, where they parted.

But Marcella was not proud any more; she was sad.

She had had many a dream of freedom, but she would have gladly given up all chances of realizing that dream, if only to feel that her father's life was not in danger. She would have gladly been a slave ten times over rather than that he should risk his life in those fearful contests.

Marcella, who was a slave in the house of Claudius Flaccus, a great Roman noble, now hastened home to her duties. Her little mistress Livia, Claudius' only daughter, wondered to see her looking so pale and sad.

"Why, you should be glad like I am, Marcella," she cried, as she showed the slave-maiden the necklace of pearls that she had just finished stringing. "See, Marcella! I shall wear these to-morrow when we go to the Circus Maximus. And what do you think? My father has promised me a brooch of precious stones if the new gladiator, Lucius, is successful to-morrow. Oh, how I hope he will be!"

Marcella tried to restrain her tears, but it was of no avail. She threw herself on the couch, and buried her face in the soft cushions, and wept as if her heart would break. Her little mistress Livia bent over her, and tried to comfort her.

"Marcella," she whispered, "it was unkind of me to say that. I forgot about your father. Please forgive me, Marcella, for I do love you, although you are only a slave. And I do not want the brooch; I should not like to wear it now. Please, Marcella, do not cry any more."

The slave raised her head and smiled through her tears.

"You did not mean to be unkind, dear little mistress," she said, as she kissed the hand which had been caressing her own golden hair. "I am sure you did not mean to be unkind; but I am in great trouble, and I have just said 'Good-bye' to my father, and I can think of no one else but him. When those we love are in danger we cannot help being anxious, can we?"

At that moment the curtains were drawn aside, and Claudius himself came into the beautiful apartment. Livia ran to greet him; she was a child of ten years old, bright and winning in her ways, in beauty and bearing every inch the child of a patrician. She was dressed in soft silk of dark purple.

"I do not want the brooch," she said, as she put

38

up her face to be kissed. "I want Marcella's father to be victorious to-morrow."

Claudius frowned.

"What has Marcella's father got to do with you, little one?" he asked roughly. "Neither he nor she is anything to you, a patrician's daughter. Slaves both of them! Let me hear no more of them. And as for the brooch, it shall be a handsome one."

But when he had gone Livia turned to the slave and said, "I shall never wear that brooch, Marcella."

So the day wore into the night, and all through the night Marcella lay awake, wondering what the morrow would bring forth. When at last she fell asleep she dreamed that she was in the Circus Maximus watching her father, who was fighting with a new gladiator. She saw her father fall. She heard the cries of the populace. She herself, a girl of fourteen summers, sprang up to help him. And then she awoke.

"Ah, it was only a dream!" she cried, with a sigh of relief. "Father will win the fight to-morrow, and then he will buy his own freedom and mine, too."

It was a beautiful day for the Public Games. People had come from all parts of the country, and the streets of Rome were crowded with all manner of folk.

The Ædile whose duty it was to arrange the Public Games had provided a very costly entertainment, and great excitement prevailed everywhere to know the issue of the contest betwen the gladiators Naevus and Lucius. It was a wonderful sight to see the Circus Maximus crowded with the rich and luxurious patrician nobles and ladies and their retinues of slaves, and the poorer classes, all bent on amusing themselves on this great public festival.

No doubt, amongst all those masses there were many anxious hearts, but none so anxious as that of the slave-girl Marcella. She sat behind her little mistress, eagerly expectant. At last a peal of trumpets and a clash of cymbals, accompanied by some wild kind of music, announced that the performance was about to begin. The folding-doors under the archway were flung open, and the gladiators marched in slowly, two by two. In all the pride of their strength and bearing they walked once round the arena, and then they stepped aside to wait until their turn came. The performance began with some fights between animals; for at the time of which we are speaking the Romans had learned to love this cruel bloodshed, and had learned to despise the less exciting, if more manly, trials of strength in which their ancestors had delighted. When this part of the cruel amusement was over the trumpets again sounded, and the gladiators made ready for their contest. Then it was that Marcella's heart beat wildly with fear. She saw her father advance together with the other gladiator; she saw their swords flash; she heard the people around her call out the name now of Naevus, and now of Lucius; she heard one near her say:

"He of the red scarf will prove the stronger, mark my words."

Marcella's father wore the red scarf.

"Nay, nay," answered the speaker's companion. "He of the green scarf will win the day."

It was all that Marcella could do to prevent herself from saying, "The gladiator with the red scarf will prove the stronger—he must prove the stronger."

She sat spell-bound, watching for the event of the contest, which had now begun between the two in real earnest. The people encouraged now the one and now the other. At this moment it seemed probable that the new man, Lucius, would be the winner; at that moment the tide had turned in the favor of Naevus. But suddenly there was a loud cry, for Lucius had felled Naevus to the ground, and now stood over him with his sword ready for use, waiting to learn from the populace whether the favorite gladiator was to be spared or killed.

The slave-girl Marcella had risen from her seat.

"That is my father," she cried; "spare him—spare him!"

But no one heard her or noticed her, and the signal for mercy was not shown; on the contrary, the thumbs of thousands of hands pointed upwards; and that meant that the vanquished man, who had been the hero of so many contests, having now failed of his accustomed valor, was to die. So Lucius gave him a thrust with his sword, and he died while he was being carried away from the arena.

"You have won your brooch, little daughter," laughed Claudius, as he bent over and fondled Livia's hair. "And it shall be a costly brooch, worthy of a patrician's daughter."

But Livia's eyes were full of tears.

"I could never wear it," she sobbed; "I should always be thinking of Marcella's father."

Poor Marcella! and she thought the little charm which he had worn for her sake would preserve his life. Ah! it was cruel to think that she would never see him again, and that all their hopes of freedom and their plans for the future had ended. Well might she weep.

That was hundreds of years ago, you know, but still the same story goes on, and all through the centuries sorrow comes to us, just as we think we are grasping happiness, and we have to be brave and bear that sorrow. But sometimes we are helped by friends, even as Livia helped Marcella. For she did help her; she loved her as a sister, and treated her as such. And as time went on the little patrician lady claimed a gift from her father Claudius, a gift which was far more costly than any brooch—it was the freedom of the Sicilian slave Marcella, the gladiator's daughter.

JULIUS CÆSAR CROSSING THE RUBICON

By Jacob Abbott

THERE was a little stream in ancient times, in the north of Italy, which flowed eastward into the Adriatic Sea, called the Rubicon. This stream has been immortalized by the transactions which we are now about to describe.

The Rubicon was a very important boundary, and yet it was in itself so small and insignificant that it is now impossible to determine which of two or three little brooks here running into the sea is entitled to its name and renown. In history the Rubicon is a grand, permanent, and conspicuous stream, gazed upon with continued interest by all mankind for nearly twenty centuries; in nature it is an uncertain rivulet, for a long time doubtful and undetermined, and finally lost.

The Rubicon originally derived its importance from the fact that it was the boundary between all that part of the north of Italy which is formed by the valley of the Po, one of the richest and most magnificent countries of the world, and the more southern Roman territories. This country of the Po constituted what was in those days called the *hither* Gaul, and was a Roman province. It belonged now to Cæsar's jurisdiction, as the commander in Gaul. All south of the Rubicon was territory reserved for the immediate jurisdiction of the city. The Romans, in order to protect themselves from any danger which might threaten their own liberties from the immense armies which they raised for the conquest of foreign nations, had imposed on every side very strict limitations and restrictions in respect to the approach of these armies to the capital. The Rubicon was the limit on this northern side. Generals commanding in Gaul were never to pass it. To cross the Rubicon with an army on the way to Rome was rebellion and treason. Hence the Rubicon became, as it were, the visible sign and symbol of civil restriction to military power.

As Cæsar found the time of his service in Gaul drawing toward a conclusion, he turned his thoughts more and more toward Rome, endeavoring to strengthen his interest there by every means in his power, and to circumvent and thwart the designs of Pompey. He had agents and partisans in Rome who acted for him and in his name. He sent immense sums of money to these men, to be employed in such ways as would most tend to secure the favor of the people. He ordered the Forum to be rebuilt with great magnificence. He arranged great celebrations, in which the people were entertained with an endless succession of games, spectacles, and public feasts. When his daughter Julia, Pompey's wife, died, he celebrated her funeral with indescribable splendor. He distributed corn in immense quantities among the people, and he sent a great many captives home, to be trained as gladiators to fight in the theatres for their amusement. In many cases, too, where he found men of talents and influence among the populace, who had become involved in debt by their dissipations and extravagance, he paid their debts, and thus secured their influence on his side. Men were astounded at the magnitude of these expenditures, and, while the multitude rejoiced thoughtlessly in the pleasures thus provided for them, the more reflecting and considerate trembled at the greatness of the power which was so rapidly rising to overshadow the land.

It increased their anxiety to observe that Pom-

pey was gaining the same kind of influence and
ascendency, too. He had not the advantage
which Cæsar enjoyed in the prodigious wealth obtained from the rich countries over which Cæsar
ruled, but he possessed, instead of it, the advantage of being all the time at Rome, and of securing, by his character and action there, a very wide
personal popularity and influence. Pompey was,
in fact, the idol of the people. At one time, when
he was absent from Rome, at Naples, he was taken
sick. After being for some days in considerable
danger, the crisis passed favorably, and he recovered. Some of the people of Naples proposed
a public thanksgiving to the gods, to celebrate his
restoration to health. The plan was adopted by
acclamation, and the example thus set extended
from city to city, until it had spread throughout
Italy, and the whole country was filled with processions, games, shows, and celebrations, which
were instituted everywhere in honor of the event.
And when Pompey returned from Naples to Rome
the towns on the way could not afford room for
the crowds that came forth to meet him. The
high roads, the villages, the ports, says Plutarch,
were filled with sacrifices and entertainments.
Many received him with garlands on their heads
and torches in their hands, and, as they conducted
him along, strewed the way with flowers.

In fact, Pompey considered himself as standing
far above Cæsar in fame and power, and this
general burst of enthusiasm and applause educed
by his recovery from sickness confirmed him in
this idea. He felt no solicitude, he said, in respect

to Cæsar. He should take no special precautions against any hostile designs which he might entertain on his return from Gaul. It was he himself, he said, that had raised Cæsar up to whatever of elevation he had attained, and he could put him down even more easily than he had exalted him.

In the meantime, the period was drawing near in which Cæsar's command in the provinces was to expire; and, anticipating the struggle with Pompey which was about to ensue, he conducted several of his legions through the passes of the Alps and advanced gradually, as he had a right to do, across the country of the Po toward the Rubicon, revolving in his capacious mind, as he came, the various plans by which he might hope to gain the ascendency over the power of his mighty rival and make himself supreme.

He concluded that it would be his wisest policy not to attempt to intimidate Pompey by great and open preparations for war, which might tend to arouse him to vigorous measures of resistance, but rather to cover and conceal his designs, and thus throw his enemy off his guard. He advanced, therefore, toward the Rubicon with a small force. He established his headquarters at Ravenna, a city not far from the river, and employed himself in objects of local interest there in order to avert as much as possible the minds of the people from imagining that he was contemplating any great design. Pompey sent to him to demand the return of a certain legion which he had lent him from his own army at a time when they were friends. Cæsar complied with this demand without any hesitation, and sent the legion home. He sent with this legion, also, some other troops which were properly his own, thus evincing a degree of indifference in respect to the amount of the force retained under his command which seemed wholly inconsistent with the idea that he contemplated any resistance to the authority of the government at Rome.

In the meantime, the struggle at Rome between the partisans of Cæsar and Pompey grew more and more violent and alarming. Cæsar, through his friends in the city, demanded to be elected consul. The other side insisted that he must first, if that was his wish, resign the command of his army, come to Rome, and present himself as a candidate in the character of a private citizen. This the constitution of the state very properly required. In answer to this requisition, Cæsar rejoined that, if Pompey would lay down his military commands, he would do so too; if not, it was unjust to require it of him. The services, he added, which he had performed for his country demanded some recompense, which, moreover, they ought to be willing to award even if in order to do it it were necessary to relax somewhat in his favor the strictness of ordinary rules. To a large part of the people of the city these demands of Cæsar appeared reasonable. They were clamorous to have them allowed. The partisans of Pompey, with the stern and inflexible Cato at their head, deemed them wholly inadmissible and contended with the most determined violence against them. The whole city was filled with the excitement of this struggle, into

which all the active and turbulent spirits of the
capital plunged with the most furious zeal, while
the more considerate and thoughtful of the population, remembering the days of Marius and Sylla,
trembled at the impending danger. Pompey himself had no fear. He urged the Senate to resist
to the utmost all of Cæsar's claims, saying if Cæsar
should be so presumptuous as to attempt to march
to Rome he could raise troops enough by stamping
with his foot to put him down.

It would require a volume to contain a full account of the disputes and tumults, the manœuvres
and debates, the votes and decrees, which marked
the successive stages of this quarrel. Pompey
himself was all the time without the city. He was
in command of an army there, and no general,
while in command, was allowed to come within
the gates. At last an exciting debate was broken
up in the Senate by one of the consuls rising to
depart, saying that he would hear the subject dis-
cussed no longer. The time had arrived for action,
and he should send a commander, with an armed
force, to defend the country from Cæsar's threatened invasion. Cæsar's leading friends, two tri-
bunes of the people, disguised themselves as slaves
and fled to the north to join their master. The
country was filled with commotion and panic.
The Commonwealth had obviously more fear of
Cæsar than confidence in Pompey. The country
was full of rumors in respect to Cæsar's power, and
the threatening attitude which he was assuming,
while they who had insisted on resistance seemed,
after all, to have provided very inadequate means

with which to resist. A thousand plans were formed, and clamorously insisted upon by their respective advocates, for averting the danger. This only added to the confusion, and the city became at length pervaded with a universal terror.

While this was the state of things at Rome, Cæsar was quietly established at Ravenna, thirty or forty miles from the frontier. He was erecting a building for a fencing school there, and his mind seemed to be occupied very busily with the plans and models of the edifice which the architects had formed. Of course, in his intended march to Rome, his reliance was not to be so much on the force which he should take with him, as on the co-operation and support which he expected to find there. It was his policy, therefore, to move as quietly and privately as possible, and with as little display of violence, and to avoid everything which might indicate his intended march to any spies which might be around him, or to any other persons who might be disposed to report what they observed, at Rome. Accordingly, on the very eve of his departure, he busied himself with his fencing school, and assumed with his officers and soldiers a careless and unconcerned air, which prevented any one from suspecting his design.

In the course of the day, he privately sent forward some cohorts to the southward, with orders for them to encamp on the banks of the Rubicon. When night came, he sat down to supper as usual and conversed with his friends in his ordinary manner, and went with them afterward to a public entertainment. As soon as it was dark and the streets were still, he set off secretly from the city, accompanied by a very few attendants. Instead of making use of his ordinary equipage, the parading of which would have attracted attention to his movements, he had some mules taken from a neighboring bakehouse and harnessed into his chaise. There were torch-bearers provided to light the way. The cavalcade drove on during the night, finding, however, the hasty preparations which had been made inadequate for the occasion. The torches went out, the guides lost their way, and the future conqueror of the world wandered about bewildered and lost, until, just after break of day, the party met with a peasant who undertook to guide them. Under his direction they made their way to the main road again, and advanced then without further difficulty to the banks of the river, where they found that portion of the army which had been sent forward encamped and awaiting their arrival.

Cæsar stood for some time upon the banks of the stream, musing upon the greatness of the undertaking in which simply passing across it would involve him. His officers stood by his side. "We can retreat *now*," said he, "but once across that river, we must go on." He paused for some time, conscious of the vast importance of the decision, though he thought only, doubtless, of its consequences to himself. Taking the step which was now before him would necessarily end either in his realizing the loftiest aspirations of his ambition, or in his utter and irreparable ruin.

There were vast public interests, too, at stake, of which, however, he probably thought but little. It proved, in the end, that the history of the whole Roman world, for several centuries, was depending upon the manner in which the question now in Cæsar's mind should turn.

There was a little bridge across the Rubicon at the point where Cæsar was surveying it. While he was standing there, the story is, a peasant or shepherd came from the neighboring fields with a shepherd's pipe—a simple musical instrument made of a reed and used much by the rustic musicians of those days. The soldiers and some of the officers gathered around him to hear him play. Among the rest came some of Cæsar's trumpeters, with their trumpets in their hands. The shepherd took one of these martial instruments from the hands of its possessor, laying aside his own, and began to sound a charge—which is a signal for a rapid advance—and to march at the same time over the bridge. "An omen! a prodigy!" said Cæsar. "Let us march where we are called by such a divine intimation. *The die is cast.*"

So saying, he pressed forward over the bridge, while the officers, breaking up the encampment, put the columns in motion to follow him.

It was shown abundantly, on many occasions in the course of Cæsar's life, that he had no faith in omens. There are equally numerous instances to show that he was always ready to avail himself of the popular belief in them, to awaken his soldiers' ardor or to allay their fears. Whether, therefore, in respect to this story of the shepherd trumpeter it was an incident that really and accidentally occurred, or whether Cæsar planned and arranged it himself, with reference to its effect, or whether, which is, perhaps, after all, the most probable supposition, the tale was only an embellishment invented out of something or nothing by the story-tellers of those days to give additional dramatic interest to the narrative of the crossing of the Rubicon, it must be left for each reader to decide.

As soon as the bridge was crossed, Cæsar called an assembly of his troops, and, with signs of great excitement and agitation, made an address to them on the magnitude of the crisis through which they were passing. He showed them how entirely he was in their power; he urged them, by the most eloquent appeals, to stand by him, faithful and true, promising them the most ample rewards when he should have attained the object at which he aimed. The soldiers responded to this appeal with promises of the most unwavering fidelity.

The first town on the Roman side of the Rubicon was Ariminum. Cæsar advanced to this town. The authorities opened its gates to him—very willing, as it appeared, to receive him as their commander. Cæsar's force was yet quite small, as he had been accompanied by only a single legion in crossing the river. He had, however, sent orders for the other legions, which had been left in Gaul, to join him without any delay, though any reinforcement of his troops seemed hardly necessary, as he found no indications of opposition to his progress. He gave his soldiers the strictest injunctions to do no injury to any property, public or private, as they advanced, and not to assume, in any respect, a hostile attitude toward the people of the country. The inhabitants, therefore, welcomed him wherever he came, and all the cities and towns followed the example of Ariminum, surrendering, in fact, faster than he could take possession of them.

In the confusion of the debates and votes in the Senate at Rome before Cæsar crossed the Rubicon, one decree had been passed deposing him from his command of the army and appointing a successor. The name of the general thus appointed was Domitius. The only real opposition which Cæsar encountered in his progress toward Rome was from him. Domitius had crossed the Apennines at the head of an army on his way northward to supersede Cæsar in his command, and had reached the town of Corfinium, which was perhaps one third of the way between Rome and the Rubicon. Cæsar advanced upon him here and shut him in.

After a brief siege the city was taken, and Domitius and his army were made prisoners. Everybody gave them up for lost, expecting that Cæsar would wreak terrible vengeance upon them. Instead of this, he received the troops at once into his own service and let Domitius go free.

In the meantime, the tidings of Cæsar's having passed the Rubicon, and of the triumphant success which he was meeting with at the commencement of his march toward Rome, reached the capital, and added greatly to the prevailing consternation. The reports of the magnitude of his force and of the rapidity of his progress were greatly exaggerated. The party of Pompey and the Senate had done everything to spread among the people the terror of Cæsar's name in order to arouse them to efforts for opposing his designs; and now, when he had broken through the barriers which had been intended to restrain him and was advancing toward the city in an unchecked and triumphant career, they were overwhelmed with dismay. Pompey began to be terrified at the danger which was impending. The Senate held meetings without the city—councils of war, as it were, in which they looked to Pompey in vain for protection from the danger which he had brought upon them. He had said that he could raise an army sufficient to cope with Cæsar at any time by stamping with his foot. They told him they thought now that it was high time for him to stamp.

In fact, Pompey found the current setting everywhere strongly against him. Some recommended that commissioners should be sent to Cæsar to make proposals for peace. The leading men, however, knowing that any peace made with him under such circumstances would be their own ruin, resisted and defeated the proposal. Cato abruptly left the city and proceeded to Sicily, which had been assigned him as his province. Others fled in other directions. Pompey himself, uncertain what to do, and not daring to remain, called upon all his partisans to join him, and set off at night, suddenly, and with very little preparation and small supplies, to retreat across the country toward the shores of the Adriatic Sea. His destination was Brundusium, the usual port of embarkation for Macedon and Greece.

Cæsar was all this time gradually advancing toward Rome. His soldiers were full of enthusiasm in his cause. As his connection with the government at home was sundered the moment he crossed the Rubicon, all supplies of money and of provisions were cut off in that quarter until he should arrive at the capital and take possession of it. The soldiers voted, however, that they would serve him without pay. The officers, too, assembled together and tendered him the aid of their contributions. He had always observed a very generous policy in his dealings with them, and he was now greatly gratified at receiving their requital of it.

The further he advanced, too, the more he found the people of the country through which he passed disposed to espouse his cause. They were struck with his generosity in releasing Domitius. It is true that it was a very sagacious policy that prompted him to release him. But, then, it was generosity too. In fact, there must be something of a generous spirit in the soul to enable a man even to see the policy of generous actions.

Among the letters of Cæsar that remain to the present day, there is one written about this time to one of his friends, in which he speaks of this subject. "I am glad," says he, "that you approve of my conduct at Corfinium. I am satisfied that such a course is the best one for us to pursue, as by so doing we shall gain the good will of all parties, and thus secure a permanent victory. Most conquerors have incurred the hatred of mankind by their cruelties, and have all, in consequence of the enmity they have thus awakened, been prevented from long enjoying their power. Sylla was an exception; but his example of successful cruelty I have no disposition to imitate. I will conquer after a new fashion, and fortify myself in the possession of the power I acquire by generosity and mercy."

Domitius had the ingratitude, after this release, to take up arms again, and wage a new war against Cæsar. When Cæsar heard of it he said it was all right. "I will act out the principles of my nature," said he, "and he may act out his."

Another instance of Cæsar's generosity occurred which is even more remarkable than this. It seems that among the officers of his army there were some whom he had appointed at the recommendation of Pompey, at the time when he and Pompey were friends. These men would, of course, feel under obligations of gratitude to Pompey as they owed their military rank to his friendly interposition in their behalf. As soon as the war broke out Cæsar gave them all his free permission to go over to Pompey's side if they chose to do so.

Cæsar acted thus very liberally in all respects. He surpassed Pompey very much in the spirit of generosity and mercy with which he entered upon the great contest before them. Pompey ordered every citizen to join his standard, declaring that he should consider all neutrals as his enemies. Cæsar, on the other hand, gave free permission to

every one to decline, if he chose, taking any part in
the contest, saying that he should consider all who
did not act against him as his friends. In the
political contests of our day it is to be observed
that the combatants are much more prone to imitate the bigotry of Pompey than the generosity of
Cæsar, condemning, as they often do, those who
choose to stand aloof from electioneering struggles,
more than they do their most determined opponents
and enemies.

When, at length, Cæsar arrived at Brundusium,
he found that Pompey had sent a part of his army
across the Adriatic into Greece and was waiting
for the transports to return that he might go over
himself with the remainder. In the meantime,
he had fortified himself strongly in the city.
Cæsar immediately laid siege to the place, and he
commenced some works to block up the mouth of
the harbor. He built piers on each side, extending out as far into the sea as the depth of the water
would allow them to be built. He then constructed a series of rafts, which he anchored on
the deep water, in a line extending from one pier
to the other. He built towers upon these rafts,
and garrisoned them with soldiers, in hopes by
this means to prevent all egress from the fort.
He thought that, when this work was completed,
Pompey would be entirely shut in, beyond all
possibility of escape.

The transports, however, returned before the
work was completed. Its progress was, of course,
slow, as the constructions were the scene of a continued conflict; for Pompey sent out rafts and

galleys against them every day, and the workmen had thus to build in the midst of continual interruptions, sometimes from showers of darts, arrows, and javelins, sometimes from the conflagrations of fireships, and sometimes from the terrible concussions of great vessels of war, impelled with prodigious force against them. The transports returned, therefore, before the defences were complete, and contrived to get into the harbor. Pompey immediately formed his plan for embarking the remainder of his army.

He filled the streets of the city with barricades and pitfalls excepting two streets which led to the place of embarkation. The object of these obstructions was to embarrass Cæsar's progress through the city in case he should force an entrance while his men were getting on board the ships. He then, in order to divert Cæsar's attention from his design, doubled the guards stationed upon the walls on the evening of his intended embarkation, and ordered them to make vigorous attacks upon all Cæsar's forces outside. Then, when the darkness came on, he marched his troops through the two streets which had been left open to the landing-place, and got them as fast as possible on board the transports. Some of the people of the town contrived to make known to Cæsar's army what was going on, by means of signals from the walls; the army immediately brought scaling ladders in great numbers, and, mounting the walls with great ardor and impetuosity, they drove all before them, and soon broke open the gates and got possession of the city. But the barricades and pitfalls, together with the darkness, so embarrassed their movements that Pompey succeeded in completing his embarkation and sailing away.

Cæsar had no ships in which to follow. He returned to Rome. He met, of course, with no opposition. He re-established the government there, organized the Senate anew, and obtained supplies of corn from the public granaries and of money from the city treasury in the capital. In going to the Capitoline Hill after this treasure, he found the officer who had charge of the money stationed there to defend it. He told Cæsar that it was contrary to law for him to enter. Cæsar said that, for men with swords in their hands, there was no law. The officer still refused to admit him. Cæsar then told him to open the doors or he would kill him on the spot. "And you must understand," he added, "that it will be easier for me to do it than it has been to say it." The officer resisted no longer, and Cæsar went in.

After this, Cæsar spent some time in vigorous campaigns in Italy, Spain, Sicily, and Gaul, wherever there was manifested any opposition to his sway. When this work was accomplished, and all these countries were completely subjected to his dominion, he began to turn his thoughts to the plan of pursuing Pompey across the Adriatic Sea.

FEARLESS SAINT GENEVIEVE, PATRON SAINT OF PARIS

By Charlotte M. Yonge

FOUR hundred years of the Roman dominion had entirely tamed the once wild and independent Gauls. Everywhere, except in the moorlands of Brittany, they had become as much like Romans themselves as they could accomplish; they had Latin names, spoke the Latin tongue, all their personages of higher rank were enrolled as Roman citizens, their chief cities were colonies where the laws were administered by magistrates in the Roman fashion, and the houses, dress, and amusements were the same as those of Italy. The greater part of the towns had been converted to Christianity, though some paganism still lurked in the more remote villages and mountainous districts.

It was upon these civilized Gauls that the terrible attacks came from the wild nations who poured out of the center and east of Europe. The Franks came over the Rhine and its dependent rivers, and made furious attacks upon the peaceful plains, where the Gauls had long lived in security, and reports were everywhere heard of villages harried by wild horsemen, with short double-headed battle-axes, and a horrible short pike covered with iron and with several large hooks, like a gigantic artificial minnow, and like it fastened to a long rope, so that the prey which it had grappled might be pulled up to the owner. Walled cities usually stopped them, but every farm or villa outside was stripped of its valuables, set on fire, the cattle driven off, and the more healthy inhabitants seized for slaves.

It was during this state of things that a girl was born to a wealthy peasant at the village now called Nanterre, about two miles from Lutetia, which was already a prosperous city, though not as yet so entirely the capital as it was destined to become under the name of Paris. She was christened by an old Gallic name, probably Gwenfrewi, or White Stream, in Latin Genovefa, but she is best known by the late French form of Geneviève. When she was about seven years old, two celebrated bishops passed through the village, Germanus, of Auxerre, and Lupus, of Troyes, who had been invited to Britain to dispute the false doctrines of Pelagius. All the inhabitants flocked into the church to see them, pray with them, and receive their blessing; and here the sweet childish devotion of Geneviève so struck Germanus, that he called her to him, talked to her, made her sit beside him at the feast, gave her his special blessing, and presented her with a copper medal with a cross engraven upon it. From that time the little maiden always deemed herself especially consecrated to the service of Heaven, but she still remained at home, daily keeping her father's sheep, and spinning their wool as she sat under the trees watching them, but always with her heart full of prayer.

After this St. Germanus proceeded to Britain, and there encouraged his converts to meet the heathen Picts at Maes Garmon, in Flintshire, where the exulting shout of the white-robed catechumens turned to flight the wild superstitious savages of the north—and the Hallelujah victory was gained without a drop of bloodshed. He never lost sight of Geneviève, the little maid whom he had so early distinguished for her piety.

After she lost her parents she went to live with her godmother, and continued the same simple habits, leading a life of sincere devotion and strict self-denial, constant prayer and much charity to her poorer neighbors.

In the year 451 the whole of Gaul was in the most dreadful state of terror at the advance of Attila, the savage chief of the Huns, who came from the banks of the Danube with a host of savages of hideous features, scarred and disfigured to render them more frightful. The old enemies, the Goths and the Franks, seemed like friends compared with these formidable beings, whose cruelties were said to be intolerable, and of whom every exaggerated story was told that could add to the horrors of the miserable people who lay in their path. Tidings came that this "Scourge of God," as Attila called himself, had passed the Rhine, destroyed Tongres and Metz, and was in full march for Paris. The whole country was in the utmost terror. Every one seized their most valuable possessions, and would have fled; but Geneviève placed herself on the only bridge across the Seine, and argued with them, assuring them, in a strain that was afterwards thought of as prophetic, that, if they would pray, repent, and defend instead of abandoning their homes, God would protect them. They were at first almost ready to stone her for thus withstanding their panic, but just then a priest arrived from Auxerre, with a present for Geneviève from St. Germanus, and they were thus reminded of the high estimation in which he held her; they became ashamed of their violence, and she led them back to pray and to arm themselves. In a few days they heard that Attila had paused to besiege Orleans, and that Aëtius, the Roman general, hurrying from Italy, had united his troops with those of the Goths and Franks, and given Attila so terrible a defeat at Châlons that the Huns were fairly driven out of Gaul. And here it must be mentioned that when in the next year, 452, Attila with his murderous host, came down into Italy, and after horrible devastation of all the northern provinces, came to the gates of Rome, no one dared to meet him but one venerable bishop, Leo, the Pope, who, when his flock were in transports of despair, went forth only accompanied by one magistrate to meet the invader, and endeavored to turn his wrath aside. The savage Huns were struck with awe by the fearless majesty of the unarmed old man. They conducted him safely to Attila, who listened to him with respect, and promised not to lead his people into Rome, provided a tribute should be paid to him. He then retreated, and, to the joy of all Europe, died on his way back to his native dominions.

But with the Huns the danger and suffering of Europe did not end. The happy state described in the Prophets as "dwelling safely, with none to make them afraid," was utterly unknown in Europe throughout the long break-up of the Roman Empire; and in a few more years the Franks were overrunning the banks of the Seine, and actually

venturing to lay siege to the Roman walls of Paris
itself. The fortifications were strong enough, but
hunger began to do the work of the besiegers, and
the garrison, unwarlike and untrained, began to
despair. But Geneviève's courage and trust never
failed; and finding no warriors willing to run the
risk of going beyond the walls to obtain food for
the women and children who were perishing around
them, this brave shepherdess embarked alone in a
little boat, and guiding it down the stream, landed
beyond the Frankish camp, and repairing to the
different Gallic cities, she implored them to send
succor to their famished brethren. She obtained
complete success. Probably the Franks had no
means of obstructing the passage of the river, so
that a convoy of boats could easily penetrate into
the town: at any rate they looked upon Geneviève
as something sacred and inspired whom they durst
not touch; probably as one of the battle-maids in
whom their own myths taught them to believe. One
account indeed says that, instead of going alone
to obtain help, Geneviève placed herself at the head
of a forage party, and that the mere sight of her inspired bearing caused them to be allowed to enter
and return in safety; but the boat version seems the
more probable, since a single boat on the broad river
would more easily elude the enemy than a troop of
Gauls pass through their army.

But a city where all the valor resided in one
woman could not long hold out, and in another in-
road, when Geneviève was absent, Paris was actually seized by the Franks. Their leader, Hilperik,
was absolutely afraid of what the mysteriously

brave maiden might do to him, and commanded
the gates of the city to be carefully guarded lest
she should enter; but Geneviève learnt that some
of the chief citizens were imprisoned, and that
Hilperik intended their death, and nothing could
withhold her from making an effort in their behalf. The Franks had made up their minds to
settle and not to destroy. They were not burning
and slaying indiscriminately, but while despising
the Romans, as they called the Gauls, for their
cowardice, they were in awe of their superior civilization and knowledge of arts. The country people
had free access to the city, and Geneviève in her
homely gown and veil passed by Hilperik's guards
without being suspected of being more than any
ordinary Gaulish village-maid; and thus she fear-
lessly made her way, even to the old Roman halls,
where the long-haired Hilperik was holding his wild
carousal. Would that we knew more of that inter-
view—one of the most striking that ever took place!
We can only picture to ourselves the Roman tessel-
ated pavement bestrewn with wine, bones, and
fragments of the barbarous revelry. There were
untamed Franks, their sun-burnt hair tied up in a
knot at the top of their heads, and falling down like
a horse's tail, their faces close-shaven, except two
huge mustaches, and dressed in tight leather garments, with swords at their wide belts. Some slept,
some feasted, some greased their long locks, some
shouted out their favorite war-songs around the
table, which was covered with the spoils of churches,
and at their head sat the wild, long-haired chieftain,
who was a few years later driven away by his own

followers for his excesses—the whole scene was all that was abhorrent to a pure, devout, and faithful nature, most full of terror to a woman. Yet there, in her strength, stood the peasant maiden, her heart full of trust and pity, her looks full of the power that is given by fearlessness of them that can kill the body. What she said we do not know—we only know that the barbarous Hilperik was overawed; he trembled before the expostulations of the brave woman, and granted all she asked—the safety of his prisoners, and mercy to the terrified inhabitants. No wonder that the people of Paris have ever since looked back to Geneviève as their protectress, and that in after-ages she has grown to be the patron saint of the city.

She lived to see the son of Hilperik, Chlodwig, or, as he was more commonly called, Clovis, marry a Christian wife, Clotilda, and after a time become a Christian. She saw the foundation of the Cathedral of Notre Dame, and of the two famous churches of St. Denys and of St. Martin of Tours, and gave her full share to the first efforts for bringing the rude and bloodthirsty conquerors to some knowledge of Christian faith, mercy, and purity. After a life of constant prayer and charity she died, three months after King Clovis, in the year 512, the 89th of her age.

GENEVIEVE ALWAYS DEEMED HERSELF CONSECRATED
TO THE SERVICE OF HEAVEN
—page 61

From the painting by Charles Sprague-Pearce

THE BOY VIKING—OLAF II OF NORWAY

By E. S. Brooks

OLD RANE, the helmsman, whose fierce mustaches and shaggy shoulder-mantle made him look like some grim old Northern wolf, held high in air the great bison-horn filled with foaming mead.

"Skoal to the Viking! Hael was-hael!"[1] rose his exultant shout. From a hundred sturdy throats the cry re-echoed till the vaulted hall of the Swedemen's conquered castle rang again.

"Skoal to the Viking! Hael was-hael!" and in the center of that throng of mail-clad men and tossing spears, standing firm and fearless upon the interlocked and uplifted shields of three stalwart fighting-men, a stout-limbed lad of scarce thirteen, with flowing light-brown hair and flushed and eager face, brandished his sword vigorously in acknowledgment of the jubilant shout that rang once again through the dark and smoke-stained hall: "Was-hael to the sea-wolf's son! Skoal to Olaf the King!"

Then above the din and clash of shouting and of steel rose the voice of Sigvat the saga-man, or song-man of the young viking, singing loud and sturdily:

> "Olaf the King is on his cruise,
> His blue steel staining,
> Rich booty gaining,
> And all men trembling at the news.

[1] "Hail and health to the Viking!"

67

Up, war-wolf's brood! our young fir's name
O'ertops the forest trees in fame,
Our stout young Olaf knows no fear.
    Though fell the fray,
    He's blithe and gay,
And warriors fall beneath his spear.
Who can't defend the wealth they have
Must die or share with the rover brave!"

A fierce and warlike song, boys and girls, to raise
in honor of so young a lad. But those were fierce
and warlike days when men were stirred by the re-
cital of bold and daring deeds—those old, old days,
eight hundred years ago, when Olaf, the boy viking,
the pirate chief of a hundred mail-clad men, stood
upon the uplifted shields of his exultant fighting-
men in the grim and smoke-stained hall of the gray
castle of captured Sigtun, oldest of Swedish cities.

Take your atlas and, turning to the map of Sweden, place your finger on the city of Stockholm. Do
you notice that it lies at the easterly end of a large
lake? That is the Maelar, beautiful with winding
channels, pine-covered islands, and rocky shores.
It is peaceful and quiet now, and palace and villa
and quaint Northern farmhouse stand unmolested
on its picturesque borders. But channels, and
islands, and rocky shores have echoed and re-echoed
with the war-shouts of many a fierce sea-rover since
those far-off days when Olaf, the boy viking, and
his Norwegian ships of war ploughed through the
narrow sea-strait and ravaged the fair shores of
the Maelar with fire and sword.

Stockholm, the "Venice of the North," as it is
called, was not then in existence; and little now remains of old Sigtun save ruined walls. But travel-

lers may still see the three tall towers of the ancient town, and the great stone-heap, alongside which young Olaf drew his ships of war, and over which his pirate crew swarmed into Sigtun town, and planted the victorious banner of the golden serpent upon the conquered walls.

For this fair young Olaf came of hardy Norse stock. His father, Harald Graenske, or "Graymantle," one of the tributary kings of Norway, had fallen a victim to the tortures of the haughty Swedish queen; and now his son, a boy of scarce thirteen, but a warrior already by training and from desire, came to avenge his father's death. His mother, the Queen Aasta, equipped a large dragon-ship or warvessel for her adventurous son, and with the lad, as helmsman and guardian, was sent old Rane, whom men called "the far-travelled," because he had sailed westward as far as England and southward to Nörvasund (by which name men then knew the Straits of Gibraltar). Boys toughened quickly in those stirring days, and this lad, who, because he was commander of the dragon-ship, was called Olaf the King—though he had no land to rule—was of viking blood, and quickly learned the trade of war. Already, among the rocks and sands of Sodermann, upon the Swedish coast, he had won his first battle over a superior force of Danish war-vessels.

Other ships of war joined him; the name of Olaf the Brave was given him by right of daring deeds, and "Skoal to the Viking!" rang from the sturdy throats of his followers as the little sea-king of thirteen was lifted in triumph upon the battledented shields.

But a swift runner bursts into the gray hall of Sigtun. "To your ships, O king; to your ships!" he cries. "Olaf, the Swedish king, men say, is planting a forest of spears along the sea-strait, and, except ye push out now, ye may not get out at all!"

The nimble young chief sprang from the upraised shields.

"To your ships, vikings, all!" he shouted. "Show your teeth, war-wolves! Up with the serpent banner, and death to Olaf the Swede!"

Straight across the lake to the sea-strait, near where Stockholm now stands, the vikings sailed, young Olaf's dragon-ship taking the lead. But all too late; for, across the narrow strait, the Swedish king had stretched great chains, and had filled up the channel with stocks and stones. Olaf and his Norsemen were fairly trapped; the Swedish spears waved in wild and joyful triumph, and King Olaf, the Swede, said with grim satisfaction to his lords: "See, jarls and lendermen, the Fat Boy is caged at last!" For he never spoke of his stout young Norwegian namesake and rival save as "Olaf Tjocke" —Olaf the Thick, or Fat.

The boy viking stood by his dragon-headed prow, and shook his clenched fist at the obstructed sea-strait and the Swedish spears.

"Shall we, then, land, Rane, and fight our way through?" he asked.

"Fight our way through?" said old Rane, who had been in many another tight place in his years of sea-roving, but none so close as this. "Why, king, they be a hundred to one!"

"And if they be, what then?" said impetuous

Olaf. "Better fall as a viking breaking Swedish spears than die a straw-death[1] as Olaf of Sweden's bonder-man. May we not cut through these chains?"

"As soon think of cutting the solid earth, king," said the helmsman.

"So; and why not, then?" young Olaf exclaimed, struck with a brilliant idea. "Ho, Sigvat," he said, turning to his saga-man, "what was that lowland under the cliff where thou didst say the pagan Upsal king was hanged in his own golden chains by his Finnish queen?"

"'Tis called the fen of Agnefit, O king," replied the saga-man, pointing toward where it lay.

"Why, then, my Rane," asked the boy, "may we not cut our way out through that lowland fen to the open sea and liberty?"

"'Tis Odin's own device," cried the delighted helmsman, catching at his young chief's great plan. "Ho, war-wolves all, bite ye your way through the Swedish fens! Up with the serpent banner, and farewell to Olaf the Swede!"

It seemed a narrow chance, but it was the only one. Fortune favored the boy viking. Heavy rains had flooded the lands that slope down to the Maelar Lake; in the dead of night the Swedish captives and stout Norse oarsmen were set to work, and before daybreak an open cut had been made in the lowlands beneath Agnefit, or the "Rock of King Agne," where, by the town of Södertelje, the viking's canal is still shown to trav-

---

[1] So contemptuously did those fierce old sea-kings regard a peaceful life that they said of one who died quietly on his bed at home: "His was but a straw-death."

ellers; the waters of the lake came rushing through the cut, and an open sea-strait awaited young Olaf's fleet.

"Unship the rudder; hoist the sail aloft!" commanded Rane the helmsman. "Sound war-horns all! Skoal to the Viking; skoal to the wise young Olaf!"

A strong breeze blew astern; the Norse rowers steered the rudderless ships with their long oars, and with a mighty rush, through the new canal and over all the shallows, out into the great Norrström, or North Stream, as the Baltic Sea was called, the fleet passed in safety while the loud war-horns blew the notes of triumph.

So the boy viking escaped from the trap of his Swedish foes, and, standing by the "grim, gaping dragon's head" that crested the prow of his war-ship, he bade the helmsman steer for Gotland Isle, while Sigvat, the saga-man, sang with the ring of triumph:

"Down the fiord sweep wind and rain;
Our sails and tackle sway and strain;
    Wet to the skin
    We're sound within.
Our sea-steed through the foam goes prancing,
While shields and spears and helms are glancing.
        From fiord to sea,
        Our ships ride free,
And down the wind with swelling sail
We scud before the gathering gale."

What a breezy, rollicking old saga it is! Can't you almost catch the spray and sea-swell in its dashing measures, boys?

Now, turn to your atlases again and look for the large island of Gotland off the southeastern coast of Sweden, in the midst of the Baltic Sea. In the time of Olaf it was a thickly peopled and wealthy district, and the principal town, Wisby, at the northern end, was one of the busiest places in all Europe. To this attractive island the boy viking sailed with all his ships, looking for rich booty, but the Gotlanders met him with fair words and offered him so great a "scatt," or tribute, that he agreed not to molest them, and rested at the island, an unwelcome guest, through all the long winter. Early in the spring he sailed eastward to the Gulf of Riga and spread fear and terror along the coast of Finland. And the old saga tells how the Finlanders "conjured up in the night, by their witchcraft, a dreadful storm and bad weather; but the king ordered all the anchors to be weighed and sail hoisted, and beat off all night to the outside of the land. So the king's luck prevailed more than the Finlander's witchcraft."

Then away "through the wild sea" to Denmark sailed the young pirate king, and here he met a brother viking, one Thorkell the Tall. The two chiefs struck up a sort of partnership; and coasting southward along the western shores of Denmark, they won a sea-fight in the Ringkiobing Fiord, among the "sand hills of Jutland." And so business continued brisk with this curiously matched pirate firm—a giant and a boy—until, under the cliffs of Kinlimma, in Friesland, hasty word came to the boy viking that the English king, Ethelred the Unready, was calling for the help of all sturdy fighters to win back his heritage and crown from young King Cnut, or Canute the Dane, whose father had seized the throne of England. Quick to respond to an appeal that promised plenty of hard knocks, and the possibility of unlimited booty, Olaf, the ever ready, hoisted his blue and crimson sails and steered his war-ships over the sea to help King Ethelred, the never ready. Up the Thames and straight for London town he rowed.

"Hail to the serpent banner! Hail to Olaf the Brave!" said King Ethelred, as the war-horns sounded a welcome; and on the low shores of the Isle of Dogs, just below the old city, the keels of the Norse war-ships grounded swiftly, and the boy viking and his followers leaped ashore. "Thou dost come in right good time with thy trusty dragon-ships, young king," said King Ethelred; "for the Danish robbers are full well entrenched in London town and in my father Edgar's castle."

And then he told Olaf how, "in the great trading place which is called Southwark," the Danes had raised "a great work and dug large ditches, and within had builded a bulwark of stone, timber, and turf, where they had stationed a large army.

"And we would fain have taken this bulwark," added the king, "and did in sooth bear down upon it with a great assault; but indeed we could make naught of it."

"And why so?" asked the young viking.

"Because," said King Ethelred, "upon the bridge betwixt the castle and Southwark have the ravaging Danes raised towers and parapets, breast high, and thence they did cast down stones and weapons upon us so that we could not prevail. And now, sea-king, what dost they counsel? How may we avenge ourselves of our enemies and win the town?"

Impetuous as ever, and impatient of obstacles, the young viking said: "How? why, pull thou down this bridge, king, and then may ye have free riverway to thy castle."

"Break down great London Bridge, young hero?" cried the amazed king. "How may that be? Have we a Duke Samson among us to do so great a feat?"

"Lay me thy ships alongside mine, king, close to this barricaded bridge," said the valorous boy, "and I will vow to break it down, or ye may call me caitiff and coward."

"Be it so," said Ethelred, the English king; and all the war-chiefs echoed: "Be it so!" So Olaf and his trusty Rane made ready the war-forces for the destruction of the bridge.

Old London Bridge was not what we should now call an imposing structure, but our ancestors of nine centuries back esteemed it quite a bridge. The chronicler says that it was "so broad that two wagons could pass each other upon it," and "under the bridge were piles driven into the bottom of the river."

So young Olaf and old Rane put their heads together, and decided to wreck the bridge by a bold viking stroke. And this is how it is told in the "Heimskringla," or Saga of King Olaf the Saint:

"King Olaf ordered great platforms of floating

wood to be tied together with hazel bands, and for this he took down old houses; and with these, as a roof, he covered over his ships so widely that it reached over the ships' sides. Under this screen he set pillars, so high and stout that there both was room for swinging their swords, and the roofs were strong enough to withstand the stones cast down upon them."

"Now, out oars and pull for the bridge," young Olaf commanded; and the roofed-over war-ships were rowed close up to London Bridge.

And as they came near the bridge, the chronicle says: "There were cast upon them, by the Danes upon the bridge, so many stones and missile weapons, such arrows and spears, that neither helmet nor shield could hold out against it; and the ships themselves were so greatly damaged that many retreated out of it."

But the boy viking and his Norsemen were there for a purpose, and were not to be driven back by stones or spears or arrows. Straight ahead they rowed, "quite up under the bridge."

"Out cables, all, and lay them around the piles," the young sea-king shouted; and the half-naked rowers, unshipping their oars, reached out under the roofs and passed the stout cables twice around the wooden supports of the bridge. The loose end was made fast at the stern of each vessel, and then, turning and heading down stream, King Olaf's twenty stout war-ships waited his word:

"Out oars!" he cried; "pull, war-birds! Pull all, as if ye were for Norway!"

Forward and backward swayed the stout Norse

rowers; tighter and tighter pulled the cables; fast down upon the straining war-ships rained the Danish spears and stones; but the wooden piles under the great bridge were loosened by the steady tug of the cables, and soon with a sudden spurt the Norse war-ships darted down the river, while the slackened cables towed astern the captured piles of London Bridge. A great shout went up from the besiegers, and "now," says the chronicle, "as the armed troops stood thick upon the bridge, and there were likewise many heaps of stones and other weapons upon it, the bridge gave way; and a great part of the men upon it fell into the river, and all the others fled—some into the castle, some into Southwark." And before King Ethelred, "the Unready," could pull his ships to the attack, young Olaf's fighting-men had sprung ashore, and, storming the Southwark earthworks, carried all before them, and the battle of London Bridge was won.

And the young Olaf's saga-man sang triumphantly:

> "London Bridge is broken down—
> Gold is won and bright renown.
> Shields resounding,
> War-horns sounding,
> Hildar shouting in the din!
> Arrows singing,
> Mail-coats ringing,
> Odin makes our Olaf win!"

And perhaps, who knows, this wrecking of London Bridge so many hundred years ago by Olaf, the boy viking of fifteen, may have been the origin

of the old song-game dear to so many generations
of children:

"London Bridge is fallen down, fallen down, fallen down—
London Bridge is fallen down, my fair lady!"

So King Ethelred won back his kingdom, and
the boy viking was honored above all others. To
him was given the chief command in perilous expeditions against the Danes, and the whole defence of all the coast of England. North and
south along the coast he sailed with all his war-
ships, and the Danes and Englishmen long remembered the dashing but dubious ways of this
young sea-rover, who swept the English coast and
claimed his dues from friend and foe alike. For
those were days of insecurity for merchant and
trader and farmer, and no man's wealth or life
was safe except as he paid ready tribute to the
fierce Norse allies of King Ethelred. But soon
after this, King Ethelred died, and young Olaf,
thirsting for new adventures, sailed away to the
south and fought his way all along the French
coast as far as the mouth of the River Garonne.
Many castles he captured; many rival vikings subdued; much spoil he gathered; until at last his
dragon-ships lay moored under the walls of old
Bordeaux, waiting for fair winds to take him
around to the Straits of Gibraltar, and so on "to
the land of Jerusalem."

One day, in the booty-filled "fore-hold" of his
dragon-ship, the young sea-king lay asleep; and
suddenly, says the old record, "he dreamed a won-
drous dream."

"Olaf, great stem of kings, attend!" he heard a deep voice call; and, looking up, the dreamer seemed to see before him "a great and important man, but of a terrible appearance withal."

"If that thou art Olaf the Brave, as men do call thee," said the vision, "turn thyself to nobler deeds than vikings' ravaging and this wandering cruise. Turn back, turn back from thy purposeless journey to the land of Jerusalem, where neither honor nor fame awaits thee. Son of King Harald, return thee to thy heritage; for thou shalt be king over all Norway."

Then the vision vanished and the young rover awoke to find himself alone, save for the sleeping foot-boy across the cabin door-way. So he quickly summoned old Rane, the helmsman, and told his dream.

"'Twas for thy awakening, king," said his stout old follower. "'Twas the great Olaf, thine uncle, Olaf Tryggvesson the king, that didst call thee. Win Norway, king, for the portent is that thou and thine shall rule thy fatherland."

And the war-ships' prows were all turned northward again, as the boy viking, following the promise of his dream, steered homeward for Norway and a throne.

Now in Norway Earl Eric was dead. For thirteen years he had usurped the throne that should have been filled by one of the great King Olaf's line; and, at his death, his handsome young son, Earl Hakon the Fair, ruled in his father's stead. And when young King Olaf heard this news, he shouted for joy and cried to Rane:

"Now, home in haste, for Norway shall be either Hakon's heritage or mine!"

" 'Tis a fair match of youth 'gainst youth," said the trusty helmsman; "and if but fair luck go with thee, Norway shall be thine!"

So from "a place called Furovald," somewhere between the mouths of Humber and of Tees, on the English coast, King Olaf, with but two stout war-ships and two hundred and twenty "well-armed and chosen persons," shook out his purple sails to the North Sea blasts, and steered straight for Norway.

As if in league against this bold young viking the storm winds came rushing down from the mountains of Norway and the cold belt of the Arctic Circle and caught the two war-ships tossing in a raging sea.

The storm burst upon them with terrific force, and the danger of shipwreck was great. "But," says the old record, "as they had a chosen company and the king's luck with them all went on well."

"Thou able chief!"

sings the faithful saga-man,

"With thy fearless crew
Thou meetest with skill and courage true
The wild sea's wrath
On thy ocean path,
Though waves mast-high were breaking round,
Thou findest the middle of Norway's ground,
With helm in hand
On Saelö's strand."

Now *Sael* was Norse for "lucky" and Saelö's Island means the lucky island.

"I'll be a lucky king for landing thus upon the Lucky Isle," said rash young Olaf, with the only attempt at a joke we find recorded of him, as, with a mighty leap, he sprang ashore where the sliding keel of his war-ship ploughed the shore of Saelö's Isle.

"True, 'tis a good omen, king," said old Rane the helmsman, following close behind.

But the soil of the "Lucky Isle" was largely clay, moist and slippery, and as the eager young viking climbed the bank his right foot slipped, and he would have fallen had not he struck his left foot firmly in the clay and thus saved himself. But to slip at all was a bad sign in those old, half-pagan, and superstitious times, and he said, ruefully: "An omen; an omen, Rane! The king falls!"

"Nay, 'tis the king's luck," says ready and wise old Rane. "Thou didst not fall, king. See; thou didst but set fast foot in this thy native soil of Norway."

"Thou art a rare diviner, Rane," laughed the young king, much relieved, and then he added solemnly: "It may be so if God doth will it so."

And now news comes that Earl Hakon, with a single war-ship, is steering north from Sogne Fiord; and Olaf, pressing on, lays his two ships on either side of a narrow strait, or channel, in Sandunga Sound. Here he stripped his ships of all their war-gear, and stretched a great cable deep in the water, across the narrow strait. Then he wound the cable-ends around the capstans, ordered all his fighting-men out of sight, and waited for his rival. Soon Earl Hakon's war-ship, crowded with rowers and fighting-men, entered the strait. Seeing, as he supposed, but two harmless merchant-vessels lying on either side of the channel, the young earl bade his rowers pull between the two. Suddenly there is a stir on the quiet merchant-vessels. The capstan bars are manned; the sunken cable is drawn taut. Up goes the stern of Earl Hakon's entrapped war-ship; down plunges her prow into the waves, and the water pours into the doomed boat. A loud shout is heard; the quiet merchant-vessels swarm with mail-clad men, and the air is filled with a shower of stones, and spears, and arrows. The surprise is complete. Tighter draws the cable; over topples Earl Hakon's vessel, and he and all his men are among the billows struggling for life. "So," says the record, "King Olaf took Earl Hakon and all his men whom they could get hold of out of the water and made them prisoners; but some were killed and some were drowned."

Into the "fore-hold" of the king's ship the captive earl was led a prisoner, and there the young rivals for Norway's crown faced each other. The two lads were of nearly the same age—between sixteen and seventeen—and young Earl Hakon was considered the handsomest youth in all Norway. His helmet was gone, his sword was lost, his ring-steel suit was sadly disarranged, and his long hair, "fine as silk," was "bound about his head with a gold ornament." Fully expecting the fate of all captives in those cruel days—instant death—

HE SHOOK HIS CLENCHED FIST AT THE OBSTRUCTED
SEA-STRAIT — page 70
From the drawing by Gertrude Demain Hammond

the young earl nevertheless faced his boy conqueror proudly, resolved to meet his fate like a man.

"They speak truth who say of the house of Eric that ye be handsome men," said the king, studying his prisoner's face. "But now, earl, even though thou be fair to look upon, thy luck hath failed thee at last."

"Fortune changes," said the young earl. "We both be boys; and thou, king, art perchance the shrewder youth. Yet, had we looked for such a trick as thou hast played upon us, we had not thus been tripped upon thy sunken cables. Better luck next time."

"Next time!" echoed the king; "dost thou not know, earl, that as thou standest there, a prisoner, there may be no 'next time' for thee?"

The young captive understood full well the meaning of the words. "Yes, king," he said; "it must be only as thou mayst determine. Man can die but once. Speak on; I am ready!" But Olaf said: "What wilt thou give me, earl, if at this time I do let thee go, whole and unhurt?"

"'Tis not what I may give, but what thou mayst take, king," the earl made answer. "I am thy prisoner; what wilt thou take to free me?"

"Nothing," said the generous young viking, advancing nearer to his handsome rival. "As thou didst say, we both be boys, and life is all before us. Earl, I give thee thy life, do thou but take oath before me to leave this my realm of Norway, to give up thy kingdom, and never to do battle against me hereafter."

The conquered earl bent his fair young head.

"Thou art a generous chief, King Olaf," he said. "I take my life as thou dost give it, and all shall be as thou wilt."

So Earl Hakon took the oath, and King Olaf righted his rival's capsized war-ship, refitted it from his own stores of booty, and thus the two lads parted; the young earl sailing off to his uncle, King Canute, in England, and the boy viking hastening eastward to Vigen, where lived his mother, the Queen Aasta, whom he had not seen for full five years.

It is harvest-time in the year 1014. Without and within the long, low house of Sigurd Sye, at Vigen, all is excitement; for word has come that Olaf the sea-king has returned to his native land, and is even now on his way to this his mother's house. Gay stuffs decorate the dull walls of the great-room, clean straw covers the earth floor, and upon the long, four-cornered tables is spread a mighty feast of mead and ale and coarse but hearty food, such as the old Norse heroes drew their strength and muscle from. At the door-way stands the Queen Aasta with her maidens, while before the entrance, with thirty "well-clothed men," waits young Olaf's stepfather, wise Sigurd Syr, gorgeous in a jewelled suit, a scarlet cloak, and a glittering golden helmet. The watchers on the housetops hear a distant shout, now another and nearer one, and soon, down the highway, they catch the gleam of steel and the waving of many banners; and now they can distinguish the stalwart forms of Olaf's chosen hundred men, their shining coats of ring-mail, their foreign helmets.

and their crossleted shields flashing in the sun. In the very front rides old Rane, the helmsman, bearing the great white banner blazoned with the golden serpent, and, behind him, cased in golden armor, his long brown hair flowing over his sturdy shoulders, rides the boy viking, Olaf of Norway.

It was a brave home-coming; and as the stout young hero, leaping from his horse, knelt to receive his mother's welcoming kiss, the people shouted for joy, the banners waved, the war-horns played their loudest; and thus, after five years of wandering, the boy comes back in triumph to the home he left when but a wild and adventurous little fellow of twelve.

The hero of nine great sea-fights, and of many smaller ones, before he was seventeen, young Olaf Haraldson was a remarkable boy, even in the days when all boys aimed to be battle-tried heroes. Toughened in frame and fiber by his five years of sea-roving, he had become strong and self-reliant, a man in action though but a boy in years.

"I am come," he said to his mother and his stepfather, "to take the heritage of my forefathers. But not from Danish nor from Swedish kings will I supplicate that which is mine by right. I intend rather to seek my patrimony with battle-axe and sword, and I will so lay hand to the work that one of two things shall happen: Either I shall bring all this kingdom of Norway under my rule, or I shall fall here upon my inheritance in the land of my fathers."

These were bold words for a boy of seventeen. But they were not idle boastings. Before a year had passed, young Olaf's pluck and courage had won the day, and in harvest-time, in the year 1015, being then but little more than eighteen years old, he was crowned King of Norway in the Dront-heim, or "Throne-home," of Nidaros, the royal city, now called on your atlas the city of Dront-heim. For fifteen years King Olaf the Second ruled his realm of Norway. The old record says that he was "a good and very gentle man"; but history shows his goodness and gentleness to have been of a rough and savage kind. The wild and stern experiences of his viking days lived again even in his attempts to reform and benefit his land. When he who had himself been a pirate tried to put down piracy, and he who had been a wild young robber sought to force all Norway to be-come Christian, he did these things in so fierce and cruel a way that at last his subjects rebelled, and King Canute came over with a great army to wrest the throne from him. On the bloody field of Sti-klestad, July 29, 1030, the stern king fell, says Sig-vat, his saga-man,

> "beneath the blows
> By his own thoughtless people given."

So King Canute conquered Norway; but after his death, Olaf's son, Magnus the Good, regained his father's throne. The people, sorrowful at their rebellion against King Olaf, forgot his stern and cruel ways, and magnified all his good deeds so mightily that he was at last declared a saint, and the shrine of Saint Olaf is still one of the glories of the old cathedral in Drontheim. And, after King Magnus died, his descendants ruled Norway for nearly four hundred years; and thus was brought to pass the promise of the dream that, in the "fore-hold" of the great dragon-ship, under the walls of old Bordeaux, came so many years before to the daring and sturdy young Olaf of Norway, the boy viking.

THE BOY-HEROES OF CRECY AND POITIERS

By Treadwell Walden

ALMOST every one has heard of the famous battles of Crecy and Poitiers, which were so much alike in all that made them remarkable that they are generally coupled together—one always reminding us of the other. Yet there is one point they had in common which has not been especially remarked, but which ought to link them memorably together in the imagination of young people.

These two great battles really took place ten years apart; for one was fought in 1346 and the other in 1356. The battle-fields also were wide apart; for Crecy was far in the north of France, near the coast of the English Channel, and Poitiers away in the south, deep in the interior, nearly three hundred miles from Crecy. But they have drawn near to each other in the minds of students of history, because in both cases the French largely outnumbered the English; in both cases the English had gone so far into the country that their retreat seemed to be cut off; in both cases there was a most surprising and unexpected result, for the French were terribly defeated; and in both cases this happened because they made the same mistake: they trusted so much to their overwhelming numbers, to their courage and their valor, that they forgot to be careful about anything else, while the English made up for their small numbers by prudence, discipline, and skill, without which courage and valor are often of no avail.

It is quite exciting to read the description of these battles, with their archery fights, the clashing together of furious knights, the first brave advance and the final running away; but, after a while, the battles at large seem to fade out in the greater interest which surrounds the figures of two youngsters—one hardly more than fifteen, the other scarcely fourteen—for one carried off all the honors of the victory of Crecy, and the other redeemed from total dishonor the defeat of Poitiers. Let us now take up the romantic story of the English lad in the former battle, and of the French lad in the latter.

When, in 1346, Edward III of England had determined upon an invasion of France, he brought over his army in a fleet of nearly a thousand sail. He had with him not only the larger portion of his great nobles, but also his eldest son, Edward Plantagenet, the Prince of Wales. He had good reasons for taking the boy. The prince was expected to become the next King of England. His father evidently thought him able to take a very important part in becoming also the King of

France. If all the accounts of him are true, he was a remarkable youth; wonderfully strong and courageous, and wonderfully discreet for his years.

There was only one road to success or fame in those days, and that was the profession of arms. The ambition of every high-born young fellow was to become a knight. Knighthood was something that both king and nobles regarded as higher in some respects than even the royalty or nobility to which they were born. No one could be admitted into an order of the great brotherhood of knights, which extended all over Europe and formed an independent society, unless he had gone through severe discipline, and had performed some distinguished deed of valor. Then he could wear the golden spurs; for knighthood had its earliest origin in the distinction of fighting on horseback, while ordinary soldiers fought on foot. Although knighthood changed afterward, the word "chivalry" always expressed it, from *cheval*, a horse. And in addition to valor, which was the result of physical strength and courage, the knight was expected to be generous, courteous, faithful, devout, truthful, high-souled, high-principled. Hence the epithet, "chivalrous," which, even to-day, is so often heard applied to men of especially fine spirit. "Honor," was the great word which included all these qualities then, as it does in some measure now.

I have only time to give you the standard, and cannot pause to tell you how well or ill it was lived up to generally. But I would not have taken this story in hand if chivalry had to be left out of the account, for it was chivalry that made my two boys the heroes they were.

As soon as King Edward landed at La Hague, he gave very clear evidence of the serious work he had cut out for his son, and of his confidence that the youngster would be equal to it. He publicly pledged his boy, beforehand, to some great deed, and to a life of valor and honor. In sight of the whole army, he went through the form of making him a knight. Young Edward, clad in armor, kneeled down before him on the wet sand, when the king touched his shoulder with his sword, saying: "I dub thee knight. Be brave, bold, and loyal!" You may imagine how proudly then the young fellow seized lance and sword and shield, and sprang into his saddle at a leap, and with what high resolve he rode on beside his mailed and gallant father to deserve the name which that impressive ceremony had given him.

The army moved rapidly forward and northward toward Calais, conquering everything on its way, till when in the neighborhood of Crecy, the intelligence came that the French king, Philip, with an army of one hundred and twenty thousand men and all the chivalry of France, had come in between it and the sea. There was no retreat possible. Edward had but thirty thousand to oppose this great host. They were four to one. He was in a dangerous spot also; but after a time he succeeded in getting away to a good position, and there he awaited the onset. No one will doubt that he was anxious enough, and yet what did he do? After arranging his troops in battle order, three battalions deep, he sent young Edward to the very front of the brilliant group of his finest barons to take the brunt of the terrible charge that was now to come! It shows of what stern material the king and the men of that time were made, for all his present love, all his future hope, lay around that gallant boy. But he knew that the value of the glory which might be earned was worth all the risk. Besides, he was as much under chivalrous necessity to send him, as the lad was under to go. That pledge to knighthood, on the seashore, had not been either lightly taken or lightly given. If chivalry was not equal to sacrifice, it was equal to nothing. There was keen wisdom, too, in the act. The king could count all the more on the enthusiasm, self-devotion and valor of the knights and men-at-arms, in whose keeping he had placed so precious a charge. That whole first battalion would be nerved to tenfold effort because the prince was among them, for every one would be as deeply concerned as the father in the boy's success.

Edward carried his feeling of devotion to his son's best interests to such a chivalrous extent that he made it a point of duty to keep out of the battle altogether.

He was nowhere to be seen. He went into a windmill on a height nearby, and watched the fight through one of the narrow windows in its upper story. He would not even put on his helmet. That was the way the father stood by his son—by showing absolute confidence in him, and denying himself all the glory that might come from a great and important battle. And the young fellow was a thousandfold nerved and strengthened by knowing that his father fully trusted in him.

I need not give the details of the battle. It is sufficient to know that the first line of the French chivalry charged with the utmost fury. Among these was an ally of note, John, King of Bohemia, who with his barons and knights was not behindhand in the deadly onset; and yet this king was old and blind! His was chivalry in another form! He would have his stroke in the battle, and he plunged into it with his horse tied by its reins to one of his knights on either side. A plume of three ostrich feathers waved from his helmet, and the chroniclers say he laid about him well. After the battle, he and his two companions were found dead, with their horses tied together.

But although the French were brave they were not wise. For not only had they brought on the fight with headlong energy before they were prepared, but they had allowed Edward to place himself so that the afternoon sun, then near its setting, blazed full in their eyes and faces. Edward's army fought in the shadow. The terrible English bowmen sent their deadly cloth-yard arrows so thick and fast into the dazzled and crowded ranks of fifteen thousand Genoese archers and the intermingled men-at-arms, that the missiles filled the air like snow. The Genoese were thrown into confusion, and this spread throughout the whole French army. The French king, with some of his dukes, flew foaming over the field in the rear, trying in vain to get up in time to swell the onset upon the English front.

But the onset had proved bad enough as it was. The knights around the young prince were frightened for his safety. One of them, Sir Thomas of Norwich, was sent back to Edward to ask him to come to the assistance of the prince.

"Sir Thomas," said the king, "is my son dead or unhorsed, or so wounded that he cannot help himself?"

"Not so, my lord, thank God; but he is fighting against great odds, and is like to have need of your help."

"Sir Thomas," replied the king, "return to them who sent you, and tell them from me not to send for me, whatever chance befall them, so long as my son is alive, and tell them that I bid them let the lad win his spurs; for I wish, if God so desire, that the day should be his, and the honor thereof remain to him and to those to whom I have given him in charge."

And there he stayed in the windmill till the battle was over. Soon the cry of victory reached him as the French fled in the darkness, leaving their dead strewn upon the field. Now the young prince appeared covered with all the glory that his father had coveted for him, bearing the ostrich plume which he had taken from the dead King of Bohemia. The boy rode up with his visor raised—his face was as fair as a girl's, and glowed under a crown of golden hair. He bore his trophy aloft, and when it was placed as a knightly decoration above the crest of his helmet, he little thought that the triple tuft was to wave for more than five hundred years, even to this day, on England's front, for such it does, and that, next to the crown, there shall be no badge so proudly known as the three feathers which nod above the coronet of the Prince of Wales. Edward Albert, son of King George V, now wears it because Edward, the Prince of Wales, when still in his teens, won it at Crecy. We will leave him there, and go on ten years.

Philip, the French king, had passed away about six years before, and John, a wild character for such a trying time, had ascended the throne. He was always plunging himself into difficulties, and was often guilty of cruelty; and yet was of such a free, generous nature, and had so many of the virtues of chivalry in that day, that he was known as "John the Good." He was the extreme opposite to the grave, prudent, sagacious Edward III, who was still alive and well, and King of England.

Some time after the victory of Crecy, Calais had been taken, and then both nations were glad to arrange a truce. Nine years of this had gone by, when Edward thought it necessary to make another attempt on France. As soon as might be, therefore, young Edward, his son, now twenty-five, came over alone, landing at Bordeaux. He had, meantime, gained great fame. He was now known as "the Black Prince," because he had a fancy for having his armor painted as black as midnight, in order, they say, to give a greater brightness to his fresh blond complexion and golden hair. Marshaling his little army of 12,000 men, he set out into the interior of France. When he had reached the neighborhood of Poitiers, he was astounded by the news that

King John was both after him and behind him, with a force of 60,000 men—five to one! Here was Crecy over again as to numbers, but there was one thing made it worse; for, as Edward III not long before had instituted the famous "Order of the Garter" which is even now one of the foremost orders of knighthood in Europe, so John, not to be behindhand, and in order to give a new chivalrous impulse to his nobles, had just instituted the "Order of the Star." He made five hundred knights of this new order, every one of whom had vowed that he would never retreat, and would sooner be slain than yield to an enemy.

The Black Prince thought it almost impossible to fight his way through such a desperately determined host. So he offered to restore all he had just conquered and to make another truce, if he might pass by unmolested. But John would not consent. He must have Calais back again, and the prince, with one hundred of his best knights, into the bargain. "This will never do," thought the prince. "Better try for another Crecy."

On the morning of September 19, 1356, the battle began. John had with him all four of his sons, Charles, Louis, John and Philip; the eldest only nineteen, and the youngest fourteen. The three former were put under good guardianship in different portions of the field; but why the hare-brained monarch took the youngest boy with him into the very front and thickest of the fight, it is hard to guess, unless it was another imitation of Edward, and he had also good reason to think that the lad was unusually well able to take care of himself, having been trained at arms and pledged to knighthood. But young "Sir Philip," as he was called, proved quite equal to the occasion.

King John himself led the van, moving down through a defile, into which, after a time, his whole army found themselves crowded. Meantime, the Prince of Wales had planted his army just where he would tempt John into that trap and had set his archers in good position. These men were clad in green, like Robin Hood's men, and carried bows seven feet long and so thick that few men of modern days could bend them. A cloth-yard shaft from one of these would fly with tremendous force. Edward had placed these archers in ambush, behind green hedges, and crouching in the green of the vineyards.

Just as the French king, with all his new chivalry around him, dashed down the narrow valley—the white standard of France on one side of him, his keen-eyed little son on the other—and began to deploy the whole advance battalion, preliminary to a grand charge—whiz! whiz! whir! whir! from both sides came the arrows, as thick as hail and as terrible as javelins, from the hidden archers. The astonished Frenchmen fell back. That crowded still more those who were yet wedged in the narrow space behind. Now came the English onset. Then a panic. Then a rout. Then a general flight. Dukes, barons, knights of all sorts fled with the rest; also Charles, Louis, John, the three elder sons of the king. The king was in great danger of being slain; but he did not move, and Philip stood fighting by his side. The standard-bearer fell, and the white ensign lay in the dust. Many a faithful knight was cut down, or swept away a prisoner. But Philip flinched not.

The assailants—some of whom knew the king, while others were wondering who he might be—pressed them fiercely on every side, striking at them, but more anxious to take them captives than to kill them, for they were worth a heavy ransom. The Englishmen shouted all together, "Yield you! Yield you, else you die!" Little Sir Philip had no yield in him, as long as his father held out. He kept close to him, trying to ward off the blows which were aimed at him, and warning him in time, as his quick eye caught a near danger on either hand. Every instant he was heard calling out, "Father, ware right! Father, ware left!" Suddenly a mounted knight appeared, who hailed the king in French. It was a French knight, who was fighting on the English side.

"Sir, sir!" he shouted, "I pray you yield!"

"To whom shall I yield me?" said John. "Where is my cousin, the Prince of Wales?"

"Sir, yield you to me; I will bring you to him."

"Who are you?" said the king.

"Denis de Morbecque, a knight of Artois; I serve the King of England, not being able to live in France, for I have lost all I possessed there."

"I yield me to you," said John, handing him his steel glove.

Then the whole crowd began to drag at him, each exclaiming: "I took him!" Both the king and the prince were sadly hustled, until two barons broke through the throng by dint of their horses, and led the two to the tent of the Prince of Wales, "and made him a present of the King of France!" says an old chronicler. "The prince also bowed full low before the king, and received him as a king, properly and discreetly, as he well knew how to do."

In the evening he entertained him and Philip at supper, "and would not sit at the king's table for all the king's entreaty, but waited as a serving man, bending the knee before him, and saying: 'Dear sir, be pleased not to put on so bad a countenance, because it hath not pleased God to consent this day to your wishes; for, assuredly, my lord and father will show you all the honor and friendship he shall be able, and he will come to terms with you so reasonably that you shall remain good friends forever.'"

Nor did all this end in words, but it went on for years during all the captivity of King John and Prince Philip—first at Bordeaux and afterward at the then new Windsor Castle, in England, where galas, tournaments, hawking and hunting, and all sorts of entertainments were devised for them. When King John was brought from Bordeaux to England, where King Edward had prepared to meet him in great state, the French king was mounted on a tall, cream-colored charger, and young Philip rode by his side in great honor also, while the Prince of Wales sat on a small black horse, like an humble attendant on them both. The two royal fathers met midway in that London street, the houses which lined the way were hung with rich tapestries, the trades were out in companies of many colors, the people thronged round the steel-clad cavalcades as they came together, and they filled the air with shouts—but what two figures now

most fill the eye when all that pageant has passed
away? Not the father who stood by his son with
such chivalrous faith, nor the father whose son stood
by him with such chivalrous devotion, but the fair
youth who carries that tuft of feathers upon his
helmet, with its motto, "I serve," and the lad whom
all have heard of as "Philip the Bold"; the boy-hero
of Crecy doing chivalrous honor to the boy-hero of
Poitiers!

THE NOBLE BURGHERS OF CALAIS

By Charlotte M. Yonge

NOWHERE does the continent of Europe approach Great Britain so closely as at the
Straits of Dover, and when the English sovereigns
were full of the vain hope of obtaining the crown of
France, or at least of regaining the great possessions that their forefathers had owned as French
nobles, there was no spot so coveted by them as the
fortress of Calais, the possession of which gave an
entrance into France.

Thus it was that when, in 1346, Edward III
had beaten Philippe VI at the battle of Crecy,
the first use he made of his victory was to march
upon Calais, and lay siege to it. The walls were
exceedingly strong and solid, mighty defenses of
masonry, of huge thickness and like rocks for
solidity, guarded it, and the king knew that it
would be useless to attempt a direct assault. Indeed, during all the middle ages, the modes of
protecting fortifications were far more efficient

than the modes of attacking them. The walls could be made enormously massive, the towers raised to a great height, and the defenders so completely sheltered by battlements that they could not easily be injured, and could take aim from the top of their turrets, or from their loophole windows. The gates had absolute little castles of their own, a moat flowed round the walls full of water, and only capable of being crossed by a drawbridge, behind which the portcullis, a grating armed beneath with spikes, was always ready to drop from the archway of the gate and close up the entrance. The only chance of taking a fortress by direct attack was to fill up the moat with earth and faggots, and then raise ladders against the walls; or else to drive engines against the defenses, battering-rams which struck them with heavy beams, mangonels which launched stones, sows whose arched wooden backs protected troops of workmen who tried to undermine the wall, and moving towers consisting of a succession of stages or shelves, filled with soldiers, and with a bridge with iron hooks, capable of being launched from the highest story to the top of the battlements. The besieged could generally disconcert the battering-ram by hanging beds or mattresses over the walls to receive the brunt of the blow, the sows could be crushed with heavy stones, the towers burnt by well directed flaming missiles, the ladders overthrown, and in general the besiegers suffered a great deal more damage than they could inflict. Cannon had indeed just been brought into use at the battle of Crecy, but they only consisted of iron bars fastened together with hoops, and were as yet of little use, and thus there seemed to be little danger to a well guarded city from any enemy outside the walls.

King Edward arrived before the place with all his victorious army early in August, his good knights and squires arrayed in glittering steel armor, covered with surcoats richly embroidered with their heraldic bearings; his stout men-at-arms, each of whom was attended by three bold followers; and his archers, with their cross-bows to shoot bolts, and long-bows to shoot arrows of a yard long, so that it used to be said that each went into battle with three men's lives under his girdle, namely the three arrows he kept there ready to his hand. With the king was his son, Edward, Prince of Wales, who had just won the golden spurs of knighthood so gallantly at Crecy when only in his seventeenth year, and likewise the famous Hainault knight, Sir Walter Mauny, and all that was noblest and bravest in England.

This whole glittering army, at their head the king's great royal standard bearing the golden lilies of France quartered with the lions of England, and each troop guided by the square banner, swallow-tailed pennon or pointed pennoncel of their leader, came marching to the gates of Calais, above which floated the blue standard of France with its golden flowers, and with it the banner of the governor, Sir Jean de Vienne. A herald, in a rich long robe embroidered with the arms of England, rode up to the gate, a trumpet sounding before him, and called upon Sir Jean de

Vienne to give up the place to Edward, King of England, and of France, as he claimed to be. Sir Jean made answer that he held the town for Philippe, King of France, and that he would defend it to the last; the herald rode back again and the English began the siege of the city.

At first they only encamped, and the people of Calais must have seen the whole plain covered with the white canvas tents, marshaled round the ensigns of the leaders, and here and there a more gorgeous one displaying the colors of the owner. Still there was no attack upon the walls. The warriors were to be seen walking about in the leathern suits they wore under their armor; or if a party was to be seen with their coats of mail on, helmet on head, and lance in hand, it was not against Calais that they came; they rode out into the country, and by and by might be seen driving back before them herds of cattle and flocks of sheep or pigs that they had seized and taken away from the poor peasants; and at night the sky would show red lights where farms and homesteads had been set on fire. After a time, in front of the tents, the English were to be seen hard at work with beams and boards, setting up huts for themselves, and thatching them over with straw or broom.

These wooden houses were all ranged in regular streets, and there was a market-place in the midst, whither every Saturday came farmers and butchers to sell corn and meat, and hay for the horses; and the English merchants and Flemish weavers would come by sea and by land to bring cloth, bread, weapons, and everything that could be needed to be sold in this warlike market.

The governor, Sir Jean de Vienne, began to perceive that the king did not mean to waste his men by making vain attacks on the strong walls of Calais, but to shut up the entrance by land, and watch the coast by sea so as to prevent any provisions from being taken in, and so to starve him into surrendering. Sir Jean de Vienne, however, hoped that before he should be entirely reduced by famine, the King of France would be able to get together another army and come to his relief, and at any rate he was determined to do his duty, and hold out for his master to the last. But as food was already beginning to grow scarce, he was obliged to turn out such persons as could not fight and had no stores of their own, and so one Wednesday morning he caused all the poor to be brought together, men, women, and children, and sent them all out of the town, to the number of 1,700. It was probably the truest mercy, for he had no food to give them, and they could only have starved miserably within the town, or have hindered him from saving it for his sovereign; but to them it was dreadful to be driven out of house and home, straight down upon the enemy, and they went along weeping and wailing, till the English soldiers met them and asked why they had come out. They answered that they had been put out because they had nothing to eat, and their sorrowful famished looks gained pity for them. King Edward sent orders that not only should they go safely through his camp, but that they should all rest, and have the first hearty dinner that they had eaten for many a day, and he sent every one a small sum of money before they left the camp, so that many of them went on their way praying aloud for the enemy who had been so kind to them.

A great deal happened whilst King Edward kept watch in his wooden town and the citizens of Calais guarded their walls. England was invaded by King David II of Scotland, with a great army, and the good Queen Philippa, who was left to govern at home in the name of her little son Lionel, assembled all the forces that were left at home, and sent them to meet him. And one autumn day, a ship crossed the Straits of Dover, and a messenger brought King Edward letters from his queen to say that the Scots army had been entirely defeated at Nevil's Cross, near Durham, and that their king was a prisoner, but that he had been taken by a squire named John Copeland, who would not give him up to her.

King Edward sent letters to John Copeland to come to him at Calais, and when the squire had made his journey, the king took him by the hand saying, "Ha! welcome, my squire, who by his valor has captured our adversary the King of Scotland."

Copeland, falling on one knee, replied, "If God, out of His great kindness, has given me the King of Scotland, no one ought to be jealous of it, for God can, when He pleases, send His grace to a poor squire as well as to a great lord. Sir, do not take it amiss if I did not surrender him to

the orders of my lady queen, for I hold my lands
of you, and my oath is to you, not to her."

The king was not displeased with his squire's
sturdiness, but made him a knight, gave him a
pension of 500*l*. a year, and desired him to surrender his prisoner to the queen, as his own
representative. This was accordingly done, and
King David was lodged in the Tower of London.
Soon after, three days before All Saints' Day,
there was a large and gay fleet to be seen crossing from the white cliffs of Dover, and the king,
his son, and his knights rode down to the landing-
place to welcome plump, fair-haired Queen
Philippa, and all her train of ladies, who had come
in great numbers to visit their husbands, fathers,
or brothers in the wooden town. Then there was
a great court, and numerous feasts and dances, and
the knights and squires were constantly striving
who could do the bravest deed of prowess to please
the ladies. The King of France had placed
numerous knights and men-at-arms in the neighboring towns and castles, and there were constant
fights whenever the English went out foraging,
and many bold deeds that were much admired
were done. The great point was to keep provisions
out of the town, and there was much fighting
between the French who tried to bring in supplies,
and the English who intercepted them. Very little
was brought in by land, and Sir Jean de Vienne
and his garrison would have been quite starved but
for two sailors of Abbeville, named Marant and
Mestriel, who knew the coast thoroughly, and
often, in the dark autumn evenings, would guide

in a whole fleet of little boats, loaded with bread
and meat for the starving men within the city.
They were often chased by King Edward's vessels,
and were sometimes very nearly taken, but they
always managed to escape, and thus they still enabled the garrison to hold out.

So all the winter passed, Christmas was kept
with brilliant feasting and high merriment by
the king and his queen in their wooden palace outside, and with lean cheeks and scanty fare by the
besieged within. Lent was strictly observed
perforce by the besieged, and Easter brought a
betrothal in the English camp; a very unwilling
one on the part of the bridegroom, the young
Count of Flanders, who loved the French much
better than the English, and had only been tor-
mented into giving his consent by his unruly vassals
because they depended on the wool of English
sheep for their cloth works. So, though King
Edward's daughter Isabel was a beautiful fair-
haired girl of fifteen, the young count would
scarcely look at her; and in the last week before
the marriage-day, while her robes and her jewels
were being prepared, and her father and mother
were arranging the presents they should make to
all their court on the wedding-day, the bridegroom,
when out hawking, gave his attendants the slip,
and galloped off to Paris, where he was welcomed
by King Philippe.

This made Edward very wrathful, and more than
ever determined to take Calais. About Whitsuntide he completed a great wooden castle upon the
seashore, and placed in it numerous warlike

engines, with forty men-at-arms and 200 archers, who kept such a watch upon the harbor that not even the two Abbeville sailors could enter it, without having their boats crushed and sunk by the great stones that the mangonels launched upon them. The townspeople began to feel what hunger really was, but their spirits were kept up by the hope that their king was at last collecting an army for their rescue.

And Philippe did collect all his forces, a great and noble army, and came one night to the hill of Sangate, just behind the English army, the knights' armor glancing and their pennons flying in the moonlight, so as to be a beautiful sight to the hungry garrison who could see the white tents pitched upon the hillside. Still there were but two roads by which the French could reach their friends in the town—one along the seacoast, the other by a marshy road higher up the country, and there was but one bridge by which the river could be crossed. The English king's fleet could prevent any troops from passing along the coast road, the Earl of Derby guarded the bridge, and there was a great tower, strongly fortified, close upon Calais. There were a few skirmishes, but the French king, finding it difficult to force his way to relieve the town, sent a party of knights with a challenge to King Edward to come out of his camp and do battle upon a fair field.

To this Edward made answer, that he had been nearly a year before Calais, and had spent large sums of money on the siege, and that he had nearly become master of the place, so that he had no intention of coming out only to gratify his adversary, who must try some other road if he could not make his way in by that before him.

Three days were spent in parleys, and then, without the slightest effort to rescue the brave, patient men within the town, away went King Philippe of France, with all his men, and the garrison saw the host that had crowded the hill of Sangate melt away like a summer cloud.

August had come again, and they had suffered privation for a whole year for the sake of the king who deserted them at their utmost need. They were in so grievous a state of hunger and distress that the hardiest could endure no more, for ever since Whitsuntide no fresh provisions had reached them. The governor, therefore, went to the battlements and made signs that he wished to hold a parley, and the king appointed Lord Basset and Sir Walter Mauny to meet him and appoint the terms of surrender.

The governor owned that the garrison was reduced to the greatest extremity of distress, and requested that the king would be contented with obaining the city and fortress, leaving the soldiers and inhabitants to depart in peace.

But Sir Walter Mauny was forced to make answer that the king, his lord, was so much enraged at the delay and expense that Calais had cost him, that he would only consent to receive the whole on unconditional terms, leaving him free to slay, or to ransom, or make prisoners whomsoever he pleased, and he was known to consider that there was a heavy reckoning to pay, both for the trouble the siege had cost him and the damage the Calesians had previously done to his ships.

The brave answer was: "These conditions are too hard for us. We are but a small number of knights and squires, who have loyally served our lord and master as you would have done, and have suffered much ill and disquiet, but we will endure far more than any man has done in such a post, before we consent that the smallest boy in the town shall fare worse than ourselves. I therefore entreat you, for pity's sake, to return to the king and beg him to have compassion, for I have such an opinion of his gallantry that I think he will alter his mind."

The king's mind seemed, however, sternly made up; and all that Sir Walter Mauny and the barons of the council could obtain from him was that he would pardon the garrison and townsmen on condition that six of the chief citizens should present themselves to him, coming forth with bare feet and heads, with halters round their necks, carrying the keys of the town, and becoming absolutely his own to punish for their obstinacy as he should think fit.

On hearing this reply, Sir Jean de Vienne begged Sir Walter Mauny to wait till he could consult the citizens, and, repairing to the market-place, he caused a great bell to be rung, at sound of which all the inhabitants came together in the town-hall. When he told them of these hard terms he could not refrain from weeping bitterly, and wailing and lamentation arose all around him. Should all starve together, or sacrifice their best and most honored after all suffering in common so long?

Then a voice was heard; it was that of the richest burgher in the town, Eustache de St. Pierre. "Messieurs, high and low," he said, "it would be a sad pity to suffer so many people to die through hunger, if it could be prevented; and to hinder it would be meritorious in the eyes of our Saviour. I have such faith and trust in finding grace before God, if I die to save my townsmen, that I name myself as first of the six."

As the burgher ceased, his fellow-townsmen wept aloud, and many, amid tears and groans, threw themselves at his feet in a transport of grief and gratitude. Another citizen, very rich and respected, rose up and said, "I will be second to my comrade, Eustache." His name was Jean Daire. After him, Jacques Wissant, another very rich man, offered himself as companion to these, who were both his cousins; and his brother Pierre would not be left behind: and two more, unnamed, made up this gallant band of men willing to offer their lives for the rescue of their fellow-townsmen.

Sir Jean de Vienne mounted a little horse—for he had been wounded, and was still lame—and came to the gate with them, followed by all the people of the town, weeping and wailing, yet, for their own sakes and their children's, not daring to prevent the sacrifice. The gates were opened, the governor and the six passed out, and the gates were again shut behind them. Sir Jean then rode up to Sir Walter Mauny, and told him how these burghers had voluntarily offered themselves, begging him to do all in his power to save them; and Sir Walter promised with his whole heart to plead their cause. De Vienne then went back into the town, full of heaviness and anxiety; and the six citizens were led by Sir Walter to the presence of the king, in his full court. They all knelt down, and the foremost said: "Most gallant king, you see before you six burghers of Calais, who have all been capital merchants, and who bring you the keys of the castle and town. We yield ourselves to your absolute will and pleasure, in order to save the remainder of the inhabitants of Calais, who have suffered much distress and misery. Condescend, therefore, out of your nobleness of mind, to have pity on us."

Strong emotion was excited among all the barons and knights who stood round, as they saw the resigned countenances, pale and thin with patiently-endured hunger, of these venerable men, offering themselves in the cause of their fellow-townsmen. Many tears of pity were shed; but the king still showed himself implacable, and commanded that they should be led away, and their heads stricken off. Sir Walter Mauny interceded for them with all his might, even telling the king that such an execution would tarnish his honor, and that reprisals would be made on his own garrisons; and all the nobles joined in entreating pardon for the citizens, but still without effect; and the headsman had been actually sent for, when Queen Philippa, her eyes streaming with tears, threw herself on her knees amongst the captives, and said, "Ah, gentle sir, since I have crossed the sea with much danger to see you, I have never asked you one favor; now I beg as a boon to myself, for the sake of the Son of the Blessed Mary, and for your love to me, that you will be merciful to these men!"

For some time the king looked at her in silence; then he exclaimed: "Dame, dame, would that you had been anywhere than here! You have entreated in such a manner that I cannot refuse you; I therefore give these men to you, to do as you please with."

Joyfully did Queen Philippa conduct the six citizens to her own apartments, where she made them welcome, sent them new garments, entertained them with a plentiful dinner, and dismissed them each with a gift of six nobles. After this, Sir Walter Mauny entered the city, and took possession of it; retaining Sir Jean de Vienne and the other knights and squires till they should ransom themselves, and sending out the old French inhabitants; for the king was resolved to people the city entirely with English, in order to gain a thoroughly strong hold of his first step in France.

The king and queen took up their abode in the city; and the houses of Jean Daire were, it appears, granted to the queen—perhaps, because she considered the man himself as her charge, and wished to secure them for him—and her little daughter Margaret was, shortly after, born in one of his houses. Eustache de St. Pierre was taken into high favor, and was placed in charge of the new citizens whom the king placed in the city.

Indeed, as this story is told by no chronicler but Froissart, some have doubted of it, and thought the violent resentment thus imputed to Edward III inconsistent with his general character; but it is evident that the men of Calais had given him strong provocation by attacks on his shipping— piracies which are not easily forgiven—and that he considered that he had a right to make an example of them. It is not unlikely that he might, after all, have intended to forgive them, and have given the queen the grace of obtaining their pardon, so as to excuse himself from the fulfillment of some over-hasty threat. But, howeyer this may have been, nothing can lessen the glory of the six grave and patient men who went forth, by their own free will, to meet what might be a cruel and disgraceful death, in order to obtain the safety of their fellow-townsmen.

THE STORY OF JOAN OF ARC, THE MAID WHO SAVED FRANCE

Anonymous

OVER five hundred years ago, the children of Domremy, a little village on the border of France, used to dance and sing beneath a beautiful beech tree. They called it "The Fairy Tree." Among these children was one named Jeanne, the daughter of an honest farmer, Jacques d'Arc. Jeanne sang more than she danced, and though she carried garlands like the other boys and girls, and hung them on the boughs of the Fairies' Tree, she liked better to take the flowers into the parish church and lay them on the altars of St. Margaret and St. Catherine.

She was brought up by her parents (as she told

113

the judges at her trial) to be industrious, to sew and spin. She did not fear to match herself at spinning and sewing, she said, against any woman in Rouen. When very young, she sometimes went to the fields to watch the cattle. As she grew older, she worked in the house; she did not any longer watch sheep and cattle. But the times were dangerous, and when there was an alarm of soldiers or robbers in the neighborhood, she sometimes helped to drive the flock into a fortified island or peninsula, for which her father was responsible, in the river near her home. She learned her creed, she said, from her mother. Twenty years after her death, her neighbors, who remembered her, described her as she was when a child. Jean Morin said that she was a good industrious girl, but that she would often be praying in church when her father and mother did not know it. Jean Waterin, when he was a boy, had seen Joan in the fields, "and when they were all playing together, she would go apart and pray to God, as he thought, and he and the others used to laugh at her. When she heard the church bell ring, she would kneel down in the fields." All those who had seen Joan told the same tale: she was always kind, simple, industrious, pious and yet merry and fond of playing with the others.

In Joan's childhood France was under a mad king, Charles VI, and was torn to pieces by two factions, the party of Burgundy and the party of Armagnac. The English took advantage of these disputes, and overran the land. The two parties of Burgundy and Armagnac divided town from town and village from village. It was as in the days of the Douglas Wars in Scotland, when the very children took sides for Queen Mary and King James, and fought each other in the streets. Domremy was for the Armagnacs—that is, against the English and for the Dauphin, the son of the mad Charles VI. But at Maxey, a village near Domremy, the people were all for Burgundy and the English. The boys of Domremy would go out and fight the Maxey boys with fists and sticks and stones. Joan did not remember having taken part in those battles, but she had often seen her brothers and the Domremy boys come home all bruised and bleeding.

When Joan was between twelve and thirteen (1424), so she swore, a *Voice came to her from God for her guidance,* but when first it came, she was in great fear. And it came, that Voice, about noonday, in the summer season, she being in her father's garden. Joan had not fasted the day before that, but was fasting when the Voice came. The Voices at first only told her to be a good girl, and go to church. The Voice later told her of the great sorrow there was in France, and that one day she must go into France and help the country. She had visions with the Voices; visions first of St. Michael, and then of St. Catherine and St. Margaret. "I saw them with my bodily eyes, as I see you," she said to her judges, "and when they departed from me I wept, and well I wished that they had taken me with them."

What are we to think about these visions and these Voices which were with Joan to her death?

In 1428 only a very few small towns in the east still held out for the Dauphin, and these were surrounded on every side by enemies. Meanwhile the Voices came more frequently, urging Joan to go into France and help her country. She asked how she, a girl, who could not ride or use sword and lance, could be of any help? At the same time she was encouraged by one of the vague old prophecies which were common in France. A legend ran that France was to be saved by a Maiden from the Oak Wood, and there was an Oak Wood (*le bois chenu*) near Domremy. Some such prophecy had an influence on Joan, and probably helped people to believe in her. The Voices often commanded her to go to Vaucouleurs, a neighboring town which was loyal, and there meet Robert de Baudricourt, who was captain of the French garrison. Now, Robert de Baudricourt was a gallant soldier, but a plain practical man, very careful of his own interest, and cunning enough to hold his own among his many enemies, English, Burgundian, and Lorrainers.

Joan had a cousin who was married to one Durand Lassois, at Burey en Vaux, a village near Vaucouleurs. This cousin invited Joan to visit her for a week. At the end of that time she spoke to her cousin's husband. There was an old saying, as we saw, that France would be rescued by a Maid, and she, as she told Lassois, was that Maid. Lassois listened, and, whatever he may have thought of her chances, he led her to Robert de Baudricourt.

Joan came, in her simple red dress, and walked straight up to the captain. She told him that the Dauphin must keep quiet, and risk no battle, for, before the middle of Lent next year (1429), God would send him help. She added that the kingdom belonged, not to the Dauphin, but to her Master, who willed that the Dauphin should be crowned, and she herself would lead him to Reims, to be anointed with the holy oil.

"And who is your Master?" said Robert.

"The King of Heaven!"

Robert, very naturally, thought that Joan was crazed, and shrugged his shoulders. He bluntly told Lassois to box her ears and take her back to her father. So she had to go home; but here new troubles awaited her. The enemy came down on Domremy and burned it; Joan and her family fled to Neufchâteau, where they stayed for a few days. When Joan looked from her father's garden to the church, she saw nothing but a heap of smoking ruins. These things only made her feel more deeply the sorrows of her country. The time was drawing near when she had prophesied that the Dauphin was to receive help from heaven—namely, in the Lent of 1429. On that year the season was held more than commonly sacred, for Good Friday and the Annunciation fell on the same day. So, early in January, 1429, Joan turned her back on Domremy, which she was never to see again. Her cousin Lassois came and asked leave for Joan to visit him again; so she said good-by to her father and mother, and to her friends. She went to her cousin's house at Burey, and there she stayed for six weeks, hearing bad news of the siege of Orleans by the English. A squire named Jean de Nouillompont met Joan one day.

"Well, my lass," said he, "is our king to be driven from France, and are we all to become English?"

"I have come here," said Joan, "to bid Robert de Baudricourt lead me to the king, but he will not listen to me. And yet to the king I must go, even if I walk my legs down to the knees; for none in all the world—king, nor duke, nor the King of Scotland's daughter—can save France, but myself only. Certainly, I would rather stay and spin with my poor mother, for to fight is not my calling; but I must go and I must fight, for so my Lord will have it."

"And who is your Lord?" said Jean de Nouillompont.

"He is God," said the Maiden.

On February 12, the story goes, she went to Robert de Baudricourt. "You delay too long," she said. "On this very day, at Orleans, the gentle Dauphin has lost a battle."

Now the people of Vaucouleurs brought clothes for Joan to wear on her journey to the Dauphin. They were such clothes as men wear—doublet, hose, surcoat, boots, and spurs—and Robert de Baudricourt gave Joan a sword. Her reason was that she would have to be living alone among men-at-arms for a ten days' journey and she thought it was more modest to wear armor like the rest. Also, her favorite saint, St. Margaret, had done this once when in danger. Besides, in all the romances of chivalry, we find fair maidens fighting in arms like men, or travelling dressed as pages.

On February 23, 1429, the gate of the little castle of Vaucouleurs, "the Gate of France," which is still standing, was thrown open. Seven travellers rode out, among them two squires, Jean de Nouillompont and Bertrand de Poulengy, with their attendants, and Joan the Maid. "Go, and let what will come of it come!" said Robert de Baudricourt. He did not expect much to come of it. It was a long journey—they were eleven days on the road—and a dangerous. But Joan laughed at danger. "God will clear my path to the king, for to this end I was born." Often they rode by night, stopping at monasteries when they could. Sometimes they slept out under the sky. Though she was young and beautiful, these two gentlemen never dreamed of paying their court to her and making love, as they do in romances, for they regarded her "as if she had been an angel." They were in awe of her, they said long afterward, and all the knights who had seen her said the same.

From Fierbois, Joan made some clerk write to the king that she was coming to help him, and that she would know him among all his men. Probably it was here that she wrote to beg her parents' pardon, and they forgave her, she says. Meanwhile, news reached the people then besieged in Orleans that a marvellous Maiden was riding to their rescue. On March 6, Joan arrived in Chinon, where for two or three days the king's advisers would not let him see her. At last they yielded, and she went straight up to him, and when he denied that he was the king, she told him that she knew well who he was.

"There is the king," said Charles, pointing to a richly dressed noble.

"No, fair sire. You are he!"

Still it was not easy to believe. Joan stayed at Chinon in the house of a noble lady. The young Duc d'Alençon was on her side from the first.

Great people came to see her and question her, but when she was alone, she wept and prayed.

Joan was weary of being asked questions. One day she went to Charles and said, "Gentle Dauphin, why do you delay to believe me? I tell you that God has taken pity on you and your people, at the prayer of St. Louis and St. Charlemagne. And I will tell you by your leave, something which will show you that you should believe me." Then she told him secretly something which, as he said, none could know but God and himself.

But the king to whom Joan brought this wonderful message, the king whom she loved so loyally, and for whom she died, spoiled all her plans. He, with his political advisers, prevented her from driving the English quite out of France. These favorites were lazy, comfortable, cowardly, disbelieving; in their hearts they hated the Maid, who put them to so much trouble. Charles, to tell the truth, never really believed in her; he never quite trusted her; he never led a charge by her side; and in the end, he shamefully deserted her, and left the Maid to her doom.

Weeks had passed, and Joan had never yet seen a blow struck in war. She used to exercise herself in horsemanship, and knightly sports of tilting, and it is wonderful that a peasant-girl became, at once, one of the best riders among the chivalry of France. The young Duc d'Alençon and his wife were her friends from the first, when the politicians and advisers were against her. It was now determined that Joan should be taken to Poitiers, and examined before all the learned men, bishops, doctors, and higher clergy who still were on the side of France. There was good reason for this delay. It was plain to all, friends and foes, that the wonderful Maid was not like other men and women, with her Voices, her visions, her prophecies, and her powers. All agreed that she had some strange help given to her; but who gave it? This aid must come, people thought then, either from heaven or hell—either from God and his saints, or from the devil and his angels. Now, if any doubt could be thrown on the source whence Joan's aid came, the English might argue (as of course they did) that she was a witch and a heretic. If she was a heretic and a witch, then her king was involved in her wickedness, and so he might be legally shut out from his kingdom. It was necessary, therefore, that Joan should be examined by learned men. They must find out whether she had always been good, and a true believer, and whether her Voices always agreed in everything with the teachings of the Church. Otherwise her angels must be devils in disguise. During three long weeks the learned men asked her questions. They said it was wonderful how wisely this girl, who "did not know A from B," replied to their puzzling inquiries. She told the story of her visions, of the command laid upon her to rescue Orleans.

At last, after examining witnesses from Domremy, and the Queen of Sicily and other great ladies to whom Joan was intrusted, the clergy found nothing in her but "goodness, humility, frank maidenhood, piety, honesty and simplicity." As for her wearing a man's dress, the Archbishop of Embrun said to the king, "It is more becoming to do these things in man's clothes, since they have to be done amongst men."

The king therefore made up his mind at last. Jean and Pierre, Joan's brothers, were to ride with her to Orleans; her old friends, her first friends, Jean de Nouillompont and Bertrand de Poulengy, had never left her. She was given a squire, a page, and a chaplain. The king gave Joan armor and horses, and offered her a sword. But her Voices told her that, behind the altar of St. Catherine de Fierbois, where she heard mass on her way to Chinon, there was an old sword, with five crosses on the blade, buried in the earth. That sword she was to wear. A man whom Joan did not know, and had never seen, was sent from Tours, and found the sword in the place which she described. The sword was cleaned of rust, and the king gave her two sheaths, one of velvet, one of cloth of gold, but Joan had a leather sheath made for use in war. She also commanded a banner to be made, with the Lilies of France on a white field.

When once it was settled that she was to lead an army to relieve Orleans, she showed her faith by writing a letter addressed to the King of England,

Bedford, the Regent, and the English generals at Orleans. If they did not yield to the Maid and the king, she will come on them to their sorrow. "Duke of Bedford, the Maid prays and entreats you not to work our own destruction!"

We may imagine how the English laughed and swore when they received this letter. They threw the heralds of the Maid into prison, and threatened to burn them as heretics. From the very first, the English promised to burn Joan as a witch and a heretic.

At last the men-at-arms who were to accompany Joan were ready. She was armed in white armor, but unhelmeted, a little axe in her hand, riding a great black charger. She turned to the church, and said, in her girlish voice, "You priests and churchmen, make prayers and processions to God." Then she cried, "Forward, Forward!" and on she rode at their head, a page carrying her banner. And so Joan went to war.

She led, she says, ten or twelve thousand soldiers. This army was to defend a great convoy of provisions of which the people of Orleans stood in sore need. The people were not starving, but food came in slowly, and in small quantities. The French general-in-chief was the famous Dunois. On the English side was the brave Talbot, who fought under arms for sixty years, and died fighting when he was over eighty.

Looking *down* the river Loire, Orleans lies on your right hand. It had strong walls, towers on the wall, and a bridge of many arches crossing to the left side of the river. At the further end of this bridge were a fort and rampart called Les Tourelles, and this fort had already been taken by the English, so that no French army could cross the bridge to help Orleans. The rampart and the fort of Les Tourelles were guarded by another strong work called Les Augustins. All round the outside of the town, on the right bank, the English had built strong redoubts, which they called *bastilles*, but on the east, above the town, and on the Orleans bank of the Loire, the English had only one bastille, St. Loup. Now, as Joan's army mustered at Blois, south of Orleans, further down the river, she might march on the *left* side of the river, cross it by boats above Orleans, and enter the town where the English were weakest and had only one fort, St. Loup. Or she might march up the *right* bank, and attack the English where they were strongest and had many bastilles. The Voices bade the Maid act on the boldest plan, and enter Orleans, where the English were strongest, on the right bank of the river. The English would not move, said the Voices. She was certain that they would not even sally out against her. But Dunois in Orleans, and the generals with the Maid, thought this plan very perilous. They, therefore, deceived her, caused her to think that Orleans was on the *left* bank of the Loire, and led her thither. When she arrived, she saw that they had not played her fair, that the river lay between her and the town, and the strongest force of the enemy.

This girl of seventeen saw that, if a large convoy of provisions was to be thrown into a besieged town, the worst way was to try to ferry the supplies across a river under the enemy's fire. But Dunois and the other generals had brought her to this pass, and the Maid was sore ill-pleased. The wind was blowing in her teeth; boats could not cross with the troops and provisions. There she sat her horse and chafed till Dunois came out and crossed the Loire to meet her. This is what he says about Joan and her conduct:

"I did not think, and the other generals did not think, that the men-at-arms with the Maid were a strong enough force to bring the provisions into the town. Above all, it was difficult to get boats and ferry over the supplies, for both wind and stream were dead against us. Then Joan spoke to me thus:

" 'Are you the general?'

" 'That am I, and glad of your coming.'

" 'Is it you who gave counsel that I should come hither by that bank of the stream, and not go straight where Talbot and the English are?'

" 'I myself, and others wiser than I, gave that advice, and we think it the better way and the surer.'

" 'In God's name, the counsel of our God is wiser and surer than yours. You thought to deceive me, and you have deceived yourselves, for I bring you a better rescue than ever shall come to soldier or city—that is, the help of the King of Heaven. * * *'

"Then instantly, and as it were in one moment, the wind changed that had been dead against us, and had hindered the boats from carrying the provisions into Orleans, and the sails filled."

Dunois now wished Joan to cross by boat and

enter the town, but her army could not cross, so the army returned to Blois, to cross by the bridge there, and come upon the Orleans bank, as Joan had intended from the first. Then Joan crossed in the boat, holding in her hand the lily standard. She and La Hire and Dunois rode into Orleans, where the people crowded round her, blessing her, and trying to kiss her hand. So they led her with great joy to the Regnart Gate, and the house of Jacques Boucher, treasurer of the Duke of Orleans, and there was she gladly received.

Next day, without leave from Joan, La Hire led a sally against the English, fought bravely, but failed, and Joan wished once more to bid the English go in peace. The English, of course, did not obey her summons, and it is said that they answered with wicked words which made her weep. For she wept readily, and blushed when she was moved. In her anger she went to a rampart, and, crying aloud, bade the English begone; but they repeated their insults, and threatened yet again to burn her. Next day, Dunois went off to bring the troops from Blois, and Joan rode round and inspected the English position. They made no attempt to take her. On May 4 the army returned from Blois. Joan rode out to meet them, priests marched in procession, singing hymns, but the English never stirred. They were expecting fresh troops under Fastolf. For some reason, probably because they did not wish her to run risk, they did not tell Joan when the next fight began. She had just lain down to sleep when she leaped up with the noise, wakening her squire. "My Voices tell me," she said, "that I must go against the English, but whether to their forts or against Fastolf I know not."

In a moment she was in the street, the page handed to her the lily flag from the upper window. Followed by her squire, D'Aulon, she galloped to the Burgundy Gate. They met wounded men. "Never do I see French blood but my hair stands up on my head," said Joan. She rode out of the gate to the English fort of St. Loup, which the Orleans men were attacking. Joan leaped into the fosse, under fire, holding her banner, and cheering on her men. St. Loup was taken by the French, in spite of a gallant defence.

The French generals now conceived a plan to make a feint, or a sham attack, on the English forts where they were strongest, on the Orleans side of the river. The English on the left side would cross to help their countrymen, and then the French would take the forts beyond the bridge. Thus they would have a free path across the river, and would easily get supplies, and tire out the English. They only told Joan of the first part of their plans, but she saw that they were deceiving her. When the plan was explained, she agreed to it; her one wish was to strike swiftly and strongly.

The French attacked the English fort of Les Augustins, beyond the river, but suddenly they fled to their bridge of boats, while the English sallied out, yelling their insults at Joan. She turned, gathered a few men, and charged. The English ran before her like sheep; she planted her banner again in the ditch. The French hurried back to her; a great Englishman, who guarded the breach, was shot; two French knights leaped in, the others followed, and the English took refuge in the re-doubt of Les Tourelles, their strong fort at the bridge-head.

The Maid returned to Orleans, and, though it was a Friday, and she always fasted on Fridays, she was so weary that she ate some supper. A bit of bread, her page reports, was all that she usually ate. Now the generals sent to Joan and said that enough had been done. They had food, and could wait for another army from the king. "You have been with your council," she said, "I have been with mine. The wisdom of God is greater than yours. Rise early to-morrow, do better than your best, keep close by me; for to-morrow have I much to do, and more than ever yet I did, and to-morrow shall my blood flow from a wound above my breast." Joan had already said at Chinon that she would be wounded at Orleans.

The generals did not wish to attack the bridge-tower, but Joan paid them no attention. They were glad enough to follow, lest she took the fort without them. About half-past six in the morning the fight began. The French and Scottish leaped into the fosse, they set ladders against the walls, they reached the battlements, and were struck down by English swords and axes. Cannon-balls and great stones and arrows rained on them. "Fight on!" cried the Maid; "the place is ours." At one o'clock she set a ladder against the wall with her own hands, but was deeply wounded by an arrow, which pierced clean through between neck and shoulder. Joan wept, but seizing the arrow with her own hands she dragged it out. "Yet," says Dunois, "she did not withdraw from the battle, nor took any medicine for the wound; and the onslaught lasted from morning till eight at night, so that there was no hope of victory. I desired that the army should go back to the town, but the Maid came to me and bade me wait a little longer. Next she mounted her horse and rode into a vineyard, and there prayed for the space of seven minutes or eight. Then she returned, took her banner, and stood on the brink of the fosse. The English trembled when they saw her, but our men returned to the charge and met with no resistance. The English fled or were slain, and we returned gladly into Orleans." The people of Orleans had a great share in this victory. Seeing the English hard pressed, they laid long beams across the broken arches of the bridge, and charged by this perilous way. The triumph was even more that of the citizens than of the army.

Next day the English drew up their men in line of battle. The French went out to meet them, and would have begun the attack. Joan said that God would not have them fight.

"If the English attack, we shall defeat them; we are to let them go in peace, if they will."

Mass was then said before the French army.

When the rite was done, Joan asked: "Do they face us, or have they turned their backs?"

It was the English backs that the French saw that day; Talbot's men were in full retreat on Meun.

From that hour, May 8 is kept a holiday at Orleans in honor of Joan the Maiden. Never was there such a deliverance. In a week the Maid had driven a strong army, full of courage and well led, out of forts like Les Tourelles. The Duc d'Alençon visited it, and said that with a few men-at-arms he would have felt certain of holding it for a week against any strength, however great. But Joan not only gave the French her spirit: her extraordinary courage in leading a new charge after so terrible a wound, "six inches deep," says D'Alençon, made the English think that they were fighting a force not of this world.

HOW JOAN THE MAID TOOK LARGESS FROM THE ENGLISH

Anonymous

THE Maid had shown her sign, as she promised; she had rescued Orleans. Her next desire was to lead Charles to Reims, through a country occupied by the English, and to have him anointed there with the holy oil. Till this was done she could only regard him as Dauphin—king, indeed, by blood, but not by consecration.

After all that Joan had accomplished, the king and his advisers might have believed in her. She went to the castle of Loches, where Charles was; he received her kindly, but still he did not seem eager to go to Reims. It was a dangerous adventure, for

"FIGHT ON!" CRIED THE MAID; "THE PLACE IS OURS"

—page 128

From the painting by William Rainey

which he and his favorites had no taste. It seems
that more learned men were asked to give their
opinion. Was it safe and wise to obey the Maid?
Councils were now held at Tours, and time was
wasted as usual. As usual, Joan was impatient.
With Dunois, she went to see Charles at the castle
of Loches. Some nobles and clergy were with him;
Joan entered, knelt, and embraced his knees.
"Noble Dauphin," she said, "do not hold so many
councils, and such weary ones, but come to Reims
and receive the crown."

Harcourt asked her if her Voices, or "counsel"
(as she called it), gave this advice. She blushed
and said: "I know what you mean, and will tell
you gladly." The king asked her if she wished
to speak before so many people. Yes, she would
speak. When they doubted her, she prayed, "and
then she heard a Voice saying to her:

" *'Fille de Dieu, va, va, je serai à ton aide, val!'* [1]

"And when she heard this Voice she was glad indeed, and wished that she could always be as she
was then; and as she spoke," says Dunois, "she rejoiced strangely, lifting her eyes to heaven." And
she repeated: "I will last for only one year, or little
more; use me while you may."

Joan stirred the favorites and courtiers at last.
They would go to Reims, but could they leave behind them English garrisons in Jargeau, where
Suffolk commanded; in Meun, where Talbot was,
and in other strong places? Already, without Joan,
the French had attacked Jargeau, after the rescue
of Orleans, and had failed. Joan agreed to assail

---

[1] Daughter of God, go on, go on, I will help thee; go!

Jargeau. Her army was led by the "fair duke,"
D'Alençon.

Let us tell what followed in the words of the
Duc d'Alençon:

"We were about six hundred lances, who wished
to go against the town of Jargeau, then held by the
English. That night we slept in a wood, and next
day came Dunois and some other captains. When
we were all met we were about twelve hundred
lances; and now arose a dispute among the captains,
some thinking that we should attack the city, others
not so, for they said that the English were very
strong, and had many men. Seeing this difference,
Jeanne bade us have no fear of any numbers, nor
doubt about attacking the English, because God
was guiding us. She herself would rather be herd-
ing sheep than fighting, if she were not certain that
God was with us. Thereon we rode to Jargeau,
meaning to occupy the outlying houses, and there
pass the night; but the English knew of our approach, and drove in our skirmishers. Seeing this,
Jeanne took her banner and went to the front, bidding our men be of good heart. And they did so
much that they held the suburbs of Jargeau that
night. * * * Next morning we got ready our
artillery, and brought guns up against the town.
After some days a council was held, and I, with
others, was ill content with La Hire, who was said
to have parleyed with Lord Suffolk. La Hire was
sent for, and came. Then it was decided to storm
the town, and the heralds cried, 'To the attack!' and
Jeanne said to me, 'Forward, gentle duke.' I
thought it was too early, but she said, 'Doubt not;

the hour is come when God pleases.' As the onslaught was given, Jeanne bade me leave the place
where I stood, 'or yonder gun,' pointing to one on
the walls, 'will slay you.' Then I withdrew, and a
little later De Lude was slain in that very place.
And I feared greatly, considering the prophecy of
the Maid. Then we both went together to the onslaught; and Suffolk cried for a parley, but no man
marked him, and we pressed on. Jeanne was climbing a ladder, banner in hand, when her flag was
struck by a stone, and she also was struck on her
head, but her light helmet saved her. She leaped
up again, crying, 'Friends, friends; on, on! Our
Lord has condemned the English. They are ours;
be of good heart.' In that moment Jargeau was
taken, and the English fled to the bridges, we following, and more than eleven hundred of them were
slain."

Once Joan saw a man-at-arms strike down a
prisoner. She leaped from her horse, and laid
the wounded Englishman's head on her breast,
consoling him, and bade a priest come and hear his
confession. From Jargeau the Maid rode back to
Orleans, where the people could not look on her
enough, and made great festival.

The garrison of the English in Beaugency did
not know whether to hold out or to yield. Fastolf
said that the English had lost heart, and that
Beaugency should be left to its fate, while the rest
held out in strong places and waited for re-enforce-
ments, but Talbot was for fighting. The English
then rode to Meun, and cannonaded the bridge-
fort, which was held by the French. They hoped

to take the bridge, cross it, march to Beaugency, and relieve the besieged there. But that very night Beaugency surrendered to the Maid! She then bade her army march on the English, who were retreating to Paris. But how was the Maid to find the English? "Ride forward," she cried, "and you shall have a sure guide." They had a guide, and a strange one.

The English were marching toward Paris, near Pathay, when their skirmishers came in with the news that the French were following. Talbot lined the hedges with five hundred archers of his best, and sent a galloper to bring thither the rest of his army. On came the French, not seeing the English in ambush. In a few minutes they would have been shot down and choked the pass with dying men and horses. But now was the moment for the strange guide.

A stag was driven from cover by the French, and ran blindly among the ambushed English bowmen. Not knowing that the French were so near, and being archers from Robin Hood's country, who loved a deer, they raised a shout, and probably many an arrow flew at the stag. The French scouts heard the cry, saw the English and hurried back with the news. "Forward!" cried the Maid; "if they were hung to the clouds, we have them. To-day the gentle king will gain such a victory as never yet did he win."

The French dashed into the pass before Talbot had secured it. Fastolf galloped up, but the English thought that he was in flight; the captain of the advanced guard turned his horse about and made off. Talbot was taken, Fastolf fled, "making more sorrow than ever yet did man." The French won a great victory. They needed their spurs, as the Maid had told them that they would, to follow their flying foes. The English lost some 3,000 men. In the evening, Talbot, as a prisoner, was presented to the Duc d'Alençon.

At last, with difficulty, Charles was brought to visit Reims and consent to be crowned like his ancestors.

Seeing that he was never likely to move, Joan left the town where he was and went off into the country. This retreat brought Charles to his senses. The towns which he passed by yielded to him; Joan went and summoned each. "Now she was with the king in the center, now with the rear guard, now with the van." The town of Troyes, where there was an English garrison, did not wish to yield. There was a council in the king's army; they said they could not take the place.

"In two days it shall be yours, by force or by good-will," said the Maid. "Six days will do," said the chancellor, "if you are sure you speak truth."

Joan made ready for an attack. She was calling "Forward!" when the town surrendered. Reims, after some doubts, yielded also, on July 16, and all the people welcomed the king. On July 17 the king was crowned and anointed with the holy oil by that very Archbishop of Reims who always opposed Joan. The Twelve Peers of France were not all present—some were on the English side—but Joan stood by Charles, her banner in her hand.

HOW JOAN TOOK LARGESS

When the ceremony was ended, and the Dauphin Charles was a crowned and anointed king, the Maid knelt weeping at his feet. "Gentle king," she said, "now is accomplished the will of God, who desired that you should come to Reims to be consecrated, and to prove that you are the true king and the kingdom is yours." Then all the knights wept for joy.

The king bade Joan choose her reward. Already horses, rich armor, jewelled daggers, had been given to her. These, adding to the beauty and glory of her aspect, had made men follow her more gladly, and for that she valued them. She made gifts to noble ladies, and gave much to the poor. She only wanted money to wage the war with, not for herself. Her family was made noble; on their shield, between two lilies, a sword upholds the crown. Her father was at Reims, and saw her in her glory. What reward, then, was Joan to choose? She chose nothing for herself, but that her native village of Domremy should be free from taxes. This news her father carried home from the splendid scene at Reims.

As they went from Reims after the coronation, Dunois and the archbishop were riding by her rein. The people cheered and shouted with joy.

"They are a good people," said Joan. "Never saw I any more joyous at the coming of their king. Ah, would that I might be so happy when I end my days as to be buried here!" Said the archbishop: "Jeanne, in what place do you hope to die?" Then she said: "Where it pleases God; for I know not that hour, nor that place, more than ye

do. But would to God, my Maker, that now I
might depart, and lay down my arms, and help my
father and mother, and keep their sheep with my
brothers and my sisters, who would rejoice to see
me!"

What was to be done after the crowning of the
king? Bedford, the regent for the child Henry
VI, expected to see Joan under the walls of Paris.
He was waiting for the troops which the Cardinal
of Winchester had collected in England. Bedford
induced Winchester to bring his men to France,
but they had not arrived. The Duke of Burgundy,
the head of the great French party which opposed
Charles, had been invited by the Maid to Reims.
Again she wrote to him: "Make a firm, good peace
with the King of France," she said; "forgive each
other with kind hearts"; "I pray and implore you,
with joined hands, fight not against France."

The Duke of Burgundy, far from listening to
Joan's prayer, left Paris and went to raise men for
the English. Meanwhile, Charles was going from
town to town, and all received him gladly. But
Joan soon began to see that instead of marching
west from Reims to Paris, the army was being led
southwest toward the Loire. There the king would
be safe among his dear castles, where he could live
indoors, and take his ease. Thus Bedford was able
to throw 5,000 men of Winchester's into Paris, and
even dared to come out and hunt for the French
king. The French should have struck at Paris at
once, as Joan desired. The delays were excused
because the Duke of Burgundy had promised to
surrender Paris in a fortnight. But this he did

merely to gain time. Joan knew this, and said there would be no peace but at the lance-point.

The French and English armies kept watching each other, and there were skirmishes near Senlis. On August 15, the Maid and d'Alençon hoped for a battle. But the English had fortified their position in the night. Come out they would not, so Joan rode up to their fortification, standard in hand, struck the palisade and challenged them to sally forth. She even offered to let them march out and draw themselves up in line of battle. The Maid stayed on the field all night and next day made a retreat, hoping to draw the English out of their fort. But they were too wary and went back to Paris.

Now the fortnight was over, after which the Duke of Burgundy was to surrender Paris, but he did nothing of the kind. The Maid was weary of words. She called the Duc d'Alençon and said: "My fair duke, array your men, for, by my staff, I would fain see Paris more closely than I have seen it yet." On August 23, the Maid and d'Alençon left the king at Compiègne and rode to St. Denis, where were the tombs of the kings of France. "And when the king heard that they were at St. Denis, he came, very sore against his will, as far as Senlis, and it seems that his advisers were contrary to the will of the Maid, of the Duc d'Alençon, and of their company." The king was afraid to go near Paris, but Bedford was afraid to stay in the town. He went to Rouen, the strongest English hold in Normandy, leaving the Burgundian army and 2,000 English in Paris.

Every day, the Maid and d'Alençon rode from St. Denis to the gates of Paris, to observe the best places for an attack. And still Charles dallied and delayed, still the main army did not come up. Thus the delay of the king gave the English time to make Paris almost impregnable and to frighten the people who, had Charles marched straight from Reims, would have yielded as Reims did. D'Alençon kept going to Senlis urging Charles to come up with the main army. He went on September 1—the king promised to start next day. D'Alençon returned to the Maid, the king still loitered. At last d'Alençon brought him to St. Denis on September 7, and there was a skirmish that day.

In the book of Perceval de Cagny, who was with his lord, the Duc d'Alençon, he says: "The assault was long and fierce, and it was marvel to hear the noise of the cannons and culverins from the walls, and to see the clouds of arrows. Few of those in the fosse with the Maid were struck, though many others on horse and foot were wounded with arrows and stone cannon-balls, but by God's grace and the Maid's good fortune, there was none of them but could return to camp unhelped. The assault lasted from noon till dusk—say eight in the evening. After sunset, the Maid was struck by a crossbow bolt in the thigh; and, after she was hurt, she cried but the louder that all should attack, and that the place was taken. But as night had now fallen and she was wounded, and the men-at-arms were weary with the long attack, De Gaucourt and others came and found her, and, against her will, brought her forth from the fosse. And so ended that onslaught.

But right sad she was to leave and said, 'By my bâton, the place would have been taken.' They put her on horseback, and led her to her quarters, and all the rest of the king's company who that day had come from St. Denis.

"Next day," says Cagny, "in spite of her wound, she was first in the field. She went to d'Alençon and bade him sound the trumpet for the charge. D'Alençon and the other captains were of the same mind as the Maid, and Montmorency with sixty gentlemen and many lances came in, though he had been on the English side before. So they began to march on Paris, but the king sent messengers, and compelled the Maid and the captains to return to St. Denis. Right sorry were they, yet they must obey the king. When she saw that they would go, she dedicated her armor, and hung it up before the statue of Our Lady at St. Denis, and so right sadly went away in company with the king. And thus were broken the will of the Maid and the army of the king."

The courtiers had triumphed. They had thwarted the Maid, they had made her promise to take Paris of no avail. They had destroyed the confidence of men in the banner that had never gone back.

The king now went from one pleasant tower on the Loire to another, taking the Maid with him. Meanwhile, the English took and plundered some of the cities which had yielded to Charles, and they carried off the Maid's armor from the chapel in St. Denis. Her Voices had bidden her stay at St. Denis, but this she was not permitted to do, and now she must hear daily how the loyal towns that she had won were plundered by the English, and all her work seemed wasted. The Duc d'Alençon offered to lead an army against the English in Normandy, if the Maid might march with him, for the people had not wholly lost faith, but the courtiers and the Archbishop of Reims, who managed the king and the war, would not consent, nor would they allow the Maid and the duke to even see each other.

Joan wanted to return to Paris, but the council sent her to take La Charité and Saint-Pierre-le-Moustier from the English. This town she attacked first. Her squire, a gentleman named d'Aulon, was with her, and described what he saw. "When they had besieged the place for some time, an assault was commanded, but for the great strength of the forts and the numbers of the enemy the French were forced to give way. At that hour I who speak was wounded by an arrow in the heel, and could not stand or walk without crutches. But I saw the Maid holding her ground with a handful of men, and, fearing ill might come of it, I mounted a horse and rode to her, asking what she was doing there alone, and why she did not retreat like the others. She took the *salade* from her head, and answered that she was not alone, but had in her company fifty thousand of her people; and that go she would not till she had taken that town.

"But, whatever she said, I saw that she had with her but four men or five, as others also saw, wherefore I bade her retreat. Then she commanded me to have fagots brought, and planks to bridge fosses. And as she spoke to me, she cried in a loud voice, 'All of you, bring fagots to fill the fosse.' And this was done, whereat I greatly marvelled, and instantly that town was taken by assault with no great resistance. And all that the Maid did seemed to me rather deeds divine than natural, and it was impossible that so young a maid should do such deeds without the will and guidance of Our Lord."

DEATH OF JOAN THE MAID

Anonymous

FROM there the Maid rode to attack La Charité. But, though the towns helped her as well as they might with money and food, her force was too small and was too ill provided with everything, for the king did not send supplies. She abandoned the siege and departed in great displeasure. The court now moved from place to place, with Joan following in its train; for three weeks she stayed with a lady who describes her as very devout and constantly in church. Thinking her already a saint, people brought her things to touch. "Touch them yourselves," she said; "your touch is as good as mine."

Winter was over and spring came on, but still the king did nothing. The Maid could be idle no longer. Without a word to the king, she rode to Lagny, "for there they had fought bravely against the English." These men were Scots, under Sir Hugh Kennedy. In mid-April she was at Melun.

There "she heard her Voices almost every day, and many a time they told her that she would presently be taken prisoner." Her year was over. She prayed that she might die as soon as she was taken, without the long sorrow of imprisonment. Then her Voices told her to bear graciously whatever befell her, for so it must be. But they told her not the hour of her captivity. "If she had known the hour she would not then have gone to war. And often she prayed them to tell her of that hour, but they did not answer." These words are Joan's. She spoke them to her judges at Rouen.

The name of Joan was now such a terror to the English that men deserted rather than face her in arms. At this time the truce with Burgundy ended, and the duke openly set out to besiege the strong town of Compiègne, held by De Flavy for France. Burgundy had invested Compiègne, when Joan, with four hundred men, rode into the town secretly at dawn. That day Joan led a sally against the Burgundians. Her Voices told her nothing, good or bad, she says. The Burgundians were encamped at Margny and at Clairoix, the English at Venette, villages on a plain near the walls. Joan crossed the bridge on a gray charger, in a surcoat of crimson silk, rode through the redoubt beyond the bridge, and attacked the Burgundians. De Flavy in the town was to prevent the English from attacking her in the rear. He had boats on the river to secure Joan's retreat, if necessary.

Joan swept through Margny, driving the Burgundians before her; the garrison of Clairoix came to their help; the battle was doubtful. Meanwhile the English came up; they could not have reached the Burgundians, to aid them, but some of the Maid's men, seeing the English standards, fled. The English followed them under the walls of Compiègne; the gate of the redoubt was closed to prevent the English from entering with the runaways. Like Hector under Troy, the Maid was shut out from the town which she came to save.

Joan was with her own foremost line when the rear fled. They told her of her danger; she heeded not. Her men seized her bridle and turned her horse's head about. The English held the entrance from the causeway; Joan and a few men were driven into a corner of the outer wall. A rush was made at Joan. "Yield! yield to me!" each man cried.

"I have given my faith to Another," she said, "and I will keep my oath."

Her enemies confess that on this day Joan did great feats of arms, covering the rear of her force when they had to fly. Some French historians hold that the gates were closed, by treason, that the Maid might be taken.

The Maid, as a prisoner, was led to Margny, where the Burgundian and English captains rejoiced over her. They had her at last, the girl who had driven them from fort and field. Not a French lance was raised to rescue her; not a sou did the king send to ransom her.

Within two days of her capture, the Vicar-General of the Inquisition in France claimed her as a heretic and a witch. The English knights let the doctors of the University of Paris judge and burn

the girl whom they seldom dared to face in war.
She was the enemy of the English, and the English
believed in witchcraft. Joan was now kept in a
high tower and was allowed to walk on the leads.
She knew she was sold to England, she had heard
that the people of Compiègne were to be massacred.
She would rather die than fall into English hands,
but she hoped to escape and relieve Compiègne.
She therefore prayed for counsel to her Saints;
might she leap from the top of the tower? Would
they not bear her up in their hands? St. Catherine
bade her not to leap; God would help her and the
people of Compiègne.

Then, for the first time, as far as we know, the
Maid wilfully disobeyed her Voices. She leaped
from the tower. They found her, not wounded, not
a limb broken, but stunned. She knew not what
had happened; they told her she had leaped down.
For three days she could not eat, "yet was she comforted by St. Catherine, who bade her confess and
seek pardon of God, and told her that, without fail,
they of Compiègne should be relieved before Mar-
tinmas." This prophecy was fulfilled. Joan was
more troubled about Compiègne than about her own
coming doom.

She was now locked up in an iron cage at Rouen.
The person who conducted the trial was her deadly
enemy, the Bishop of Beauvais, Cauchon, whom
she and her men had turned out of his bishopric.
Next, Joan was kept in strong irons day and night,
always guarded by five English soldiers. Weak-
ened by long captivity and ill usage, she, an un-
taught girl, was questioned repeatedly for three

months by the most cunning and learned doctors of law of the Paris University. Often many spoke at once, to perplex her mind. But Joan always showed a wisdom which confounded them, and which is at least as extraordinary as her skill in war. She would never swear an oath to answer *all* their questions. About herself, and all matters bearing on her own conduct, she would answer. About the king, and the secrets of the king, she would not answer. If they forced her to reply about these things, she frankly said, she would not tell them the truth. The whole object of the trial was to prove that she dealt with powers of evil, and that her king had been crowned and aided by the devil. Her examiners, therefore, attacked her day by day, in public and in her dungeon, with questions about these visions which she held sacred and could only speak of with a blush among her friends. She maintained that she certainly did see and hear her Saints, and that they came to her by the will of God. This was called blasphemy and witchcraft.

Most was made of her refusal to wear woman's dress. For this she seems to have had two reasons: first, that to give up her old dress would have been to acknowledge that her mission was ended; next, for reasons of modesty, she being alone in prison among ruffianly men. She would wear woman's dress if they would let her take the Holy Communion, but this they refused. To these points she was constant: she would not deny her visions; she would not say one word against her king, "the noblest Christian in the world," she called him, who had deserted her. She would not wear woman's dress in prison. They took her to the torture-chamber, and threatened her with torture. Finally, they put her up in public, opposite a pile of wood ready for burning, where she was solemnly preached to for the last time. All through her trial, her Voices bade her answer boldly, in three months she would give her last answer, in three months "she would be free with great victory, and come into the Kingdom of Paradise."

At last, in fear of the fire and the stake before her, and on promise of being taken to a kindlier prison among women, and released from chains, she promised to renounce her visions, and submit to Cauchon and her other enemies. Some little note on paper she now signed with a cross, and repeated a short form of words. By some trick this signature was changed for a long document, in which she was made to confess all her visions false.

Cauchon had triumphed. The blame of heresy and witchcraft was cast on Joan, and on her king as an accomplice. But the English were not satisfied; they made an uproar, they threatened Cauchon, for Joan's life was to be spared. She was to be in prison all her days, on bread and water, but while she lived they dared scarcely stir against the French. They were soon satisfied.

Joan's prison was not changed. There soon came news that she had put on man's dress again. The judges went to her. She told them (they say) that she put on this dress of her own free will. In confession, later, she told her priest that she had been refused any other dress, and had been brutally treated both by the soldiers and by an English lord.

DEATH OF JOAN

In any case, the promises made to her had been broken. The judge asked her if her Voices had been with her again.

"Yes."

"What did they say?"

"God told me by the Voices of the great sorrow of my treason, when I abjured to save my life."

"Do you believe the Voices came from St. Margaret and St. Catherine?"

"Yes, and that they are from God."

She added that she had never meant to deny this, had not understood that she had denied it.

All was over now; she was a "relapsed heretic." Enough. They burned Joan the Maid. She did not suffer long. Her eyes were fixed on a cross which a priest, Martin l'Advenu, held up before her. She maintained, he says, to her dying moment, the truth of her Voices. With a great cry of JESUS! she gave up her life. Even the English wept, even a secretary of the English king said that they had burned a Saint.

Twenty years after her death Charles VII, in his own interest, induced the Pope to try the case of Joan over again. They collected the evidence of most of the living people who had known her, the Domremy peasants, from Dunois, d'Alençon, d'Aulon, from Isambart and l'Advenu, they learned how nobly she died, and how she never made one complaint, but forgave all her enemies freely. All these old Latin documents were collected, edited, and printed, in 1849, by Monsieur Jules Quicherat, a long and noble labor.

HOW CATHERINE DOUGLAS TRIED TO SAVE KING JAMES OF SCOTLAND

By Charlotte M. Yonge

IT was bedtime, and the old vaulted chambers of the Dominican monastery at Perth echoed with sounds that would seem incongruous in such a home of austerity, but that the disturbed state of Scotland rendered it the habit of her kings to attach their palaces to convents, that they themselves might benefit by the "peace of the Church," which was in general accorded to all sacred spots.

Thus it was that Christmas and Carnival time of 1435-6 had been spent by the court in the cloisters of Perth, and the dance, the song, and the tourney had strangely contrasted with the grave and self-denying habits to which the Dominicans were devoted in their neighboring cells. The festive season was nearly at an end, for it was the 20th of February, but the evening had been more than usually gay, and had been spent in games at chess, tables, or backgammon, reading romances of chivalry, harping and singing. King James himself, brave and handsome, and in the prime of life, was the blithest of the whole joyous party. He was the most accomplished man in his dominions; for though he had been basely kept a prisoner at Windsor throughout his boyhood by Henry IV of England, an education had been bestowed on him far above what he would have otherwise obtained; and he was naturally a man of great ability, refinement,

149

and strength of character. Not only was he a perfect knight on horseback, but in wrestling and running, throwing the hammer, and "putting the stane," he had scarcely a rival, and he was skilled in all the learned lore of the time, wrote poetry, composed music both sacred and profane, and was a complete minstrel, able to sing beautifully and to play on the harp and organ. His queen, the beautiful Joan Beaufort, had been the lady of his minstrelsy in the days of his captivity, ever since he had watched her walking on the slopes of Windsor Park, and wooed her in verses that are still preserved. They had now been eleven years married, and their court was one bright spot of civilization, refinement, and grace, amid the savagery of Scotland. And now, after the pleasant social evening, the queen, with her long fair hair unbound, was sitting under the hands of her tirewomen, who were preparing her for the night's rest; and the king, in his furred nightgown, was standing before the bright fire on the hearth of the wide chimney, laughing and talking with the attendant ladies.

Yet dark hints had already been whispered, which might have cast a shadow over that careless mirth. Always fierce and vindictive, the Scots had been growing more and more lawless and savage ever since the disputed succession of Bruce and Balliol had unsettled all royal authority, and led to one perpetual war with the English. The twenty years of James's captivity had been the worst of all—almost every noble was a robber chief, Scottish borderer preyed upon English borderer, Highlander upon Lowlander, knight upon traveller, every one who had armor upon him who had not; each clan was at deadly feud with its neighbor; blood was shed like water from end to end of the miserable land, and the higher the birth of the offender the greater the impunity he claimed.

Indeed, James himself had been brought next to the throne by one of the most savage and horrible murders ever perpetrated—that of his elder brother, David, by his own uncle; and he himself had probably been only saved from sharing the like fate by being sent out of the kingdom. His earnest words on his return to take the rule of this unhappy realm were these: "Let God but grant me life, and there shall not be a spot in my realm where the key shall not keep the castle, and the bracken bush the cow, though I should lead the life of a dog to accomplish it."

This great purpose had been before James through the eleven years of his reign, and he had worked it out resolutely. The lawless nobles would not brook his ruling hand, and strong and bitter was the hatred that had arisen against him. In many of his transactions he was far from blameless: he was sometimes tempted to craft, sometimes to tyranny; but his object was always a high and kingly one, though he was led by the horrible wickedness of the men he had to deal with more than once to forget that evil is not to be overcome with evil, but with good. In the main, it was his high and uncompromising resolution to enforce the laws upon high and low alike that led to the nobles' conspiracies against him; though, if he had always been true to his purpose of swerving neither to the right nor to the left, he might have avoided the last fatal offense that armed the murderer against his life.

The chief misdoers in the long period of anarchy had been his uncles and cousins; nor was it till after his eldest uncle's death that his return home had been possible. With a strong hand had he avenged upon the princes and their followers the many miseries they had inflicted upon his people; and in carrying out these measures he had seized upon the great earldom of Strathern, which had descended to one of their party in right of his wife, declaring that it could not be inherited by a female. In this he appears to have acted unjustly, from the strong desire to avail himself by any pretext of an opportunity of breaking the overweening power of the great turbulent nobles; and, to make up for the loss, he created the new earldom of Menteith, for the young Malise Graham, the son of the dispossessed earl. But the proud and vindictive Grahams were not thus to be pacified. Sir Robert Graham, the uncle of the young earl, drew off into the Highlands, and there formed a conspiracy among other discontented men who hated the resolute government that repressed their violence. Men of princely blood joined in the plot, and 300 Highland catherans were ready to accompany the expedition that promised the delights of war and plunder.

Even when the hard-worked king was setting forth to enjoy his holiday at Perth, the traitors had fixed upon that spot as the place of his doom; but the scheme was known to so many, that it could not be kept entirely secret, and warnings began to gather round the king. When, on his way to Perth, he was about to cross the Firth of Forth, the wild figure of a Highland woman appeared at his bridle rein, and solemnly warned him "that, if he crossed that water, he would never return alive." He was struck by the apparition, and bade one of his knights to inquire of her what she meant; but the knight must have been a dullard or a traitor, for he told the king that the woman was either mad or drunk, and no notice was taken of her warning.

There was likewise a saying abroad in Scotland, that the new year, 1436, should see the death of a king; and this same carnival night, James, while playing at chess with a young friend, whom he was wont to call the king of love, laughingly observed that "it must be you or I, since there are but two kings in Scotland—therefore, look well to yourself."

Little did the blithe monarch guess that at that moment one of the conspirators, touched by a moment's misgiving, was hovering round, seeking in vain an opportunity of giving him warning; that even then his chamberlain and kinsman, Sir Robert Stewart, was enabling the traitors to place boards across the moat for their passage, and to remove the bolts and bars of all the doors in their way. And the Highland woman was at the door, earnestly entreating to see the king if but for one moment! The message was even brought to him, but alas! he bade her wait till the morrow, and she turned away, declaring that she should never more see his face!

And now, as before said, the feast was over, and the king stood, gayly chatting with his wife and her ladies, when the clang of arms was heard, and the glare of torches in the court below flashed on the windows. The ladies flew to secure the doors. Alas! the bolts and bars were gone! Too late the warnings returned upon the king's mind, and he knew it was he alone who was sought. He tried to escape by the windows, but here the bars were but too firm. Then he seized the tongs, and tore up a board in the floor, by which he let himself down into the vault below, just as the murderers came rushing along the passage, slaying on their way a page named Walter Straiton.

There was no bar to the door. Yes, there was. Catherine Douglas, worthy of her name, worthy of the cognizance of the bleeding heart, thrust her arm through the empty staples to gain for her sovereign a few moments more for escape and safety! But though true as steel, the brave arm was not as strong. It was quickly broken. She was thrust fainting aside, and the ruffians rushed in. Queen Joan stood in the midst of the room, with her hair streaming round her, and her mantle thrown hastily on. Some of the wretches even struck and wounded her, but Graham called them off, and bade them search for the king. They sought him in vain in every corner of the women's apartments, and dispersed through the other rooms in search of their prey. The ladies began to hope that the citizens and nobles in the town were coming to their help, and that the king might have escaped through an opening that led from the vault into the tennis-court. Presently, however, the king called to them to draw him up again, for he had not been able to get out of the vault, having a few days before caused the hole to be bricked up, because his tennis-balls used to fly into it and be lost. In trying to draw him up by the sheets, Elizabeth Douglas, another of the ladies, was actually pulled down into the vault; the noise was heard by the assassins, who were still watching outside, and they returned.

There is no need to tell of the foul and cruel slaughter that ensued, nor of the barbarous vengeance that visited it. Our tale is of golden, not of brazen deeds; and if we have turned our eyes for a moment to the Bloody Carnival of Perth, it is for the sake of the king, who was too upright for his bloodthirsty subjects, and, above all, for that of the noble-hearted lady whose frail arm was the guardian of her sovereign's life in the extremity of peril.

THE BRAVE QUEEN OF HUNGARY

By Charlotte M. Yonge

OF all the possessions of the old kingdom of Hungary, none was more valued than what was called the Crown of St. Stephen, so called from one which had, in the year 1000, been presented by Pope Sylvester II to Stephen, the second Christian Duke, and first King of Hungary. A crown and a cross were given to him for his coronation, which took place in the Church of the Holy Virgin, at

Alba Regale, also called in German Weissenburg, where thenceforth the kings of Hungary were anointed to begin their troubled reigns, and at the close of them were laid to rest beneath the pavement, where most of them might have used the same epitaph as the old Italian leader: "He rests here, who never rested before." For it was a wild realm, bordered on all sides by foes, with Poland, Bohemia, and Austria, ever casting greedy eyes upon it, and afterwards with the Turk upon the southern border, while the Magyars, or Hungarian nobles, themselves were a fierce and untamable race, bold and generous, but brooking little control, claiming a voice in choosing their own sovereign, and to resist him, even by force of arms, if he broke the laws. No prince had a right to their allegiance unless he had been crowned with St. Stephen's crown; but if he had once worn that sacred circle, he thenceforth was held as the only lawful monarch, unless he should flagrantly violate the Constitution. In 1076, another crown had been given by the Greek emperor to Geysa, King of Hungary, and the sacred crown combined the two. It had the two arches of the Roman crown, and the gold circlet of the Constantinopolitan; and the difference of workmanship was evident.

In the 1439 died King Albert, who had been appointed King of Hungary in right of his wife, Queen Elizabeth. He left a little daughter only four years old, and as the Magyars had never been governed by a female hand, they proposed to send and offer their crown, and the hand of their young widowed queen, to Wladislas, the King of Poland.

But Elizabeth had hopes of another child, and in case it should be a son, she had no mind to give away its rights to its father's throne. How, then, was she to help herself among the proud and determined nobles of her court? One thing was certain, that if once the Polish king were crowned with St. Stephen's crown, it would be his own fault if he were not King of Hungary as long as he lived; but if the crown were not to be found, of course he could not receive it, and the fealty of the nobles would not be pledged to him.

The most trustworthy person she had about her was Helen Kottenner, the lady who had the charge of her little daughter, Princess Elizabeth, and to her she confided her desire that the crown might be secured, so as to prevent the Polish party from getting access to it. Helen herself has written down the history of these strange events, and of her own struggles of mind at the risk she ran, and the doubt whether good would come of the intrigue; and there can be no doubt that, whether the queen's conduct were praiseworthy or not, Helen dared a great peril for the sake purely of loyalty and fidelity. "The queen's commands," she says, "sorely troubled me; for it was a dangerous venture for me and my little children, and I turned it over in my mind what I should do, for I had no one to take counsel of but God alone; and I thought if I did it not, and evil arose therefrom, I should be guilty before God and the world. So I consented to risk my life on this difficult undertaking; but desired to have some one to help me." This was permitted; but the first person to whom the Lady of Kottenner confided her intention, a Croat, lost his color from alarm, looked like one half dead, and went at once in search of his horse. The next thing that was heard of him was that he had had a bad fall from his horse, and had been obliged to return to Croatia, and the queen remained much alarmed at her plans being known to one so faint-hearted. However, a more courageous confidant was afterwards found in a Hungarian gentleman, whose name has become illegible in Helen's old manuscript.

The crown was in the vaults of the strong castle of Plintenburg, also called Vissegrad, which stands upon a bend of the Danube, about twelve miles from the twin cities of Buda and Pesth. It was in a case, within a chest, sealed with many seals, and since the king's death, it had been brought up by the nobles, who closely guarded both it and the queen, into her apartments, and there examined and replaced it in the chest. The next night, one of the queen's ladies upset a wax taper, without being aware of it, and before the fire was discovered, and put out, the corner of the chest was singed, and a hole burnt in the blue velvet cushion that lay on the top. Upon this, the lords had caused the chest to be taken down again into the vault, and had fastened the doors with many locks and with seals. The castle had further been put into the charge of Ladislas von Gara, the queen's cousin, and Ban, or hereditary commander, of the border troops, and he had given it over to a Burggraf, or seneschal, who had placed his bed in the chamber where was the door leading to the vaults.

The queen removed to Komorn, a castle higher

up the Danube, in charge of her faithful cousin, Count Ulric of Eily, taking with her her little daughter Elizabeth, Helen Kottenner, and two other ladies. This was the first stage on the journey to Presburg, where the nobles had wished to lodge the queen, and from thence she sent back Helen to bring the rest of the maids of honor and her goods to join her at Komorn. It was early spring, and snow was still on the ground, and the Lady of Kottenner and her faithful nameless assistant travelled in a sledge; but two Hungarian noblemen went with them, and they had to be most careful in concealing their arrangements. Helen had with her the queen's signet, and keys; and her friend had a file in each shoe, and keys under his black velvet dress.

On arriving in the evening, they found that the Burggraf had fallen ill, and could not sleep in the chamber leading to the vault, because it belonged to the ladies' chambers, and that he had therefore put a cloth over the padlock of the door and sealed it. There was a stove in the room, and the maidens began to pack up their clothes there, an operation that lasted till eight o'clock; while Helen's friend stood there, talking and jesting with them, trying all the while to hide the files, and contriving to say to Helen: "Take care that we have a light." So she begged the old housekeeper to give her plenty of wax tapers, as she had many prayers to say. At last every one was gone to bed, and there only remained in the room with Helen, an old woman, whom she had brought with her, who knew no German, and was fast asleep. Then the accomplice came back through the chapel, which opened into this same hall. He had on his black velvet gown and felt shoes, and was followed by a servant, who, Helen says, was bound to him by oath, and had the same Christian name as himself, this being evidently an additional bond of fidelity. Helen, who had received from the queen all the keys of this outer room, let them in, and, after the Burggraf's cloth and seal had been removed, they unlocked the padlock and the other two locks of the outer door of the vault, and the two men descended into it. There were several other doors, whose chains required to be filed through, and their seals and locks broken, and to the ears of the waiting Helen the noise appeared fatally loud. She says: "I devoutly prayed to God and the Holy Virgin, that they would support and help me; yet I was in greater anxiety for my soul than for my life, and I prayed to God that He would be merciful to my soul, and rather let me die at once there, than that anything should happen against His will, or that should bring misfortune on my country and people."

She fancied she heard a noise of armed men at the chapel door, but finding nothing there, believed that it was a spirit, and returning to her prayers, vowed, poor lady, to make a pilgrimage to St. Maria Zell, in Styria, if the Holy Virgin's intercessions obtained their success, and till the pilgrimage could be made, "to forego every Saturday night my feather bed!" After another false alarm at a supposed noise at the maidens' door, she ventured into the vault to see how her companions were getting on, when she found they had filed away all the locks, except that of the case containing the crown, and this they were obliged to burn, in spite of their apprehension that the smell and smoke might be observed. They then shut up the chest, replaced the padlocks and chains with those they had brought for the purpose, and renewed the seals with the queen's signet, which, bearing the royal arms, would baffle detection that the seals had been tampered with. They then took the crown into the chapel, where they found a red velvet cushion, so large that by taking out some of the stuffing a hiding-place was made in which the crown was deposited, and the cushion sewn up over it.

By this time day was dawning, the maidens were dressing, and it was the hour for setting off for Komorn. The old woman who had waited on them came to the Lady of Kottenner to have her wages paid, and be dismissed to Buda. While she was waiting, she began to remark on a strange thing lying by the stove, which, to the Lady Helen's great dismay, she perceived to be a bit of the case in which the crown was kept. She tried to prevent the old woman from noticing it, pushed it into the hottest part of the stove, and, by way of further precaution, took the old woman away with her, on the plea of asking the queen to make her a bedes-woman at Vienna, and this was granted to her.

When all was ready, the gentleman desired his servant to take the cushion and put it into the sledge designed for himself and the Lady of Kottenner. The man took it on his shoulders, hiding it under an old ox-hide, with the tail hanging down, to the laughter of all beholders. Helen further records the trying to get some breakfast in the market-place and finding nothing but herrings, also the going to mass, and the care she took not to sit upon the holy crown, though she had to sit on its cushion in the sledge. They dined at an inn, but took care to keep the cushion in sight, and then in the dusk crossed the Danube on the ice, which was becoming very thin, and half-way across it broke under the maidens' carriage, so that Helen expected to be lost in the Danube, crown and all. However, though many packages were lost under the ice, her sledge got safe over, as well as all the ladies, some of whom she took into her conveyance, and all safely arrived at the castle of Komorn late in the evening.

The very hour of their arrival a babe was born to the queen, and to her exceeding joy it was a son. Count von Eily, hearing "that a king and a friend was born to him," had bonfires lighted, and a torch-light procession on the ice that same night, and early in the morning came the Archbishop of Gran to christen the child. The queen wished her faithful Helen to be godmother, but Helen refused in favor of some lady whose family it was probably needful to propitiate. She took off the little Princess Eliza-beth's mourning for her father and dressed her in red and gold, all the maidens appeared in gay apparel, and there was great rejoicing and thanksgiving when the babe was christened Ladislas, after a sainted king of Hungary.

The peril was, however, far from ended; for many of the Magyars had no notion of accepting an in-

THEN HE OFFERED A FERVENT PRAYER OF THANKS
—page 176

fant for their king, and by Easter, the King of
Poland was advancing upon Buda to claim the
realm to which he had been invited. No one had
discovered the abstraction of the crown, and Elizabeth's object was to take her child to Weissenburg,
and there have him crowned, so as to disconcert the
Polish party. She had sent to Buda for cloth of
gold to make him a coronation dress, but it did not
come in time, and Helen therefore shut herself
into the chapel at Komorn, and, with doors fast
bolted, cut up a rich and beautiful vestment of his
grandfather's, the Emperor Sigismund, of red and
gold, with silver spots, and made it into a tiny
coronation robe, with surplice and humeral (or
shoulder-piece), the stole and banner, the gloves and
shoes. The queen was much alarmed by a report
that the Polish party meant to stop her on her way
to Weissenburg; and if the baggage should be seized
and searched, the discovery of the crown might
have fatal consequences. Helen, on this, observed
that the king was more important than the crown,
and that the best way would be to keep them together; so she wrapped up the crown in a cloth,
and hid it under the mattress of his cradle, with a
long spoon for mixing his pap upon the top, so,
said the queen, he might take care of his crown
himself.

On Tuesday before Whitsunday the party set
out, escorted by Count Ulric, and several other
knights and nobles. After crossing the Danube
in a large boat, the queen and her little girl were
placed in a carriage, or more probably a litter, the
other ladies rode, and the cradle and its precious

contents were carried by four men; but this the poor little Lassla, as Helen shortens his lengthy name, resented so much, that he began to scream so loud that she was forced to dismount and carry him in her arms, along a road rendered swampy by much rain.

They found all the villages deserted by the peasants, who had fled into the woods, and as most of their lords were of the other party, they expected an attack, so the little king was put into the carriage with his mother and sister, and the ladies formed a circle round it "that if any one shot at the carriage we might receive the stroke." When the danger was over the child was taken out again, for he would be content nowhere but in the arms of either his nurse or of faithful Helen, who took turns to carry him on foot nearly all the way, sometimes in a high wind which covered them with dust, sometimes in great heat, sometimes in rain so heavy that Helen's fur pelisse, with which she covered his cradle, had to be wrung out several times. They slept at an inn, round which the gentlemen lighted a circle of fires, and kept watch all night.

Weissenburg was loyal, five hundred armed gentlemen came out to meet them, and on Whitsun Eve they entered the city, Helen carrying her little king in her arms in the midst of a circle of these five hundred holding their naked swords aloft. On Whitsunday, Helen rose early, bathed the little fellow, who was twelve weeks old that day, and dressed him. He was then carried in her arms to the church, beside his mother. According to the old Hungarian customs the choir door was closed—

the burghers were within, and would not open till
the new monarch should have taken the great coronation oath to respect the Hungarian liberties and
laws.

This oath was taken by the queen in the name
of her son, the doors were opened, and all the train
entered, the little princess being lifted up to stand
by the organ, lest she should be hurt in the throng.
First Helen held her charge up to be confirmed,
and then she had to hold him while he was knighted,
with a richly adorned sword bearing the motto "In-
destructible," and by a stout Hungarian knight
called Mikosch Weida, who struck with such a good
will that Helen felt the blow on her arm, and the
queen cried out to him not to hurt the child.

The Archbishop of Gran anointed the little
creature, dressed him in the red and gold robe, and
put on his head the holy crown, and the people
admired to see how straight he held up his neck
under it; indeed, they admired the loudness and
strength of his cries, when, as the good lady
records, "the noble king had little pleasure in his
coronation, for he wept aloud." She had to hold
him up for the rest of the service, while Count Ulric
of Eily held the crown over his head, and afterwards to seat him in a chair in St. Peter's Church,
and then he was carried home in his cradle, with
the count holding the crown over his head, and the
other regalia borne before him.

And thus Ladislas became King of Hungary at
twelve weeks old, and was then carried off by his
mother into Austria for safety. Whether this secret
robbery of the crown, and coronation by stealth

was wise or just on the mother's part is a question not easy of answer—though of course she deemed it her duty to do her utmost for her child's rights. Of Helen Kottenner's deep fidelity and conscientious feeling there can be no doubt, and her having acted with her eyes fully open to the risk she ran, her trust in Heaven overcoming her fears and terrors, rendered her truly a heroine.

The crown has had many other adventures, and afterwards was kept in an apartment of its own in the castle of Ofen, with an antechamber guarded by two grenadiers. The door was of iron, with three locks, and the crown itself was contained in an iron chest with five seals. All this, however, did not prevent it from being taken away and lost in the Revolution of 1849.

A STORY OF CHRISTOPHER COLUMBUS FOR LITTLE CHILDREN

By Elizabeth Harrison

ONCE upon a time, far across the great ocean there lived a little boy named Christopher. The city in which he lived was called Genoa. It was on the coast of the great sea, and from the time that little Christopher could first remember he had seen boats come and go across the water. I doubt not that he had little boats of his own which he tried to sail, or paddle about on the small pools near his home.

Soon after he was old enough to read books,

which in those days were very scarce and very much valued, he got hold of an account of the wonderful travels of a man named Marco Polo. Over and over again little Christopher read the marvelous stories told by this old traveller, of the strange cities which he had seen and of the dark-colored people whom he had met; of the queer houses; of the wild and beautiful animals he had encountered; of the jewels and perfumes and flowers which he had come across.

All day long the thoughts of little Christopher were busy with this strange far-away land which Marco Polo described. All night long he dreamed of the marvelous sights to be seen on those distant shores. Many a time he went down to the water's edge to watch the queer ships as they slowly disappeared in the dim distance, where the sea and sky seemed to meet. He listened eagerly to everything about the sea and the voyages of adventure, or of trade which were told by the sailors near.

When he was fourteen years old he went to sea with an uncle, who was commander of one of the vessels that came and went from the port of Genoa. For a number of years he thus lived on a vessel, learning everything that he could about the sea. At one time the ship on which he was sailing had a desperate fight with another ship; both took fire and were burned to the water's edge. Christopher Columbus, for that was his full name, only escaped, as did the other sailors, by jumping into the sea and swimming to the shore. Still this did not cure him of his love for the ocean life.

We find after a time that he left Italy, his native

country, and went to live in Portugal, a land near the great sea, whose people were far more venturesome than had been those of Genoa. Here he married a beautiful maiden, whose father had collected a rich store of maps and charts, which showed what was then supposed to be the shape of the earth and told of strange and wonderful voyages which brave sailors had from time to time dared to make out into the then unknown sea. Most people in those days thought it was certain death to any one who ventured very far out on the ocean.

There were all sorts of queer and absurd ideas afloat as to the shape of the earth. Some people thought it was round like a pancake and that the waters which surrounded the land gradually changed into mist and vapor and that he who ventured out into these vapors fell through the mist and clouds down into—they knew not where. Others believed that there were huge monsters living in the distant waters ready to swallow any sailor who was foolish enough to venture near them.

But Christopher Columbus had grown to be a very wise and thoughtful man, and from all he could learn from the maps of his father-in-law and the books which he read, and from the long talks which he had with some other learned men, he grew more and more certain that the world was round like an orange, and that by sailing westward from the coast of Portugal one could gradually go round the world and find at last the wonderful land of *Cathay,* the strange country which lay far beyond the sea, the accounts of which had so thrilled him as a boy.

CHRISTOPHER COLUMBUS

We, of course, know that he was right in his belief concerning the shape of the earth, but people in those days laughed him to scorn when he spoke of making a voyage out on the vast and fearful ocean. In vain he talked and reasoned and argued, and drew maps to explain matters. The more he proved to his own satisfaction that this must be the shape of the world, the more other people shook their heads and called him crazy.

He remembered in his readings of the book of Marco Polo's travels that the people whom Polo had met were heathen who knew little about the God who had made the world, and nothing at all about His Son, Christ Jesus, and as Christopher Columbus loved very dearly the Christian religion, his mind became filled with a longing to carry it across the great seas to this far-away country. The more he thought about it the more he wanted to go, until his whole life was filled with the one thought of how to get hold of some ships to prove that the earth was round, and that these far-away heathens could be reached.

Through some influential friends he obtained admission to the court of the King of Portugal. Eagerly he told the rich monarch of the great enterprise which filled his heart. It was of little or no use, the king was busy with other affairs, and only listened to the words of Columbus as one might listen to the wind. Year after year passed by, Columbus' wife had died, and their one little son, Diego, had grown to be quite a boy. Finally Columbus decided he would leave Portugal and would go over to Spain, a rich country near by, and see if the Spanish monarchs would not give him boats in which to make his longed-for voyage.

The Spanish king was named Ferdinand, and the Spanish queen was a beautiful woman named Isabella. When Columbus told them of his belief that the world was round, and of his desire to help the heathen who lived in this far-off country, they listened attentively to him, for both King Ferdinand and Queen Isabella were very earnest people and very desirous that all the world should become Christians; but their ministers and officers of state persuaded them that the whole thing was a foolish dream of an enthusiastic, visionary man; and again Columbus was disappointed in his hope of getting help.

Still he did not give up in despair. *The thought was too great for that.* He sent his brother over to England to see if the English king would not listen to him and give the necessary help, but again he was doomed to disappointment. Only here and there could he find any one who believed that it was possible for him to sail round the earth and reach the land on the other side. Long years passed by. Columbus grew pale and thin with waiting and hoping, with planning and longing.

Sometimes as he walked along the streets of the Spanish capital people would point their fingers at him and say: "There goes the crazy old man who thinks the world is round." Again and again Columbus tried to persuade the Spanish king and queen that if they would aid him, his discoveries would bring great honor and riches to their kingdom, and that they would also become the benefactors of the world by helping to spread the knowledge of Christ and His religion. Nobody believed in his theory. Nobody was interested in his plan. He grew poorer and poorer.

At last he turned his back on the great Spanish court, and in silent despair he took his little son by the hand and walked a long way to a small seaport called Palos, where there was a queer old convent in which strangers were often entertained by the kind monks who lived in it. Weary and footsore he reached the gate of the convent. Knocking upon it he asked the porter, who answered the summons, if he would give little Diego a bit of bread and a drink of water. While the two tired travellers were resting, as the little boy ate his dry crust of bread, the prior of the convent, a man of thought and learning, whose name was Juan Perez, came by and at once saw that these two were no common beggars. He invited them in and questioned Columbus closely about his past life. He listened quietly and thoughtfully to Columbus and his plan of crossing the ocean and converting the heathen to Christianity.

Juan Perez had at one time been a very intimate friend of Queen Isabella; in fact, the priest to whom she told all her sorrows and troubles. He was a quiet man and talked but little. After a long conference with Columbus, in which he was convinced that Columbus was right, he borrowed a mule and getting on his back rode for many miles across the open country to the palace in which the queen was then staying. I do not know how he convinced her of the truth of Columbus' plan, when all the ministers and courtiers and statesmen about her considered it the absurdly foolish and silly dream of an old man; but, somehow, he did it.

He then returned on his mule to the old convent at Palos, and told Columbus to go back once more to the court of Spain and again petition the queen to give him money with which to make his voyage of discovery. The state treasurer said the queen had no money to spare, but this noble-hearted woman, who now, for the first time, realized that it was a grand and glorious thing Columbus wished to do, said she would give her crown jewels for money with which to start Columbus on his dangerous journey across the great ocean.

This meant much in those days, as queens were scarcely considered dignified or respectable if they did not wear crowns of gold inlaid with bright jewels on all public occasions, but Queen Isabella cared far more to send the gospel of Christ over to the heathen than how she might look, or what other people might say about her. The jewels were pawned and the money was given to Columbus. With a glad heart he hastened back to the little town of Palos where he had left his young son with the kind of priest Juan Perez.

But now a new difficulty arose. Enough sailors could not be found who would venture their lives by going out on this unknown voyage with a crazy old man such as Columbus was thought to be. At last the convicts from the prisons were given liberty by the queen on condition that they would go with the sailors and Columbus. So, you see, it was not altogether a very nice crew, still it was the best he could get, and Columbus' heart was so filled with the great work that he was willing to undertake the voyage no matter how great or how many the difficulties might be. The ships were filled with food and other provisions for a long, long voyage.

Nobody knew how long it would be before the land on the other side could be reached, and many people thought there was no possible hope of its ever being found.

Early one summer morning, even before the sun had risen, Columbus bade farewell to the few friends who had gathered at the little seaport of Palos to say good-bye to him. The ships spread their sails and started on the great untried voyage. There were three boats, none of which we would think, nowadays, was large enough or strong enough to dare venture out of sight and help of land and run the risk of encountering the storms of mid-ocean.

The names of the boats were the *Santa Maria,* which was the one that Columbus himself commanded, and two smaller boats, one named the *Pinta* and the other the *Nina.*

Strange, indeed, must the sailors have felt, as hour after hour they drifted out into the great unknown waters, which no man ever ventured into before. Soon all land faded from their sight, and on, and on, and on they went, not knowing where or how the voyage would end. Columbus alone was filled with hope, feeling quite sure that in time he would reach the never before visited shores of a New World, and would thus be the means of bringing the Christian religion to these poor, ignorant people. On and on they sailed, day after day—far beyond the utmost point which sailors had ever before reached.

Many of the men were filled with a strange dread and begged and pleaded to return home. Still on and on they went, each day taking them further and further from all they had ever known or loved before. Day after day passed, and week after week until two months had elapsed.

The provisions which they had brought with them were getting scarce, and the men now dreaded starvation. They grew angry with Columbus, and threatened to take his life if he did not command the ships to be turned back toward Spain, but his patience did not give out, nor was his faith one whit the less. He cheered the hearts of the men as best he could, often telling them droll, funny stories to distract their thoughts from the terrible dread which now filled all minds.

He promised a rich reward to the first man who should discover land ahead. This somewhat renewed their courage, and day and night watches were set and the western horizon before them was scanned at all hours. Time and again they thought they saw land ahead, only to find they had mistaken a cloud upon the horizon for the longed-for shore. Flocks of birds flying westward began to be seen. This gave some ground for hope. For surely the birds must be flying toward some land where they could find food, and trees in which to build their nests. Still fear was great in the hearts of all, and Columbus knew that he could not keep the men much longer in suspense, and that if land did not appear soon they would compel him to turn around and retrace his steps whether he wished to or not.

Then he thought of all the benighted heathen who had never heard of God's message of love to man through Christ, and he prayed almost incessantly that courage might be given him to go on. Hour after hour he looked across the blue water, day and night, longing for the sight of land. In fact, he watched so incessantly that his eyesight became injured and he could scarcely see at all.

At last one night as he sat upon the deck of the ship he was quite sure that a faint light glimmered for a few moments in the distant darkness ahead. Where there is a light there must be land, he thought. Still he was not sure, as his eyesight had become so dim. So he called one of the more faithful sailors to him and asked him what he saw. The sailor exclaimed:

"A light, a light!"

Another sailor was called, but by this time the light had disappeared and the sailor saw nothing, and Columbus' hopes again sank. Still he felt they must be nearing land. About two o'clock that night the commander of one of the other boats started the cry:

"Land! land ahead!"

You can well imagine how the shout was taken up, and how the sailors, one and all, rushed to the edge of their ships, leaning far over, no doubt, and straining their eyes for the almost unhoped-for sight.

CHRISTOPHER COLUMBUS

Early the next morning some one of the sailors picked up a branch of a strange tree, lodged in the midst of which was a tiny bird's nest. This was sure evidence that they were indeed near land, for branches of trees do not grow in water.

Little by little the land came in sight. First it looked like a dim ghost of a shore, but gradually it grew distinct and clear. About noon the next day the keel of Columbus' boat grounded upon the sand of the newly discovered country. No white man had ever before set eyes upon it. No ship had ever before touched this coast.

At last after a long life of working and studying, of hoping and planning, of trying and failing, and trying yet again, he had realized his dream.

The great mystery of the ocean was revealed, and Columbus had achieved a glory which would last as long as the world lasted. *He had given a new world to mankind!* He had reached the far distant country across the ocean, which scarcely any of his countrymen had even believed to have any existence. He now *knew* that the whole round world could in time have the Christian religion.

He sprang upon the shore, and dropping on his knees he first stooped and kissed the ground, and then he offered a fervent prayer of thanks to God.

A learned attorney who had come with him across the water next planted the flag of Spain upon the unknown land, and claimed the newly discovered country in the name of King Ferdinand and Queen Isabella of Spain.

Wonderful, wonderful indeed were the things which Columbus and the sailors now saw! Strange naked men and women of a copper, or bronze color, strange new birds with gorgeous tails that glittered like gems such as they had never seen before; beautiful and unknown fruits and flowers met their gaze on every side.

The savages were kind and gentle and brought them food and water. They had little else to offer as they had no houses, nor streets, nor carriages, nor cars, nor conveniences of any kind. Do you know, my dear children, that this strange, wild, savage country which Columbus had travelled so far and so long to discover was *our country, America?*

But it was not long after Columbus had gone back to Europe and told the people there of the wonderful things which he had seen in this far, far away land that ship-loads of white people, who were educated and who had been taught to love God and to keep His commandments, came over and settled in this wild, new country. They plowed the land and planted seed; they built houses for themselves, their wives and little ones, and in time they made school-houses for the children, and churches in which to worship God. Long and hard was the struggle which these first white men had to make in this strange, new country.

Year after year more and more white men came. These new settlers prospered, and new towns were built, and roads were made from one town to another, and stores and manufactories began to be seen.

At last the little handful of people had grown so strong that they established a government of their own, which welcomed all newcomers, providing they were law-abiding citizens. The poor and oppressed, the persecuted and discouraged in other lands came to this new shore, where they found wealth if they were willing to work for it.

Here they need no longer fear the persecutions from which they had suffered. Here they gained new hope and became honored and respected citizens.

Little by little the small country grew into a great nation, the greatest on earth, because it is the freest, and each citizen in it has his rights respected. But for the courage and determination and self-sacrifice of Columbus this great new world might have remained for hundreds of years unknown to men.

Four hundred years afterwards the children of the children's children of these early settlers had a grand celebration in honor of the brave old man, Christopher Columbus, whom the people of his day called crazy, and all the nations of the earth were invited to bring their most beautiful, their richest and rarest products to this celebration, in order that not we of America alone, but *the whole world might celebrate the wisdom and the courage of the great Columbus, "the finder of America."*

In the rejoicing and in the celebration the nations did not forget the good Queen Isabella, who was willing to give up her most precious jewels in order that she might help Columbus in his voyage of discovery.

A SEA-FIGHT IN THE TIME OF QUEEN BESS

By Charles Kingsley

WHEN the sun leaped up the next morning, and the tropic night flashed suddenly into the tropic day, Amyas was pacing the deck, with dishevelled hair and torn clothes, his eyes red with rage and weeping, his heart full—how can I describe it? Picture it to yourselves, picture it to yourselves, you who have ever lost a brother; and you who have not, thank God that you know nothing of his agony. Full of impossible projects, he strode and staggered up and down, as the ship thrashed close-hauled through the rolling seas. He would go back and burn the villa. He would take Guayra, and have the life of every man in it in return for his brother's. "We can do it, lads!" he shouted. "If Drake took Nombre de Dios, we can take La Guayra." And every voice shouted, "Yes."

"We will have it, Amyas, and have Frank too, yet," cried Cary; but Amyas shook his head. He knew, and knew not why he knew, that all the ports in New Spain would never restore to him that one beloved face.

"Yes, he shall be well avenged. And look there! There is the first crop of our vengeance." And he pointed toward the shore, where between them and the now distant peaks of the Silla three sails appeared, not five miles to windward.

"There are the Spanish bloodhounds on our heels,

179

the same ships which we saw yesterday off Guayra. Back, lads, and welcome them, if they were a dozen."

There was a murmur of applause from all around; and if any young heart sank for a moment at the prospect of fighting three ships at once, it was awed into silence by the cheer which rose from all the older men, and by Salvation Yeo's stentorian voice:

"If there were a dozen, the Lord is with us, who has said, 'One of you shall chase a thousand.' Clear away, lads, and see the glory of the Lord this day."

"Amen!" cried Cary; and the ship was kept still closer to the wind.

Amyas had revived at the sight of battle. He no longer felt his wounds, or his great sorrow; even Frank's last angel's look grew dimmer every moment as he bustled about the deck; and ere a quarter of an hour had passed, his voice cried firmly and cheerfully as of old:

"Now, my masters, let us serve God, and then to breakfast, and after that clear for action."

Jack Brimblecombe read the daily prayers, and the prayers before a fight at sea, and his honest voice trembled as, in the Prayer for all Conditions of Men (in spite of Amyas' despair), he added, "and especially for our dear brother Mr. Francis Leigh, perhaps captive among the idolators;" and so they rose.

"Now, then," said Amyas, "to breakfast. A Frenchman fights best fasting, a Dutchman drunk, an Englishman full, and a Spaniard when the devil is in him, and that's always."

"And good beef and the good cause are a match for the devil," said Cary. "Come down, captain; you must eat too."

Amyas shook his head, took the tiller from the steersman, and bade him go below and fill himself. Will Cary went down, and returned in five minutes, with a plate of bread and beef, and a great jack of ale, coaxed them down Amyas' throat, as a nurse does with a child, and then scuttled below again with tears hopping down his face.

Amyas stood still steering. His face was grown seven years older in the last night. A terrible set calm was on him. Woe to the man who came across him that day!

"There are three of them, you see, my masters," said he, as the crew came on deck again. "A big ship forward, and two galleys astern of her. The big ship may keep; she is a race ship, and if we can but recover the wind of her, we will see whether our height is not a match for her length. We must give her the slip, and take the galleys first."

"I thank the Lord," said Yeo, "who has given so wise a heart to so young a general; a very David and Daniel, saving his presence, lads; and if any dare not follow him, let him be as the men of Meroz and Succoth. Amen! Silas Stavely, smite me that boy over the head, the young monkey; why is he not down at the powder-room door?"

And Yeo went about his gunnery, as one who knew how to do it, and had the most terrible mind to do it thoroughly, and the most terrible faith that it was God's work.

So all fell to; and though there was comparatively little to be done, the ship having been kept as far as could be in fighting order all night, yet there was "clearing the decks, lacing the nettings, making of bulwarks, fitting of waist-cloths, arming of tops, tallowing of pikes, slinging of yards, doubling of sheets and tacks," enough to satisfy even the pedantical soul of Richard Hawkins himself.

Amyas took charge of the poop, Cary of the forecastle, and Yeo, as gunner, of the main deck, while Drew, as master, settled himself in the waist; and all was ready, and more than ready, before the great ship was within two miles of them.

And now, while the mastiffs of England and the bloodhounds of Spain are nearing and nearing over the rolling surges, thirsting for each other's blood, let us spend a few minutes at least in looking at them both, and considering the causes which in those days enabled the English to face and conquer armaments immensely superior in size and number of ships, and to boast that in the whole Spanish war but one queen's ship, the *Revenge,* and (if I recollect right) but one private man-of-war, Sir Richard Hawkins' *Dainty,* had ever struck their colors to the enemy.

What was it which enabled Sir Richard Grenvil's *Revenge,* in his last fearful fight off the Azores, to endure, for twelve hours before she struck, the attack of eight Spanish armadas, of which two (three times her own burden) sank at her side; and after all her masts were gone, and she had been boarded three times without success, to defy to the last the whole fleet of fifty-four sail, which lay around her, waiting for her to sink, "like dogs around the dying forest king?"

What was it that enabled young Richard Hawkins' *Dainty*, though half her guns were useless through the carelessness or treachery of the gunner, to maintain for three days a running fight with two Spaniards of equal size with her, double weight of metal, and ten times the number of men?

What enabled Sir George Cary's illustrious ship, the *Content*, to fight single-handed, from seven in the morning till eleven at night, with four great armadas and two galleys, though her heaviest gun was but one nine-pounder, and for many hours she had but thirteen men fit for service?

What enabled, in the very year of which I write, those two "valiant Turkey merchantmen of London, the *Merchant Royal* and the *Tobie*, with their three small consorts, to cripple, off Pantellaria in the Mediterranean, the whole fleet of Spanish galleys sent to intercept them, and return triumphant through the Straits of Gibraltar?

And lastly, what in the fight of 1588, whereof more hereafter, enabled the English fleet to capture, destroy, and scatter that Great Armada, with the loss (but not the capture) of one pinnace, and one gentleman of note?

There were more causes than one: the first seems to have lain in the build of the English ships; the second in their superior gunnery and weight of metal; the third (without which the first would have been useless) in the hearts of the English men.

The English ship was much shorter than the

Spanish; and this (with the rig of those days) gave them an ease in manœuvring, which utterly confounded their Spanish foes. "The English ships in the fight of 1588," says Camden, "charged the enemy with marvellous agility, and having discharged their broadsides, flew forth presently into the deep, and levelled their shot directly, without missing, at those great ships of the Spaniards, which were altogether heavy and unwieldy." Moreover, the Spanish fashion, in the West Indies at least, though not in the ships of the Great Armada, was, for the sake of carrying merchandise, to build their men-of-war flush decked, or as it was called "race" (razés), which left those on deck exposed and open; while the English fashion was to heighten the ship as much as possible at stem and stern, both by the sweep of her lines, and also by stockades ("close fights and cage-works") on the poop and forecastle, thus giving to the men a shelter, which was further increased by strong bulkheads ("co-bridge-heads") across the main-deck below, dividing the ship thus into a number of separate forts, fitted with swivels ("bases, fowlers and murderers") and loopholed for musketry and arrows.

But the great source of superiority was, after all, in the men themselves. The English sailor was then, as now, a quite amphibious and all-cunning animal, capable of turning his hand to everything, from needlework and carpentry to gunnery or hand-to-hand blows; and he was, moreover, one of a nation, every citizen of which was not merely permitted to carry arms, but compelled by law to practice from childhood the use of the bow, and accustomed to consider sword-play and quarter-staff as a necessary part and parcel of education, and the pastime of every leisure hour. The "fiercest nation upon earth," as they were then called, and the freest also, each man of them fought for himself with the self-help and self-respect of a Yankee ranger, and once bidden to do his work, was trusted to carry it out by his own wit as best he could. In one word, he was a free man.

The English officers, too, as now, lived on terms of sympathy with their men unknown to the Spaniards, who raised between the commander and the commanded absurd barriers of rank and blood, which forbade to his pride any labor but that of fighting. The English officers, on the other hand, brought up to the same athletic sports, the same martial exercise, as their men, were not ashamed to care for them, to win their friendship, even on emergency to consult their judgment; and used their rank, not to differ from their men, but to outvie them; not merely to command and be obeyed, but like Homer's heroes, or the old Norse vikings, to lead and be followed. Drake touched the true mainspring of English success when he once (in his voyage round the world) indignantly rebuked some coxcomb gentleman-adventurers with, "I should like to see the gentleman that will refuse to set his hand to a rope. I must have the gentlemen to hale and draw with the mariners." But those were days in which her Majesty's service was as little overridden by absurd rules of seniority as by that etiquette which is at once the counterfeit and the ruin of true discipline. Under Elizabeth and her ministers, a brave and a shrewd man was certain of promotion, let his rank or his age be what they might; the true honor of knighthood covered once and for all any lowliness of birth; and the merchant service (in which all the best sea-captains, even those of noble blood, were more or less engaged) was then a nursery, not only for seamen, but for warriors, in days when Spanish and Portuguese traders (whenever they had a chance) got rid of English competition by salvoes of cannon-shot.

Hence, as I have said, that strong fellow-feeling between officers and men; and hence mutinies (as Sir Richard Hawkins tells us) were all but unknown in the English ships, while in the Spanish they broke out on every slight occasion. For the Spaniards, by some suicidal pedantry, had allowed their navy to be crippled by the same despotism, etiquette, and official routine by which the whole nation was gradually frozen to death in the course of the next century or two; forgetting that, fifty years before, Cortez, Piazarro, and the early conquistadores of America had achieved their miraculous triumphs on the exactly opposite methods; by that very fellow-feeling between commander and commanded by which the English were now conquering them in their turn.

Their navy was organized on a plan complete enough; but on one which was, as the event proved, utterly fatal to their prowess and unanimity, and which made even their courage and honor useless against the assaults of free men. "They do, in their armadas at sea, divide themselves into three bodies; to wit, soldiers, mariners, and gunners. The soldiers and officers watch and ward as if on shore; and this is the only duty they undergo, except cleaning their arms, wherein they are not over curious. The gunners are exempted from all labor and care, except about the artillery; and these are either Almaines, Flemings, or strangers; for the Spaniards are but indifferently practiced in this art. The mariners are but as slaves to the rest, to moil and to toil day and night; and those but few and bad, and not suffered to sleep or harbor under the decks. For in fair or foul weather, in storms, sun, or rain, they must pass void of covert or succor."

This is the account of one who was long prisoner on board their ships; let it explain itself, while I return to my tale. For the great ship is now within two musket-shots of the *Rose*, with the golden flag of Spain floating at her poop; and her trumpets are shouting defiance up the breeze, from a dozen brazen throats, which two or three answer lustily from the *Rose*, from whose poop flies the flag of England, and from her fore the arms of Leigh and Cary side by side, and over them the ship and bridge of the good town of Bideford. And then Amyas calls:

"Now, silence trumpets, waits, play up! 'Fortune my foe!' and God and the Queen be with us!"

Whereon (laugh not, reader, for it was a fashion of those musical as well as valiant days) up rose that noble old favorite of good Queen Bess, from cornet and sackbut, fife and drum; while Parson Jack, who had taken his stand with the musicians on the poop, worked away lustily at his violin.

"Well played, Jack; thy elbow flies like a lamb's tail," said Amyas, forcing a jest.

"It shall fly to a better fiddle-bow presently, sir, if I have the luck—"

"Steady, helm!" said Amyas. "What is he after now?"

The Spaniard, who had been coming upon them right down the wind under a press of sail, took in his light canvas.

"He don't know what to make of our waiting for him so bold," said the helmsman.

"He does, though, and means to fight us," cried another. "See, he is hauling up the foot of his mainsail; but he wants to keep the wind of us."

"Let him try, then," quoth Amyas. "Keep her closer still. Let no one fire till we are about. Man the starboard guns; to starboard, and wait, all small-arm men. Pass the order down to the gunner, and bid all fire high, and take the rigging."

Bang went one of the Spaniard's bow guns, and the shot went wide. Then another and another, while the men fidgeted about, looking at the priming of their muskets, and loosened arrows in the sheaf.

"Lie down, men, and sing a psalm. When I want you, I'll call you. Closer still, if you can, helmsman, and we will try a short ship against a long one. We can sail two points nearer the wind than he."

As Amyas had calculated, the Spaniard would gladly enough have stood across the *Rose's* bows, but knowing the English readiness, dare not for fear of being raked; so her only plan, if she did not intend to shoot past her foe down to leeward, was to put her head close to the wind, and wait for her on the same tack.

Amyas laughed to himself. "Hold on yet awhile. More ways of killing a cat than choking her with cream. Drew, there, are your men ready?"

"Ay, ay, sir!" and on they went, closing fast with the Spaniard, till within a pistol-shot.

"Ready about!" and about she went like an eel, and ran upon the opposite tack right under the Spaniard's stern. The Spaniard, astounded at the quickness of the manœuvre, hesitated a moment, and then tried to get about also, as his only chance; but it was too late, and while his lumbering length was still hanging in the wind's eye, Amyas' bowsprit had all but scraped his quarter, and the *Rose* passed slowly across his stern at ten yards' distance.

"Now, then!" roared Amyas. "Fire, and with a will! Have at her—archers, have at her, muskets all!" and in an instant a storm of bar and chain-shot, round and canister, swept the proud Don from stem to stern, while through the white cloud of smoke the musket-balls, and the still deadlier cloth-yard arrows, whistled and rushed upon their venomous errand. Down went the steersman, and every soul who manned the poop. Down went the mizzen topmast, in went the stern windows and quarter galleries; and as the smoke cleared away, the gorgeous painting of the Madre Dolorosa, with her heart full of seven swords, which, in a gilded frame, bedizened the Spanish stern, was shivered in splinters; while, most glorious of all, the golden flag of Spain, which the last moment flaunted above their heads, hung trailing in the water. The ship, her tiller shot away, and her helmsman killed, staggered helplessly a moment, and then fell up into the wind.

"Well done, men of Devon!" shouted Amyas, as cheers rent the welkin.

"She has struck!" cried some, as the deafening hurrahs died away.

"Not a bit," said Amyas. "Hold on, helmsman, and leave her to patch her tackle while we settle the galleys."

On they shot merrily, and long ere the armada could get herself to rights again, were two good miles to windward, with the galleys sweeping down fast upon them.

And two venomous-looking craft they were, as they shot through the short chopping sea upon some forty oars apiece, stretching their long swordfish snouts over the water, as if snuffing for their prey. Behind this long snout, a strong square forecastle was crammed with soldiers, and the muzzles of cannon grinned out through port-holes, not only in the sides of the forecastle, but forward in the line of the galley's course, thus enabling her to keep up a continual fire on a ship right ahead.

The long low waist was packed full of the slaves, some five or six to each oar, and down the center, between the two banks, the English could see the slave-drivers walking up and down a long gangway, whip in hand. A raised quarter-deck at the stern held more soldiers, the sunlight flashing merrily upon their armor and their gun-barrels; as they neared, the English could hear plainly the cracks of the whips, and the yells as of wild beasts which answered them; the roll and rattle of oars, and the loud "Ha!" of the slaves which accompanied every stroke, and the oaths and curses of the drivers; while a sickening musky smell, as of a pack of kennelled hounds, came down the wind from off those dens of misery. No wonder if many a young heart shuddered as it faced, for the first time, the horrible reality of those floating hells, the cruelties whereof had rung so often in the English ears, from the stories of their own countrymen, who had passed them, fought them, and now and then passed years of misery on board of them. Who knew but what there might be English among those sun-browned, half-naked masses of panting wretches?

"Must we fire upon the slaves?" asked more than one, as the thought crossed him.

Amyas sighed.

"Spare them all you can, in God's name; but if they try to run us down, rake them we must, and God forgive us."

The two galleys came on abreast of each other, some forty yards apart. To out-manœuvre their oars as he had done the ship's sails, Amyas knew was impossible. To run from them, was to be caught between them and the ship.

He made up his mind, as usual, to the desperate game.

"Lay her head upon the wind, helmsman, and we will wait for them."

They were now within musket-shot, and opened fire from their bow-guns; but, owing to the chopping sea, their aim was wild. Amyas, as usual, withheld his fire.

The men stood at quarters with compressed lips, not knowing what was to come next. Amyas, towering motionless on the quarter-deck, gave orders calmly and decisively. The men saw that he trusted himself, and trusted him accordingly.

The Spaniards, seeing him wait for them, gave a shout of joy—was the Englishman mad? And the two galleys converged rapidly, intending to strike him full, one on each bow.

They were within forty yards—another minute, and the shock would come.

The Englishman's helm went up, his yards creaked round, and gathering way he plunged upon the larboard galley.

"A dozen gold nobles to him who brings down the steersman!" shouted Carey, who had his cue.

And a flight of arrows from the forecastle rattled upon the galley's quarter-deck.

Hit or not hit, the steersman lost his nerve, and shrank from the coming shock. The galley's helm went up to port, and her beak slid all but harmless along Amyas' bow; a long dull grind, and then loud crack on crack, as the *Rose* sawed slowly through the bank of oars from stem to stern, hurling the wretched slaves in heaps upon each other; and ere her mate on the other side could swing round, to strike him in his new position, Amyas' whole broadside, great and small, had been poured into her at pistol-shot, answered by a yell which rent their ears and hearts.

"Spare the slaves! Fire at the soldiers!" cried

Amyas; but the work was too hot for much dis-
crimination, for the larboard galley, crippled but
not undaunted, swung round across his stern, and
hooked herself venomously on to him.

It was a move more brave than wise; for it prevented the other galley from returning to the attack without exposing herself a second time to the
English broadside; and a desperate attempt of the
Spaniards to board at once through the stern ports,
and up the quarter, was met with such a demurrer
of shot and steel that they found themselves in three
minutes again upon the galley's poop, accompanied,
to their intense disgust, by Amyas Leigh and
twenty English swords.

Five minutes' hard cutting, hand to hand, and
the poop was clear. The soldiers in the forecastle
had been able to give them no assistance, open as
they lay to the arrows and musketry from the
Rose's lofty stern. Amyas rushed along the central gangway, shouting in Spanish, "Freedom to
the slaves! death to the masters!" clambered into
the forecastle, followed close by his swarm of wasps,
and set them so good an example how to use their
stings, that in three minutes more there was not
a Spaniard on board who was not dead or dying.

"Let the slaves free!" shouted he. "Throw us
a hammer down, men. Hark! there's an English
voice!" There is indeed. From amid the wreck of
broken oars and writhing limbs, a voice is shrieking
in broadest Devon to the master, who is looking
over the side:

"Oh, Robert Drew! Robert Drew! Come down
and take me out of hell!"

"Who be you, in the name of the Lord?"

"Don't you mind William Prust, that Captain Hawkins left behind in the Honduras, years and years agone? There's nine of us aboard, if your shot hasn't put 'em out of their misery. Come down —if you've a Christian heart, come down!"

Utterly forgetful of all discipline, Drew leaps down, hammer in hand, and the two old comrades rush into each other's arms.

Why make a long story of what took but five minutes to do? The nine men (luckily none of them wounded) are freed, and helped on board, to be hugged and kissed by all comrades and young kinsmen; while the remaining slaves, furnished with a couple of hammers, are told to free themselves and help the English. The wretches answered by a shout; and Amyas, once more safe on board again, dashes after the other galley, which has been hovering out of reach of his guns; but there is no need to trouble himself about her; sickened with what she has got, she is struggling right up wind, leaning over to one side, and seemingly ready to sink.

"Are there any English on board of her?" asked Amyas, loth to lose the chance of freeing a countryman.

"Never a one, sir, thank God."

So they set to work to repair damages; while the liberated slaves, having shifted some of the galley's oars, pull away after their comrade; and that with such a will, that in ten minutes they have caught her up, and careless of the Spaniard's fire, boarded her en masse, with yells as of a thousand wolves.

A SEA-FIGHT

There will be fearful vengeance taken on those tyrants, unless they play the man this day.

And in the meanwhile half the crew are clothing, feeding, questioning, caressing those nine poor fellows thus snatched from living death; and Yeo, hearing the news, has rushed up on deck to welcome his old comrades, and:

"Is Michael Heard, my cousin, here among you?"

Yes, Michael Heard is there, white-headed rather from misery than age; and the embracings and questionings begin afresh.

"Where is my wife, Salvation Yeo?"

"With the Lord."

"Amen!" says the old man, with a short shudder.

"I thought so much; and my two boys?"

"With the Lord."

The old man catches Yeo by the arm.

"How, then?" It is Yeo's turn to shudder now.

"Killed in Panama, fighting the Spaniards; sailing with Mr. Oxenham; and 'twas I led 'em into it. May God and you forgive me!"

"They couldn't die better, Cousin Yeo. Where's my girl Grace?"

"Dead."

The old man covers his face with his hands for a while. "Well, I've been alone with the Lord these fifteen years, so I must not whine at being alone a while longer—it won't be long."

"Put this coat on your back, uncle," says some one.

"No; no coats for me. You'd better go to your work, lads, or the big one will have the wind of you yet."

"So she will," said Amyas, who has overheard; but so great is the curiosity on all hands, that he has some trouble in getting the men to quarters again; indeed, they only go on condition of parting among themselves the new-comers, each to tell his sad and strange story. How after Captain Hawkins, constrained by famine, had put them ashore, they wandered in misery till the Spaniards took them; how, instead of hanging them (as they at first intended), the Dons fed and clothed them, and allotted them as servants to various gentlemen about Mexico, where they throve, turned their hands (like true sailors) to all manner of trades, and made much money, and some of them were married, even to women of wealth; so that all went well, until the fatal year 1574, when, "much against the minds of many of the Spaniards themselves, that cruel and bloody Inquisition was established for the first time in the Indies"; and how, from that moment, their lives were one long tragedy.

The history even of their party was not likely to improve the good feeling of the crew toward the Spanish ship which was two miles to leeward of them, and which must be fought with, or fled from, before a quarter of an hour was past. So, kneeling down upon the deck, as many a brave crew in those days did in like case, they "gave God thanks devoutly for the favor they had found"; and then with one accord, at Jack's leading, sang one and all the ninety-fourth Psalm:

"O, Lord, Thou dost revenge all wrong,
    Vengeance belongs to Thee," etc.

And then again to quarters; for half the day's
work, or more than half, still remained to be done;
and hardly were the decks cleared afresh, and the
damage repaired as best it could be, when she came
ranging up to leeward, as closehauled as she could.

She was, as I said, a long flush-decked ship of
full five hundred tons, more than double the size,
in fact, of the *Rose,* though not so lofty in pro-
portion; and many a bold heart beat loud, and no
shame to them, as she began firing away merrily,
determined, as all well knew, to wipe out in English blood the disgrace of her late foil.

"Never mind, my merry masters," said Amyas,
"she has quantity and we quality."

"That's true," said one, "for one honest man is
worth two rogues."

"And one of our guns, three of theirs," said another. "So when you will, captain, and have at
her."

"Let her come abreast of us, and don't burn powder. We have the wind, and can do what we like
with her. Serve the men out a horn of ale all
round, steward, and all take your time."

So they waited for five minutes more, and then
set to work quietly, after the fashion of English
mastiffs, though they waxed right mad before three
rounds were fired, and the white splinters began
to crackle and fly.

Amyas, having, as he had said, the wind, and
being able to go nearer it than the Spaniard, kept
his place at easy point-blank range for his two
eighteen-pounder guns, which Yeo and his mate
worked with terrible effect.

"We are lacking her through and through every shot," said he. "Leave the small ordnance alone yet awhile, and we shall sink her without them."

"Whing, whing," went the Spaniard's shot like so many humming-tops, through the rigging far above their heads; for the ill-constructed ports of those days prevented the guns from hulling an enemy who was to windward, unless close alongside.

"Blow, jolly breeze," cried one, "and lay the Don over all thou canst. What's the matter aloft there?"

Alas! a crack, a flap, a rattle; and blank dismay! An unlucky shot had cut the foremast in two, and all forward was a mass of dangling wreck.

"Forward, and cut away the wreck!" said Amyas, unmoved. "Small-arm men, be ready. He will be aboard of us in five minutes!"

It was too true. The *Rose,* unmanageable from the loss of her head-sail, lay at the mercy of the Spaniard; and the archers and musketeers had hardly time to range themselves to leeward, when the *Madre Dolorosa's* chains were grinding against the *Rose's,* and grapples tossed on board from stem to stern.

"Don't cut them loose!" roared Amyas. "Let them stay and see the fun! Now, dogs of Devon, show your teeth, and hurrah for God and the Queen!"

And then began a fight most fierce and fell; the Spaniards, according to their fashion, attempted to board, the English, amid fierce shouts of "God and the Queen!" "God and St. George for England!" sweeping them back by showers of arrows and musket balls, thrusting them down with pikes, hurling grenades from the tops; while the swivels on both sides poured their grape, and bar, and chain, and the great main-deck guns, thundering muzzle to muzzle, made both ships quiver and recoil, as they smashed the round shot through and through each other.

So they roared and flashed, fast clenched to each other under a cloud of smoke beneath the cloudless tropic sky; while all around, the dolphins gamboled, and the flying-fish shot on from swell to swell, and the rainbow-hued jellies opened and shut their cups of living crystal to the sun, as merrily as if nothing had happened.

So it raged for an hour or more, till all arms were weary, and all tongues clove to the mouth. Sick men scrambled up on deck and fought with the strength of madness; and tiny powder-boys, handing up cartridges from the hold, laughed and cheered as the shots ran past their ears; and old Salvation Yeo, a text upon his lips, and a fury in his heart as of Joshua or Elijah in old time, worked on, calm and grim, but with the energy of a boy at play. And now and then an opening in the smoke showed the Spanish captain, in his suit of black steel armor, standing cool and proud, guiding and pointing, careless of the iron hail, but too lofty a gentleman to soil his glove with aught but a knightly sword-hilt; while Amyas and Will, after the fashion of the English gentlemen, had stripped themselves nearly as bare as their own sailors, and were cheering, thrusting, hewing, and hauling, here, there, and everywhere, like any common mariner, and filling them with a spirit of self-respect, fellow-feeling, and personal daring, which the discipline of the Spaniards, more perfect mechanically, but cold and tyrannous, and crushing spiritually, never could bestow. The black-plumed señor was obeyed; but the golden-locked Amyas was followed; and would have been followed to the end of the world.

The Spaniards, ere five minutes had passed, poured into the *Rose's* waist, but only to their destruction. Between the poop and forecastle (as was then the fashion) the upper deck beams were left open and unplanked, with the exception of a narrow gangway on either side; and off that fatal ledge the boarders, thrust on by those behind, fell headlong between the beams to the maindeck below to be slaughtered helpless in that pit of destruction, by the double fire from the bulkheads fore and aft; while the few who kept their footing on the gangway, after vain attempts to force the stockades on poop and forecastle, leaped overboard again amid a shower of shot and arrows. The fire of the English was as steady as it was quick; and though three-fourths of the crew had never smelled powder before, they proved well the truth of the old chronicler's saying (since proved again more gloriously than ever at Alma, Balaklava, and Inkermann), that "the English never fight better than in their first battle."

Thrice the Spaniards clambered on board; and thrice surged back before that deadly hail. The decks on both sides were very shambles; and Jack

Brimblecombe, who had fought as long as his conscience would allow him, found enough to do in carrying poor wretches to the surgeon. At last there was a lull in that wild storm. No shot was heard from the Spaniard's upper-deck.

Amyas leaped into the mizzen rigging, and looked through the smoke. Dead men he could descry through the blinding veil, rolled in heaps, laid flat; dead men and dying; but no man upon his feet. The last volley had swept the deck clear; one by one had dropped below to escape that fiery shower: and alone at the helm, grinding his teeth with rage, his mustachios curling up to his very eyes, stood the Spanish captain.

Now was the moment for a counter-stroke. Amyas shouted for the boarders, and in two minutes more he was over the side, and clutching at the Spaniard's mizzen rigging.

What was this? The distance between him and the enemy's side was widening. Was she sheering off? Yes—and rising too, growing bodily higher every moment, as if by magic. Amyas looked up in astonishment and saw what it was. The Spaniard was keeling fast over to leeward away from him. Her masts were all sloping forward, swifter and swifter—the end was come then!

"Back! in God's name back, men! She is sinking by the head!"

And with much ado some were dragged back, some leaped back—all but old Michael Heard.

With hair and beard floating in the wind, the bronzed naked figure, like some weird old Indian fakir, still climbed on steadfastly up the mizzen-chains of the Spaniard, hatchet in hand.

"Come back, Michael! Leap while you may!" shouted a dozen voices. Michael turned:

"And what should I come back for, then, to go home where no one knoweth me? I'll die like an Englishman this day, or I'll know the reason why!" and turning, he sprang in over the bulwarks, as the huge ship rolled up more and more, like a dying whale, exposing all her long black bulk almost down to the keel, and one of her lower-deck guns, as if in defiance, exploded upright into the air, hurling the ball to the very heavens.

In an instant it was answered from the *Rose* by a column of smoke, and the eighteen-pound ball crashed through the bottom of the defenceless Spaniard.

"Who fired? Shame to fire on a sinking ship!"

"Gunner Yeo, sir," shouted a voice up from the maindeck. "He's like a madman down here."

"Tell him if he fires again, I'll put him in irons, if he were my own brother. Cut away the grapples aloft, men. Don't you see how she drags us over? Cut away, or we shall sink with her."

They cut away, and the *Rose,* released from the strain, shook her feathers on the wave-crest like a freed sea-gull, while all men held their breath.

Suddenly the glorious creature righted herself, and rose again, as if in noble shame, for one last struggle with her doom. Her bows were deep in the water, but her afterdeck still dry. Righted:

but only for a moment, long enough to let her crew come pouring wildly up on deck, with cries and prayers, and rush aft to the poop, where, under the flag of Spain, stood the tall captain, his left hand on the standard-staff, his sword pointed in his right.

"Back, men!" they heard him cry, "and die like valiant mariners."

Some of them ran to the bulwarks, and shouted "Mercy! We surrender!" and the English broke into a cheer and called to them to run her alongside.

"Silence!" shouted Amyas. "I take no surrender from mutineers. Señor," cried he to the captain, springing into the rigging and taking off his hat, "for the love of God and these men, strike! and surrender *á buena querra.*"

The Spaniard lifted his hat and bowed courteously, and answered, "Impossible, señor. No *querra* is good which stains my honor."

"God have mercy on you, then!"

"Amen!" said the Spaniard, crossing himself.

She gave one awful lunge forward, and dived under the coming swell, hurling her crew into the eddies. Nothing but the point of her poop remained, and there stood the stern and steadfast Don, cap-à-pie in his glistening black armor, immovable as a man of iron, while over him the flag, which claimed the empire of both worlds, flaunted its gold aloft and upward in the glare of the tropic noon.

"He shall not carry that flag with him! I will have it yet, if I die for it!" said Will Cary, and rushed to the side to leap overboard, but Amyas stopped him.

"Let him die as he has lived, with honor."

A wild figure sprang out of the mass of sailors who struggled and shrieked amid the foam, and rushed upward at the Spaniard. It was Michael Heard. The Don, who stood above him, plunged his sword into the old man's body; but the hatchet gleamed, nevertheless: down went the blade through headpiece and through head; and as Heard sprang onward, bleeding, but alive, the steel-clad corpse rattled down the deck into the surge. Two more strokes, struck with the fury of a dying man, and the standard-staff was hewn through. Old Michael collected all his strength, hurled the flag far from the sinking ship, and then stood erect one moment and shouted, "God save Queen Bess!" and the English answered with a "Hurrah!" which rent the welkin.

Another moment and the gulf had swallowed his victim, and the poop, and him; and nothing remained of the *Madre Dolorosa* but a few floating spars and struggling wretches, while a great awe fell upon all men, and a solemn silence, broken only by the cry

"Of some strong swimmer in his agony."

And then, suddenly collecting themselves, as men awakened from a dream, half-a-dozen desperate gallants, reckless of sharks and eddies, leaped overboard, swam toward the flag, and towed it alongside in triumph.

A BRAVE SCOTTISH CHIEF

Anonymous

THIS is the story of the life of Alexander Gordon of Earlstoun, in the province of Galloway, Scotland. Earlstoun is a bonny place, sitting above the waterside of the river Ken. The gray tower stands ruinous and empty to-day, but once it was a pleasant dwelling, and dear to the hearts of those that had dwelt in it, when they were in foreign lands or hiding out on the wild wide moors. It was the time when Charles II wished to compel the most part of the people of Scotland to change their religion and worship as he bade them. Some obeyed the king; but most hated the new order of things, and cleaved in their hearts to their own ways and to their old ministers, who had been put out of their churches and homes at the coming of the king. Many even set themselves to resist the king in open battle rather than obey him in the matter of their consciences. It was only in this that they were rebellious, for many of them had been active in bringing him again to the throne.

Among those who thus went out to fight were William Gordon and his son Alexander. William Gordon was a grave, courteous, and venerable man, and his estate was one of the best in all Galloway. Like nearly all the lairds in the south and west, he was strongly of the Presbyterian party, and resolved to give up life and lands rather than his principles. Now, the king was doubtless ill-advised, and his councillors did not take the kindly or the wise way with the people at this time; for a host of wild Highlanders had been turned into the land, who plundered in cotter's and laird's hall without much distinction between those that stood for the Covenants and those that held for the king. So in the year 1679 Galloway was very hot and angry, and many were ready to fight the king's forces wherever they could be met with.

So, hearing news of a revolt in the west, William Gordon rode away, with many good riders at his back, to take his place in the ranks of the rebels. His son Alexander, whose story we are to tell, was there before him. The Covenanting army had gained one success in Drumclog, which gave them some hope, but at Bothwell Bridge their forces were utterly broken, largely through their own quarrels, by the Duke of Monmouth and the disciplined troops of the government.

Alexander Gordon had to flee from the field of Bothwell. He came home to Earlstoun alone, for his father had been met about six miles from the battle-field by a troop of horse, and as he refused to surrender, he was slain there and buried in the parish of Glassford.

Immediately after Bothwell, Alexander Gordon was compelled to go into hiding with a price upon his head. Unlike his father, he was very ready-witted, free with his tongue, even boisterous upon occasion, and of very great bodily strength. These qualities stood him in good stead during the long period of his wandering and when lying in concealment among the hills.

The day after Bothwell, he was passing through

the town of Hamilton, when he was recognized by an old retainer of the family.

"Save us, Maister Alexander," said the man, who remembered the ancient kindnesses of his family, "do you not know that it is death for you to be found here?"

So saying he made his young master dismount, and carried away all his horseman's gear and his arms, which he hid in a heap of field-manure behind the house. Then he took Earlstoun to his own house, and put upon him a long dress of his wife's. Hardly had he been clean-shaven and arrayed in a clean white cap, when the troopers came clattering into the town. They had heard that he and some others of the prominent rebels had passed that way; and they went from door to door, knocking and asking, "Saw ye anything of Sandy Gordon of Earlstoun?"

So going from house to house they came to the door of the ancient Gordon retainer, and Earlstoun had hardly time to run to the corner and begin to rock the cradle with his foot before the soldiers came to ask the same question there. But they passed on without suspicion, only saying one to the other as they went out, "My certes, Billy, but yon was a sturdy hizzie!"

After that there was nothing but the heather and the mountain cave for Alexander Gordon for many a day. He had wealth of adventures, travelling by night, hiding and sleeping by day. Sometimes he would venture to the house of one who sympathized with the Covenanters, only to find that the troopers were already in possession.

Sometimes, in utter weariness, he slept so long that when he awoke he would find a party searching for him quite close at hand; then there was nothing for it but to lie close like a hare in a covert till the danger passed by.

Once when he came to his own house of Earlstoun he was only an hour or two there before the soldiers arrived to search for him. His wife had hardly time to stow him in a secret recess behind the ceiling of a room over the kitchen, in which place he abode several days, having his meals passed to him from above, and breathing through a crevice in the wall.

After this misadventure he was sometimes in Galloway and sometimes in Holland for three or four years. He might even have remained in the Low Countries, but his services were so necessary to his party in Scotland that he was repeatedly summoned to come over into Galloway and the west to take up the work of organizing resistance to the government.

During most of this time the tower of Earlstoun was a barracks of the soldiers, and it was only by watching his opportunity that Alexander Gordon could come home to see his wife, and put his hand upon his bairns' heads as they lay a-row in their cots. Yet come he sometimes did, especially when the soldiers of the garrison were away on duty in the more distant parts of Galloway. Then the wanderer would steal indoors in the gloaming, soft-footed, like a thief, into his own house, and sit talking with his wife and an old retainer or two who were fit to be trusted with the secret. Yet while he sat there, one was ever on the watch, and at the slightest signs of king's men in the neighborhood Alexander Gordon rushed out and ran to the great oak tree, which you may see to this day standing in sadly diminished glory in front of the great house of Earlstoun.

Now it stands alone, all the trees of the forest having been cut away from around it during the subsequent poverty which fell upon the family.

A rope ladder lay snugly concealed among the ivy that clad the trunk of the tree. Up this Alexander Gordon climbed. When he arrived at the top he pulled the ladder after him, and found himself upon an ingeniously constructed platform built with a shelter over it from the rain, high among the branchy tops of the great oak. His faithful wife, Jean Hamilton, could make signals to him out of one of the top windows of Earlstoun whether it was safe for him to approach the house, or whether he had better remain hidden among the leaves. If you go now to look for the tree, it is indeed plain and easy to be seen. But though now so shorn and lonely, there is no doubt that two hundred years ago it stood undistinguished among a thousand others that thronged the woodland about the tower of Earlstoun.

Often, in order to give Alexander Gordon a false sense of security, the garrison would be withdrawn for a week or two, and then in the middle of some mirky night or early in the morning twilight the house would be surrounded and the whole place ransacked in search of its absent master.

On one occasion, the man who came running along the narrow river path from Dalry had hardly time to arouse Gordon before the dragoons were heard clattering down through the wood from the high-road. There was no time to gain the great oak in safety, where he had so often hid in time of need. All Alexander Gordon could do was to put on the rough jerkin of a laboring man, and set to cleaving firewood in the courtyard with the scolding assistance of a maid-servant. When the troopers entered to search for the master of the house, they heard the maid vehemently "flyting" the great hulking lout for his awkwardness, and threatening to "draw a stick across his back" if he did not work to a better tune.

The commander ordered him to drop his axe, and to point out the different rooms and hiding-places about the castle. Alexander Gordon did so with an air of indifference, as if hunting Whigs were much the same to him as cleaving firewood. He did his duty with a stupid unconcern which successfully imposed on the soldiers; and as soon as they allowed him to go, he fell to his wood-chopping with the same stolidity and rustic boorishness that had marked his conduct.

Some of the officers came up to him and questioned him as to his master's hiding-place in the woods. But as to this he gave them no satisfaction.

"My master," he said, "has no hiding-place that I know of. I always find him here when I have occasion to seek for him, and that is all I care about. But I am sure that if he thought you were seeking him he would immediately show himself to you, for that is ever his custom."

This was one of the answers with a double meaning that were so much in the fashion of the time and so characteristic of the people.

On leaving, the commander of the troop said, "Ye are a stupid kindly nowt, man. See that ye get no harm in such a rebel service."

Sometimes, however, searching waxed so hot and close that Gordon had to withdraw himself altogether out of Galloway and seek quieter parts of the country. On one occasion he was speeding up the Water of Æ when he found himself so weary that he was compelled to lie down under a bush of heather and rest before proceeding on his journey. It so chanced that a noted king's man, Dalyell of Glenæ, was riding homeward over the moor. His horse started back in astonishment, having nearly stumbled over the body of a sleeping man. It was Alexander Gordon. Hearing the horse's feet, he leaped up, and Dalyell called upon him to surrender. But that was no word to say to a Gordon of Earlstoun. Gordon instantly drew his sword, and, though unmounted, his lightness of foot on the heather and moss more than counterbalanced the advantages of the horseman, and the king's man found himself matched at all points; for the Laird of Earlstoun was in his day a famous swordsman.

Soon the Covenanter's sword seemed to wrap itself about Dalyell's blade and sent it twirling high in the air. In a little while he found himself lying on the heather at the mercy of the man whom he had attacked. He asked for his life, and Alexander Gordon granted it to him, making him promise by his honor as a gentleman that whenever he had the fortune to approach a conventicle (church meeting) he would retire, if he saw a white flag elevated in a particular manner upon a flagstaff. This seemed but a little condition to weigh against a man's life, and Dalyell agreed.

Now, the cavalier was an exceedingly honorable man and valued his spoken word. So on the occasion of a great conventicle at Mitchelslacks, in the parish of Closeburn, he permitted a great field meeting to disperse, drawing off his party in another direction, because the signal streaming from a staff told him the man who had spared his life was among the company of worshippers.

After this, the white signal was frequently used in the neighborhood over which Dalyell's jurisdiction extended, and to the great credit of the cavalier it is recorded that on no single occasion did he violate his plighted word, though he is said to have remarked bitterly that the Whig with whom he fought must have been the devil, "forever going to and fro in the earth, and walking up and down in it."

But Alexander Gordon was too great a man in the affairs of the Praying Societies to escape altogether. He continually went and came from Holland, and some of the letters that he wrote from that country are still in existence. At last, in 1683, having received many letters and valuable papers for delivery to people in refuge in Holland, he went secretly to Newcastle, and agreed with the master of a ship for his voyage to the Low Countries. But just as the vessel was setting out from the mouth of the Tyne, it was accidentally stopped. Some watchers for fugitives came on board, and Earlstoun and his companion were challenged. Earlstoun, fearing the taking of his papers, threw the box that contained them overboard; but it floated, and was taken along with himself.

Then began a long series of misfortunes for Alexander Gordon. He was five times tried, twice threatened with torture—which he escaped, in the judgment hall itself, by such an exhibition of his great strength as terrified his judges. He simulated madness, foamed at the mouth, and finally tore up the benches in order to attack the judges with the fragments. He was sent first to the castle of Edinburgh and afterward to the Bass (an island), "for a change of air," as the record quaintly says. Finally, he was despatched to Blackness Castle, where he remained close in hold till the revolution.

Not till June 5, 1689, were his prison doors thrown open, but even then Alexander Gordon would not go till he had obtained signed documents from the governor and officials of his prison to the effect that he had never altered any of his opinions in order to gain privilege or release.

Alexander Gordon returned to Earlstoun, and lived there quietly far into the next century, taking his share in local and county business with Grierson of Lag and others who had hunted him for years—which is a strange thing to think on, but one also very characteristic of those times.

On account of his great strength and the power of his voice, he was called "the Bull of Earlstoun," and it is said that when he was rebuking his servants the bellowing of the Bull could plainly be heard in Dalry, which is two miles away across hill and stream.

THE ADVENTURE OF GRIZEL COCHRANE

By Arthur Quiller-Couch

AT Edinburgh, almost under the shadow of the spire of St. Giles's, in the pavement between that old cathedral church and the County Hall, the passer-by will mark the figure of a heart let into the causeway, and know that he is standing on the "Heart of Midlothian," [1] the site of the old Tolbooth. That gloomy pile vanished in the autumn of 1817; as Mr. Stevenson says, "the walls are now down in the dust; there is no more *squalor carceris* for merry debtors, no more cage for the old acknowledged prison-breaker; but the sun and the wind play freely over the foundations of the gaol;" this place, "old in story and name-father to a noble book." The author of that same "noble book" possessed himself of some memorials of the keep he had rendered so famous, securing the stones of the gateway, and the door with its ponderous fastenings to decorate the entrance of his kitchen-court at Abbotsford. And this is all that is left.

[1] The title of one of Sir Walter Scott's romances.

GRIZEL COCHRANE

But in the summer and autumn of 1685 the Tolbooth held prisoners enough, notwithstanding the many gloomy processions that were from time to time walking to the axe and halter in the Grassmarket; and in a narrow cell, late one August evening, two persons were sitting of whom this story shall treat. These two were Sir John Cochrane, of Ochiltree, and his daughter Grizel—here on the saddest of errands, to visit her father in prison and help in his preparations for death.

For Sir John, a stout Whig, had been one of the leaders of Argyle's insurrection; had been beaten with his troops by Lord Ross at Muirdykes; had disbanded his handful of men, and fled for hiding to the house of his uncle, Mr. Gavin Cochrane, of Craigmuir; had been informed against by his uncle's wife, seized, taken to Edinburgh; had been paraded, bound and bareheaded, through the streets by the common executioner; and then on the 3d of July flung into the Tolbooth to await his trial for high treason. And now the trial, too, was over, and Sir John was condemned to die.

As he now sat, with bowed head, on the bench of his cell, it was not the stroke of death that terrified him—for Sir John was a brave man—but the parting with his children, who would through his rashness be left both orphaned and penniless (for the crown would seize his goods), and chiefly the parting with his daughter, who had been his one comfort in the dark days of waiting for the king's warrant of execution to arrive.

Between his apprehension and his trial no friend or kinsman had been allowed to visit him; but now that his death was assured, greater license had been granted. But, anxious to deprive his enemies of a chance to accuse his sons, he had sent them his earnest entreaties and commands that they should abstain from using this permission until the night before his execution. They had obeyed; but obedience of this sort did not satisfy the conscience of his daughter Grizel. On the very night of his condemnation he heard the key turn in his door; thinking it could only be the gaoler, he scarcely lifted his eyes. But the next moment a pair of soft arms were flung round his neck, and his daughter was weeping on his breast. From that day she had continued to visit him; and now as she sat beside him, staring at the light already fading in the narrow pane, both father and daughter knew that it was almost the last time.

Presently she spoke—

"And this message—tell me truly, have you any hope from it?"

It was an appeal made by Sir John's father, the Earl of Dundonald, to Father Peters, the king's confessor, who often dictated to him, as was well known, on matters of state. But in the short time left, would there be time to press this appeal, and exert that influence in London which alone could stay the death-warrant?

"There is no hope in that quarter," said Sir John.

Grizel knew that he spoke only what was her own conviction, and her despair.

"Argyle is dead these three days," pursued her father, "and with him men of less consequence than

I. Are they likely to spare me—a head of the rising? Would they spare any man now, in the heat of their revenge?"

"Father," said Grizel suddenly, "could you spare me from your side for a few days?"

Sir John looked up. He knew by her manner that she had formed some plan in her mind; he knew, too, from her heart, that nothing but chance of winning his safety could take her from him now, of all times.

"My child," he said, "you are going to attempt something."

She nodded, with a brighter face than she had worn for many days.

"And what you would attempt," he went on, "is an impossibility."

"Nothing is impossible to a true heart," she said.

"And who will help you?"

"No one." She was standing before him now, and in the twilight he could see her eyes lit up with hope, her figure upright, and as if full of a man's strength.

"My girl, you will run into danger—into blame. They will not spare you, and—do you know the characters of those men whom you would have to sue?"

She bent and kissed him.

"I am a Cochrane, my father."

Early next morning, before the world was up, Grizel Cochrane was mounted on horseback and riding towards the border. She had dressed herself—this girl of eighteen—as a young serving-woman, and when she drew rein at a wayside cottage for food and drink, professed herself journeying on a borrowed horse to visit her mother's house across the Tweed.

By noon Edinburgh was some leagues behind, but she pressed on through that day and most of the following night.

On the second day after leaving Edinburgh she crossed the Tweed, and came in safety to the home of an old nurse, on the English side, four miles beyond the town of Berwick.

"Gude sakes!" cried the old woman, who was standing at her cottage door and was rather astonished to find the horsewoman draw rein, leap to the ground, and plant a kiss on either cheek— "Gude sakes! if it isna Miss Grizel!"

"Quickly, into the house!" commanded her young mistress; "I have somewhat to tell that will not wait an hour."

She knew the old nurse was to be trusted, and therefore told her story and her secret. "Even now," she said at the end of her story, "the postman is riding from London with the warrant in his bag. I must stop him and make him give it up to me, or my father's head is the penalty.

"But what use to talk o' this, when the postman is a stout rider, and armed to boot? How is a mere girl, saving your presence, to do this at all?"

"Look here."

Grizel unrolled a bundle which she had brought on her saddle-crutch from Edinburgh; it held a horseman's cloak and a brace of pistols.

"Now," said she, "where are the clothes of

Donald, my foster-brother? He was a slight lad
in times syne, and little doubt they'll fit me."

For this was indeed the brave girl's plan:—In
those times the mail from London took eight days
on its journey to Edinburgh; by possessing herself
of the warrant for her father's death and detaining
it, she could count on the delay of sixteen or seventeen days at least before application could be made
for a second, and that signed and sent to the Scotch
capital. By this delay, time enough would be won
for her friends in London to use all their influence
to quash the sentence.

It was a mad scheme; but, as she had said, nothing is impossible to a true heart. She had possessed herself, too, of the minutest information with
regard to the places where the postmen rested on
their journey. One of these places, she knew was
a small inn kept by a widow on the outskirts of the
little town of Belford. There the man who received
the bag at Durham was accustomed to arrive at
about six in the morning, and take a few hours'
sleep before going on with his journey. And at
Belford, Grizel Cochrane had determined to meet
him.

Taking leave of her faithful nurse, she rode
southwards again, and, timing her pace, drew up
before the inn at Belford just an hour after the
postman had come in from the south and disposed
himself to sleep.

The mistress of the inn had no ostler, so Grizel
stabled her horse with her own hands, and striding
into the inn-parlor, demanded food and drink.

"Sit ye down, then," answered the old woman,

"at the end of yon table, for the best I have to give you is there already. And be pleased, my bonny man, to make as little noise as may be; for there's one asleep in that bed that I like ill to disturb."

She pointed to the victuals on the board, which were indeed the remains of the sleeping man's meal. Grizel sat down before them, considered to herself while she played with a mouthful or two, and then asked—

"Can I have a drink of water?"

" 'Deed," answered the hostess, "and are ye a water-drinker? 'Tis but an ill-custom for a change-house."

" Why, that I know; and so, when I put up at an inn, 'tis my custom always to pay for it the price of stronger drink, which I cannot take."

"Indeed—well, that's fairly spoken; and, come to think of it, 'tis but just." The landlady brought a jug of water and set it on the board.

"Is the well where you got this water near at hand?" said Grizel, pouring out a glass and sipping at it; "for if 'tis no trouble to fetch some fresh for me, I will tell you this is rather over-warm and flat. Your trouble shall be considered in the lawing," added she.

" 'Tis a good step off," answered the dame; "but I cannot refuse to fetch for so civil, discreet a lad —and a well-favored one, besides. So bide ye here, and I'll be as quick as I maun. But for any sake take care and don't meddle with the man's pistols there, for they are loaded, the both; and every time I set eyes on them they scare me out of my senses, almost."

She took up a pitcher and went out to draw the water. No sooner was Grizel left alone than, starting up, she waited for a moment, listening to the footsteps as they died away in the distance, and then crept swiftly across the floor to the place where the postman lay asleep. He lay in one of those close wooden bedsteads, like cupboards, which were then common in the houses of the poor, and to this day may be seen in many a house in Brittany. The door of it was left half-open, to give the sleeper air, and from this aperture the noise of his snoring issued in a way that shook the house.

Nevertheless, it seemed to the girl that he must be awakened by the creaking of the floor under her light footfall. With heart in mouth she stole up to the bedstead, and gently pulling the door still wider ajar, peeped in, in the hope of seeing the mail-bag and being able to pounce upon it.

She saw it, indeed; but to her dismay, it lay beneath the shaggy head of its guardian—a giant in size. The postman used his charge as a pillow, and had flung himself so heavily across it as to give not the faintest hope that any one could pull it away without disturbing its keeper from his nap. Nothing could be done now. In those few bitter moments, during which she stood helplessly looking from the bag which contained the fatal warrant to the unconscious face of the man before her, Grizel made up her mind to another plan.

She turned to the table, caught up the postman's

holsters, and pulled out the pistols of which the old woman had professed herself in such terror. Quickly drawing and secreting the charges, she returned them to their cases, with many an anxious look over her shoulder towards the bedstead, and took her seat again at the foot of the table.

Hardly had she done so when she heard the old woman returning with the pitcher. Grizel took a draught, for her throat felt like a lime-kiln, and having settled her bill, much to the landlady's satisfaction, by paying for the water the price of a pot of beer, prepared to set off. She carelessly asked and ascertained how much longer the other guest was likely to sleep.

"By the noise he makes he intends sleeping till Doomsday," she said, laughing.

"Ay, poor man! his is a hard life," said the hostess; "and little more than half an hour more before he must be on the highway again."

Grizel laughed once more, and, mounting her horse, set off at a trot along the road southward, as if continuing her journey in that direction.

Hardly had she got beyond the town, however, when turning the horse's head she galloped back, making a circuit around Belford and striking into the high road again between that place and Berwick. Having gained it, she walked the horse gently on, awaiting the coming up of the postman.

Though all her mind was now set on the enterprise before her, she could not help a shiver of terror as she thought on the chance of her tampering with the pistols being discovered, and their loading replaced. But she had chosen her course, and now she must go through with it. She was a woman, after all; and it cannot be wondered that her heart began to beat quickly as her ear caught the sound of hoofs on the road behind her, and, turning, she saw the man on whose face she had been gazing not an hour before, trotting briskly towards her—the mail-bags (there were two—one containing the letters direct from London, the other those taken up at the different post-offices on the road) strapped one on each side of his saddle in front, close to the holsters.

At the last moment her nerve came back, and as he drew near she saluted him civilly and with perfect calmness, put her horse into the same pace with his, and rode on for some way in his company.

The postman was a burly, thick-set man, with a good-humored face. You may be sure that Miss Cochrane inspected it anxiously enough, and was relieved to find that it did not contain any vast amount of hardy courage.

The man was well enough inclined for conversation, too, and as they rode had a heap of chat, which it seemed a pity to interrupt. At length, however, when they were about half way between Belford and Berwick, Grizel judged now or never was the time. Pulling her horse's rein gently so as to bring her close to her company, she said in a low but perfectly determined voice—

"Friend, I have taken a fancy for those mail-bags of yours, and I must have them: therefore take my advice, and deliver them up quietly, for I am provided for all hazards. I am mounted, as you see, on a fleet horse; I carry fire-arms; and, moreover, I am allied with those who are stronger, though not bolder, than I. You see that wood, yonder?" she continued, pointing to one about a mile off, with an accent and air meant to corroborate her bold words. "Then take my advice: give me up your bags, and speed back the road you came for the present, nor dare to approach that wood for at least two or three hours to come."

The postman, whose eyes had been growing rounder and rounder during this speech from the stripling beside him, pulled up and looked at her in dumb amazement for some moments.

"If," said he, as soon as he found his tongue, "you mean, young master, to make yourself merry at my expense, you are heartily welcome. I can see a joke, I trust, as well as another man; so have your laugh out, and don't think I'm one to take offence at the words of a foolish boy. But if," and here he whipped a pistol from his holster and turned the muzzle on her face—"if y'are mad enough to think seriously of such a business, then I am ready for you."

They had come to a stand now, in the middle of the road; and Grizel felt an ugly sinking at the heart as she looked at the mouth of the pistol, now not a yard from her cheek. Nevertheless she answered, very quietly and coolly—

"If you have a doubt, dismiss it; I am quite in earnest."

The postman, with his hand on the trigger, hesitated.

"Methinks, my lad, you seem of an age when robbing a garden or an old woman's fruit-stall would befit you better, if so be you *must* turn thief, than taking his Majesty's mails upon his highway from a stout and grown man. So be thankful, then, you have met with one who will not shed blood if he can help it, and go your way before I am provoked to fire."

"Sir," said Grizel, "you are a worthy man; nor am I fonder of bloodshed than you; but if you will not be persuaded, what shall I do? For I have said—and it is truth—that mail I must and will have. Choose, then;" and with this she pulled out a pistol from under her cloak, and, cocking it, presented it in his face.

"Nay, then, your blood be on your own head," cried the postman, and raising his pistol again he pulled the trigger; it flashed in the pan. Dashing the weapon to the ground, he pulled out the other in a moment, and aiming it in Grizel's face, fired— with the same result. In a furious passion he flung down this pistol, too, sprang from his horse, and dashed forward to seize her. She dug her spurs into her horse's flank and just eluded his grasp. Meanwhile the postman's horse, frightened at the noise and the struggle, had moved forward a pace or two. The girl saw her opportunity, and seized it in the same instant. Another dig with the spurs, and her own horse was level with the other; leaning forward she caught at the bridle, and calling to the pair, in an instant was galloping off along the highway, leaving the postman helplessly staring.

She had gone about a hundred yards with her prize, when she pulled up to look back. Her discomfited antagonist was still standing in the middle of the road, apparently stupefied with amazement at the unlooked-for turn which affairs had taken. Shouting to him to remember her advice about the wood, she put both the horses to their speed, and on looking back once more was gratified to find that the postman, impressed with the truth of her mysterious threat, had turned and was making the best of his way back to Belford.

On gaining the wood to which she had pointed, Grizel tied the postman's horse to a tree, at a safe distance from the road, and set about unfastening the straps of the mail-bags. With a sharp pen-knife she ripped them open, and searched for the government despatches among their contents. To find these was not difficult, owing to their address to the council in Edinburgh, and of the imposing weight of their seals. Here she discovered, not only the warrant for her father's death, but also many other sentences inflicting punishment in varying degrees on the unhappy men who had been taken in the late rising. Time was pressing; she could not stop to examine the warrants, but, quickly tearing them in small pieces, placed them carefully in her bosom.

This done, and having arranged all the private papers as far as possible as she had found them, Grizel mounted her horse again and rode off. The postman's horse and the mail-bags, she imagined, would soon be found, from the hints which she had given to the man about the wood—and this after-wards proved to be the case. She now set her horse at a gallop again, and did not spare whip or spur until she reached the cottage of her nurse, where her first care was to burn, not only the warrant for her father's death, but the remainder of the sentences on his fellow-prisoners. Having satisfied herself that all trace of the obnoxious papers was now consumed, she put on again her female garments, and was once more the gentle and unassuming Miss Grizel Cochrane.

It was high time, however, to be making her way northwards again; accordingly she left her pistols and cloak to be concealed by the nurse, and again set forward on her journey. By avoiding the highroad, resting only at the most sequestered cottages —and then but for an hour or so—and riding all the while as hard as she might, she reached Edinburgh in safety early next morning.

It remains only to say that the time thus won by this devoted girl was enough to gain the end for which she strove; and Father Peters plied the ear of King James so importunately that at length the order was signed for Sir John Cochrane's pardon.

The state of public affairs rendered it prudent for many years that this action of Grizel Cochrane's should be kept secret; but after the Revolution, when men could speak more freely, her heroism was known and applauded. She lived to marry Mr. Ker, of Morriston, in Berwickshire, and doubtless was as good a wife as she had proved herself a daughter.

THE SUNKEN TREASURE

By Nathaniel Hawthorne

PICTURE to yourselves a handsome, old-fashioned room, with a large, open cupboard at one end, in which is displayed a magnificent gold cup, with some other splendid articles of gold and silver plate. In another part of the room, opposite to a tall looking-glass, stands our beloved chair, newly polished, and adorned with a gorgeous cushion of crimson velvet, tufted with gold.

In the chair sits a man of strong and sturdy frame, whose face has been roughened by northern tempests and blackened by the burning sun of the West Indies. He wears an immense periwig, flowing down over his shoulders. His coat has a wide embroidery of golden foliage; and his waistcoat, likewise, is all flowered over and bedizened with gold. His red, rough hands, which have done many a good day's work with the hammer and adze, are half covered by the delicate lace ruffles at his wrists. On a table lies his silver-hilted sword; and in the corner of the room stands his gold-headed cane, made of a beautifully polished West India wood. Somewhat such an aspect as this did Phips present when he sat in Grandfather's chair after the king had appointed him Governor of Massachusetts.

But Sir William Phips had not always worn a gold-embroidered coat, nor always sat so much at his ease as he did in Grandfather's chair. He was a poor man's son, and was born in the province of Maine, where in his boyhood he used to tend sheep upon the hills. Until he had grown to be a man, he did not even know how to read and write. Tired of tending sheep, he apprenticed himself to a ship-carpenter, and spent about four years in hewing the crooked limbs of oak trees into knees for vessels.

In 1673, when he was twenty-two years old, he came to Boston, and soon afterwards was married to a widow lady, who had property enough to set him up in business. It was not long before he lost all the money that he had acquired by his marriage, and became a poor man again. Still, he was not discouraged. He often told his wife that he should be very rich, and would build a "fair brick house" in the Green Lane of Boston.

Several years passed away; and Phips had not yet gained the riches which he promised to himself. During this time he had begun to follow the sea for a living. In the year 1684 he happened to hear of a Spanish ship which had been cast away near Porto de la Plata. She had now lain for fifty years beneath the waves. This old ship had been laden with immense wealth; and nobody had thought of the possibility of recovering any part of it from the deep sea which was rolling and tossing it about. But though it was now an old story, Phips resolved that the sunken treasure should again be brought to light.

He went to London and obtained admittance to King James. He told the king of the vast wealth that was lying at the bottom of the sea. King James listened with attention, and thought this a fine opportunity to fill his treasury with Spanish gold. He appointed William Phips to be captain of a vessel, called the *Rose Algier,* carrying eighteen guns and ninety-five men. So now he was Captain Phips of the English navy.

The captain sailed from England and cruised for two years in the West Indies, trying to find the wrecked Spanish ship. But the sea is so wide and deep that it is no easy matter to discover the exact spot where a sunken vessel lies. The prospect of success seemed very small, and most people thought that Phips was as far from having money enough to build a "fair brick house" as he was while he tended sheep.

The seamen became discouraged, and gave up all hope of making their fortunes by discovering the Spanish wreck. They wanted Phips to turn pirate. There was a much better prospect of growing rich by plundering vessels which still sailed in the sea than by seeking for a ship that had lain beneath the waves full half a century. They broke out in open mutiny, but were finally mastered by Phips, and compelled to obey his orders. It would have been dangerous to continue much longer at sea with such a crew of mutinous sailors; and the ship was unseaworthy. So Phips judged it best to return to England.

Before leaving the West Indies, he met with an old Spaniard who remembered the wreck of the Spanish ship, and gave him directions how to find the very spot. It was on a reef of rocks, a few leagues from Porto de la Plata.

On his arrival in England Phips solicited the king to let him have another vessel and send him back again to the West Indies. But King James

refused to have anything more to do with the affair.
Phips might never have been able to renew the
search if the Duke of Albemarle and some other
noblemen had not lent their assistance.

They fitted out a ship, and he sailed from
England, and arrived safely at La Plata, where
he took an adze and assisted his men to build a
large boat.

The boat was intended for going closer to the
rocks than a large vessel could safely venture.
When it was finished, the captain sent several men
in it to examine the spot where the Spanish ship
was said to have been wrecked. They were accompanied by some Indians, who were skilful
divers, and could go down a great way into the
depths of the sea.

The boat's crew proceeded to the reef of rocks,
and gazed down into the transparent water. Nothing could they see more valuable than a curious sea
shrub growing beneath the water, in a crevice of the
reef of rocks. It flaunted to and fro with the swell
and reflux of the waves, and looked as bright and
beautiful as if its leaves were gold.

"We won't go back empty-handed," cried an
English sailor; and then he spoke to one of the
Indian divers. "Dive down and bring me that
pretty sea shrub there. That's the only treasure
we shall find!"

Down plunged the diver, and soon rose dripping
from the water, holding the sea shrub in his hand.
But he had learned some news at the bottom of
the sea. "There are some ship's guns," said he, the
moment he had drawn breath, "some great cannon,

among the rocks, near where the shrub was growing."

No sooner had he spoken than the English sailors knew that they had found the spot where the Spanish galleon had been wrecked, so many years before. The other Indian divers plunged over the boat's side and swam headlong down, groping among the rocks and sunken cannon. In a few moments one of them rose above the water with a heavy lump of silver in his arms. That single lump was worth more than a thousand dollars. The sailors took it into the boat, and then rowed back as speedily as they could, being in haste to inform Captain Phips of their good luck.

But, confidently as the captain had hoped to find the Spanish wreck, yet, now that it was really found, the news seemed too good to be true. He could not believe it till the sailors showed him the lump of silver. "Thanks be to God!" then cries Phips. "We shall every man of us make our fortunes!"

Hereupon the captain and all the crew set to work, with iron rakes and great hooks and lines, fishing for gold and silver at the bottom of the sea. Up came the treasures in abundance. Now they beheld a table of solid silver, once the property of an old Spanish grandee. Now they found an altar vessel, which had been destined as a gift to some Catholic church. Now they drew up a golden cup, fit for the King of Spain to drink his wine out of. Now their rakes were loaded with masses of silver bullion. There were also precious stones among the treasure, glittering and sparkling, so that it is a

wonder how their radiance could have been concealed.

After a day or two they discovered another part
of the wreck where they found a great many bags
of silver dollars. But nobody could have guessed
that these were money-bags. By remaining so long
in the salt-water they had become covered over with
a crust which had the appearance of stone, so that
it was necessary to break them in pieces with hammers and axes. When this was done, a stream of
silver dollars gushed out upon the deck of the
vessel.

The whole value of the recovered treasure, plate,
bullion, precious stones, and all, was estimated at
more than two millions of dollars. It was dangerous even to look at such a vast amount of wealth.
A captain, who had assisted Phips in the enterprise,
lost his reason at the sight of it. He died two years
afterward, still raving about the treasures that
lie at the bottom of the sea.

Phips and his men continued to fish up plate,
bullion, and dollars, as plentifully as ever, till their
provisions grew short. Then, as they could not
feed upon gold and silver any more than old King
Midas could, they found it necessary to go in
search of food. Phips returned to England, arriving there in 1687, and was received with great joy
by the Albemarles and other English lords who
had fitted out the vessel. Well they might rejoice;
for they took the greater part of the treasures to
themselves.

The captain's share, however, was enough to
make him comfortable for the rest of his days. It

also enabled him to fulfil his promise to his wife, by building a "fair brick house" in the Green Lane of Boston. The Duke of Albemarle sent Mrs. Phips a magnificent gold cup, worth at least five thousand dollars. Before Captain Phips left London, King James made him a knight; so that, instead of the obscure ship-carpenter who had formerly dwelt among them, the inhabitants of Boston welcomed him on his return as the rich and famous Sir William Phips.

THE LOST EXILES OF TEXAS

By Arthur Gilman

IF we could have stood upon the shores of Matagorda Bay with the Indians on a certain day over two hundred years ago we might have been witness to a strange sight. Before us would have been spread out the waters of a broad and sheltered harbor opening towards the sea through a narrow passage which was obstructed by sandbars and an island. One's eyes could not reach to the end of the bay, which is fifty miles long; nor could they see land beyond the sea-passage, for that opens into the broad Gulf of Mexico. Let us take our stand on the shore and see what we can see.

There appear to us, as if by magic, the forms of two French gentlemen accompanied by a small party of soldiers, who come from the mouth of the bay, and carefully thread their way along the shore,

It is a strange company of men. The leader is a native of Rouen, and he says that few of his companions are fit for anything but eating. He thought that his band comprised creatures of all sorts, like Noah's ark, but unlike the collection of the great patriarch, they seemed to be few of them worth saving.

As we look, the men begin to gather together the pieces of drift-wood that the peaceful waves throw up on to the shore. They are evidently planning to make a raft; but as one of them casts his lazy eyes in the direction in which ours were at first thrown, he exclaims with evident joy, in his native French, "*Voila les vaisseaux!*" or words to that effect, for he has descried two ships entering the bay from the Gulf. The ships slowly keep their way towards the inland coast, and from one of them there lands a man evidently higher in authority than any we have seen. His air is calm, dignified, forceful, persistent. He announces to those about him that they are at one of the mouths of the great Mississippi, or, as he well calls it, "*La rivière funeste,*" the fatal river. "Here shall we land all our men," he adds, "and here shall our vessels be placed in safe harbor."

In vain does the commander of one of the little ships protest that the water of the bay is too shallow and that the currents are too powerful; the strong man has given his order, and it must be obeyed. The channel was duly marked out, and on the twentieth of February, one of the ships, the *Aimable*, weighed anchor and began to enter the bay. The commander was on the shore, anxiously watching to see the result, when, suddenly, some of his men who had been cutting down a tree to make a canoe, rushed up and exclaimed, with terror in their faces, "The Indians have attacked us and one of our number is even now a captive in their hands." There was nothing to be done but go in pursuit of the savages.

It did not take long to arm a few men, and off they started with their leader in the direction that the Indians had taken. The savages were overtaken and a parley ensued. The leader's thoughts were now in two places at once, and he was not far enough from the shore not to be able to cast a glance towards the *Aimable*, and to say to his lieutenants, as he saw the vessel drifting near shoal water, "if she keeps on in that course, she will soon be aground." Still, no time was to be lost. The parley with the Indians did not hinder them long, and soon they were on the way towards the village whither the captive had been taken. Just as they entered its precincts and looked upon its inhabitants, clustered in groups among the dome-shaped huts, the loud boom of a cannon burst upon their ears. The savages were smitten with terror, and the commander felt his heart beat quickly as he looked again towards the water and saw the *Aimable* furling its sails, a sure token to him that she had indeed struck the rock and would be lost, with all the stores intended for use when her passengers should be landed.

Undaunted by the prospect, or even by the dark picture that his imagination conjured up, he pressed onward among the miserable savages, until his man had been recovered. Then he returned, and found his vessel on her side, a forlorn spectacle. Now the wind rose, and the sea beat upon the helpless hulk. It rocked backwards and forwards on its uneasy bed; its treasures of boxes and bales and casks were strewn over the waters; the greedy Indians made haste to seize what they could; and as night approached the hurriedly organized patrol of soldiers had all that they could do to face the deepening storm and protect their goods from the treacherous natives, as the less treacherous waves cast them upon the sands of the shore.

Who were these men, thus unceremoniously thrust upon the shores of the New World? How did it happen that they were found at a point that no European had before seen? Perhaps it is not necessary to ask how they happened to mistake the entrance to Matagorda Bay for one of the broad mouths of the Mississippi. They were Frenchmen. So much their speech has told us. The leader was Robert Cavelier, Sieur de La Salle, a man whom the historian Bancroft says that he had no superior among his countrymen for force of will and vast conceptions; for various knowledge, and quick adaptation of his genius to untried circumstances; for sublime magnanimity that resigned itself to the will of Heaven and yet triumphed over affliction by energy of purpose and unfaltering hope.

In early life he had renounced his inheritance and devoted himself to the service of the Church, but he soon left the order of Jesuits which he had entered, because, as Mr. Parkman surmises, he did not relish being all his life the moved and not the mover; because he could not give up his individuality and remain one of the great body, all of whom were compelled to march in a track pointed out to them by a superior. It is pleasant to know that he left the order with good feelings on both sides.

In 1667, we find the young man already entered upon the career of adventure in which the rest of his life was to be spent. He had sailed to Canada, the place of attraction for ambitious French youth, and there he remained several years, making the familiar acquaintance of the Indians and learning their language, while he was dreaming, like many others, of the passage to China through the rivers that came down from the westward. He had looked, too, in his vivid imagination over the vast plains of the great West, and had become filled with brilliant visions of an empire that he hoped some day to see established there for France. We have already learned how France took possession of the region, at this very period.

In such state of mind, La Salle sailed back to France in the autumn of 1674. He was well received and the next year returned, ennobled, and more than ever determined to push his grand scheme for the acquisition of the great West. His was no plan to indulge in theatrical spectacles, but to take actual possession. Year after year we see him steadily pursuing his single plan. He thinks nothing of crossing the Atlantic, of pushing his course through the trackless woods, or of paddling his frail canoe over the wild waters of the broad lakes. Indians did not daunt him by their cruelty, nor wild beasts affright him by their numbers and ferocity. Onward, ever onward, he pressed.

In the year 1680, we find him taking possession by actual occupation, of the region now comprising the State of Illinois. It was the first time that civilization had asserted itself there. La Salle built a fort, and, in memory of the trials of the way, called it *Crèvecœur*, which signified Broken-heart; but it did not testify to any broken courage on his part—rather it was a monument to the obstacles that his persistence had surmounted.

Two years later, we find his canoe, which seems to our eyes now the emblem of an aggressive civilization, flitting along the Illinois River, entering the muddy Mississippi, and floating down its thousand miles to the Gulf. This is not the whole picture, however. We see the party start from the Chicago River, in the cold weather of December. The rivers are frozen. Canoes must be dragged over their snowy and icy surfaces, and baggage can be transported in no way but upon rough sledges. Can you not see the slow procession of fifty persons dragging themselves along day after day through the region inhabited but by savages and wild beasts, suffering from cold and hunger, and all held to their duty by the persevering leader who had brought them there?

There are twenty-three Frenchmen, eighteen Indian braves, belonging to those terrible Abenakis and Mohegans whose "midnight yells had," as Mr. Parkman says, "startled the border hamlets of New England; who had danced around Puritan scalps, and whom Puritan imaginations painted as incarnate fiends." There were besides, ten squaws and three children. A motley collection and one not calculated to inspire confidence nor hope for the success of any undertaking. It was not until they had passed the point where the river broadens into Lake Peoria that they found water in which they could float their canoes. Then they continued on, until early in February they found themselves on the banks of the Mississippi. It was filled with ice, and no canoe could navigate it.

After a delay of a few days, they found the river free, and again took up their course southwards. A day more brought them to the confluence of the muddy Missouri, which some of my readers have probably seen, where a mighty stream coming down from distant mountains, enters another not so mighty as itself, and plowing its way across its current, burrows under the soil on the opposite shore. This did not detain the voyagers, though they encamped there over night, and then pursued their course towards the unknown. A few days showed them the mouth of the Ohio, but still they pressed onward. It was near the end of February, the temperature was growing perceptibly warmer as they approached the South.

At a certain point they encamped and sent out their hunters for game. One did not return at night, and a horror seized the others, as they thought that he had been overtaken and killed by hostile Indians. Day after day the woods were scoured in the hope of finding the missing companion, but it seemed vain. A fort was erected for the protection of the party on a high bluff, and named for the lost hunter, Prudhomme. At last they met some Chickasaw Indians, and messages of amity were exchanged through them with the people of their village, not far distant. Soon afterwards Prudhomme was discovered, half-dead from exposure, for he had lost his way while hunting.

Thus the expedition progressed for many days, until at last the little canoes found themselves thrust out through the turbid channels of the delta, into the clear salt waters of the Gulf of Mexico. They had stopped on the way after leaving Fort Prudhomme, at several Indian towns, had been well treated by the natives, and they had seen the mouths of the Arkansas and the Red rivers.

The whole valley of the Fatal River had been laid bare to them, and now La Salle thought the time had come to take formal possession for his sovereign.

Near the mouth of the river, the party came together on the ninth of April, 1682, and a ceremony took place that was very similar to the one at the Sault Ste. Marie, a few days less than eleven years before, by which France had taken possession of the Northwest. It did not rival that in the magnificence with which it was conducted, though the ceremonial was, perhaps, a little more elaborated, but it seemed to have a better basis of fact, for La Salle had actually passed through the heart of the region which he now claimed. A column was erected, of course, and a tablet of lead was buried near it, such as those that had been placed in the ground at various other places by Frenchmen, bearing testimony to the fact that Louis the Great claimed to rule the land.

It was nearly the end of November of the following year, when La Salle reached Quebec, after having retraced his route by long and tedious stages up the rivers that he had followed down to the Gulf. Then he returned to France to tell the story of his travels, and began to use his influence to induce the government to send out an expedition to take controlling possession of the Mississippi region. He argued with all his powers, saying that by fortifying the river, the French might control the contient. It was really a grand and brilliant proposition, and the king and his minister gave more than was demanded. Four vessels were prepared, instead of the two that La Salle asked for. The expedition comprised a hundred soldiers, thirty volunteers, many mechanics and laborers, several families and a few girls, who looked forward to certain marriage in the new land.

On the twenty-fourth of July, La Salle set sail from Rochelle, with four hundred men in his four vessels, leaving an affectionate and comforting letter as his last farewell to his mother at Rouen. We have already seen how he was thrown upon the shores of the New World. There, on the sands of Matagorda Bay, with nothing to eat but oysters and a sort of porridge made of the flour that had been saved, the homesick party of downcast men and sorrowing women encamped until their leader could tell them what to do. They did not even know where they were. They were intending to conquer the Spaniards, but they knew nothing of their whereabouts. They were attacked by Indians, and finally, some three weeks after the wreck, the commander of the ships sailed away for France leaving La Salle and his forlorn company behind!

A site was soon chosen on the river now called Lavaca (a corruption of *La Vache*, the cow, a name given it because buffaloes had been seen there), and a fort was built called St. Louis. La Salle had scarcely finished this establishment, when he determined to search for the Mississippi River, for he had by that time concluded from explorations that he had not found it. On the last day of October, he started, and towards the end of March, the party returned, tattered and worn, almost ready to die; but though the strong body of the leader had given away, his stronger spirit was still unbroken, and he soon determined to set out to find the Illinois region where he left a colony formerly, and where he felt sure he could obtain relief. There was no chance for them to return directly to France since their vessels were all gone, and this seemed their only hope.

A party of twenty was formed to undertake the perilous enterprise, and on the twenty-second of April, 1686, they took their way from the fort, bearing on their persons the contributions that their fellows who were to remain had been able to bring together for their comfort.

The party experienced a variety of hardships, quarrelled among themselves, and finally, on the morning of the eighteenth of March, 1687, one of them shot and killed the brave leader. The remainder kept on, finally reached Canada and were taken to their native land. To the colonists at Fort St. Louis, no ground of hope ever appeared, though they felt that the people of France must have an interest in them, and so they kept a lookout over the water for a ship coming to their relief. It never came, alas, and no one knows to this day what became of the Lost Exiles of Texas!

THE BOY CONQUEROR—CHARLES XII OF SWEDEN

By E. S. Brooks

IN an old, old palace on the rocky height of the *Slottsbacke*, or Palace Hill, in the northern quarter of the beautiful city of Stockholm, the capital of Sweden, there lived, just two hundred years ago, a bright young prince. His father was a stern and daring warrior-king—a man who had been a fighter from his earliest boyhood; who at fourteen had been present in four pitched battles with the Danes, and who, while yet scarce twelve years old, had charged the Danish line at the head of his guards had shot down the stout Danish colonel, who could not resist the spry young warrior. His mother was a sweet-faced Danish princess, a loving and gentle lady, who scarce ever heard a kind word from her stern-faced husband, and whose whole life was bound up in her precious little prince.

And this little Carolus, Karl, or Charles, dearly loved his tender mother. From her he learned lessons of truth and nobleness that even through all his stormy and wandering life never forsook him. Often while he had swung gently to and fro in his quaint, carved, and uncomfortable-looking cradle, had she crooned above him the old saga-songs that told of valor and dauntless courage and all the stern virtues that made up the heroes of those same old saga-songs. Many a time she had trotted the little fellow on her knee to the music of the ancient nursery rhyme that has a place in all lands and languages, from the steppes of Siberia to the homes of New York and San Francisco:

"Ride along, ride a cock-horse,
   His mane is dapple-gray;
Ride along, ride a cock-horse,
   Little boy, ride away.
Where shall the little boy ride to?
To the king's court to woo"—

and so forth, and so forth, and so forth—in different phrases but with the same idea, as many and many a girl and boy can remember. And she had told him over and over again the saga-stories and fairy tales that every Scandinavian boy and girl, from prince to peasant, knows so well—of Frithiof and Ingeborg, and the good King Rene; and about the Stone Giant and his wife Guru; and about the dwarfs, and trolls, and nixies, and beautiful mermaids and stromkarls. And she told him also many a story of brave and daring deeds, of noble and knightly lives, and how his ancestors, from the great Gustavus, and, before, from the still greater Gustavus Vasa, had been kings of Sweden, and had made the name of that Northern land a power in all the courts of Europe.

Little Prince Charles was as brave as he was gentle and jolly, and as hardy as he was brave. At five years old he killed his first fox; at seven he could manage his horse like a young centaur; and at twelve he had his first successful bear hunt. He was as obstinate as he was hardy; he steadily refused to learn Latin or French—the languages of the court — until he heard that the kings of Denmark and Poland understood them, and then he speedily mastered them.

His lady-mother's death, when he was scarce twelve years old, was a great sadness, and nearly caused his own death, but, recovering his health, he accompanied his father on hunting parties and military expeditions, and daily grew stronger and hardier than ever.

In April, 1697, when the prince was not yet fifteen, King Charles XI, his stern-faced father, suddenly died, and the boy king succeeded to the throne as absolute lord of "Sweden and Finland, of Livonia, Carelia, Ingria, Wismar, Wibourg, the islands of Rugen and Oesel, of Pomerania, and the duchies of Bremen and Verdun" — one of the finest possessions to which a young king ever succeeded, and representing what is now Sweden, Western Russia, and a large part of Northern Germany.

A certain amount of restraint is best for us all. As the just restraints of the law are best for men and women, so the proper restraints of home are best for boys and girls. A lad from whom all restraining influences are suddenly withdrawn—who can have his own way unmolested—stands in the greatest danger of wrecking his life. The temptations of power have been the cause of very much of the world's sadness and misery. And this temptation came to this boy King of Sweden called in his fifteenth year to supreme sway over a large realm of loyal subjects. Freed from the severity of his stern father's discipline, he found himself responsible to no one—absolutely his own master. And he did what too many of us, I fear, would have done in his position—he determined to have a jolly good time, come what might; and he had it—in his way.

He and his brother-in-law, the wild young Duke of Holstein, turned the town upside down. They snapped cherry-pits at the king's gray-bearded councillors, and smashed in the windows of the staid and scandalized burghers of Stockholm. They played ball with the table dishes, and broke all the benches in the palace chapel. They coursed hares through the council-chambers of the Parliament House, and ran furious races until they had ruined several fine horses. They beheaded sheep in the palace till the floors ran with blood, and then pelted the passers-by with sheep's heads. They spent the money in the royal treasury like water, and played so many heedless and ruthless boy-tricks that the period of these months of folly was known, long after, as the "Gottorp Fury," because the harum-scarum young brother-in-law, who was the ringleader in all these scrapes, was Duke of Holstein-Gottorp.

But at last, even the people—serfs of this boy autocrat though they were—began to murmur, and when one Sunday morning three clergymen preached from the text, "Woe to thee, O land, when thy king is a child," the young sovereign remembered the counsels of his good mother and recalled the glories of his ancestors, saw how foolish and dangerous was all this reckless sport, turned over a new leaf, became thoughtful and care-taking, and began his career of conquest with the best victory of all—the conquest of himself!

But though he curbed his tendency to profitless and hurtful "skylarking," he had far too much of the Berserker blood of his ancestors—those rough old vikings who "despised mail and helmet and went into battle unharnessed"—to become altogether gentle in manners or occupation. He hated his fair skin, and sought in every way to tan and roughen it, and to harden himself by exposure and neglect of personal comfort. Many a night was passed by the boy on the bare floor, and for three nights in the cold Swedish December he slept in the hay-loft of the palace stables, without undressing and with but a scanty covering.

So he grew to be a lad of seventeen, sturdy, strong, and hardy, and at the date of our story, in the year of 1699, the greater part of his time was given up to military exercises and field sports, with but little attention to debates in council or to the cares of state.

Among his chief enjoyments were the sham fights on land and water. Many a hard-fought battle was waged between the boys and young men who made up his guards and crews, and who would be divided into two or more opposing parties, as the plan of battle required. This was rough and dangerous sport, and was attended often with really serious results. But the participants were stout and sturdy Northern lads, used to hardships and trained to physical endurance. They thought no more of these encounters than do the boys of to-day of the crush of football and the hard hitting of the baseball field, and blows were given and taken with equal good nature and unconcern.

One raw day in the early fall of 1699, sturdy young Arvid Horn, a stout, blue-eyed Stockholm boy, stripped to the waist, and with a gleam of fun in his eyes, stood upright in his little boat as it bobbed on the crest of the choppy Maelar waves. He hailed the king's yacht.

"Holo; in the boat there! Stand for your lives!" he shouted, and levelled his long squirt-gun full at the helmsman.

Swish! came the well-directed stream of water plump against the helmsman's face. Again and again it flew, until dripping and sore he dropped the tiller and dashed down the companion-way calling loudly for help.

Help came speedily, and as the crew of the king's yacht manned the rail and levelled at their single assailant the squirt-guns, which were the principal weapons of warfare used in these "make-believe" naval engagements, the fun grew fast and furious; but none had so sure an aim or so strong an arm to send an unerring and staggering stream as young Arvid Horn. One by one he drove them back, while as his boat drifted still nearer the yacht he made ready to spring to the force-chains and board his prize. But even before he could steady himself for the jump, another tall and fair-haired Stockholm lad, darting out from the high cabin, rallied the defeated crew and bade them man the pumps at once.

A clumsy-looking fire-engine stood amidship, and the crew leaped to its pumps as directed, while the newcomer, catching up a line of hose, sprang to the rail and sent a powerful stream of water straight against the solitary rover.

"Repel boarders!" he cried, laughingly, and the sudden stream from the fire-engine's nozzle sent young Arvid Horn staggering back into his boat.

But he rallied quickly, and with well-charged squirt-gun attacked the new defender of the yacht. The big nozzle, however, was more than a match for the lesser squirt-gun, and the small boat speedily began to fill under the constant deluge of water from the engine.

"Yield thee, yield thee, Arvid Horn; yield thee to our unconquerable nozzle," came the summons from the yacht; "yield thee, or I will drown you out like a rat in a cheese-press!"

"Arvid Horn yields to no one," the plucky boy in the boat made answer, and with a parting shot and a laughing *"Farväl!"* he leaped from the sinking boat into the dancing Maelar water. Striking boldly out, he swam twice round the boat in sheer bravado, defying the enemy; now ducking to escape the pursuing stream, or now, while floating on his back, sending a return shot with telling force against the men at the pump—for he still clung to his trusty squirt-gun.

The fair-faced lad in the yacht looked at the swimmer in evident admiration.

"Is it, then, hard to swim, Arvid Horn?" he inquired.

"Not if one is fearless," called back the floating boy.

"How; fearless?" exclaimed the lad on the yacht, hastily. "Do you perhaps think that I am afraid?"

"I said not so," replied young Arvid, coolly sending a full charge from his squirt-gun straight up in the air.

"No; but you mean it—good faith, you mean it, then," said the lad, and flinging off wig, cocked hat, and long coat only, without an instant's hesitation he, too, leaped into the Maelar Lake.

There is nothing so cooling to courage or reckless enthusiasm as cold water—if one cannot swim. The boy plunged and floundered, and weighty with his boots and his clothing, soon sank from sight. As he came spluttering to the surface again, "Help, help, Arvid," he called despairingly; "I am drowning!"

Arvid, who had swum away from his friend, thinking that he would follow after, heard the cry and caught a still louder one from the yacht: "The king, the king is sinking!"

A few strokes brought him near to the over-confident diver, and clutching him by his shirt-collar, he kept the lad's head above water until, after a long and laborious swim, he brought his kingly burden safe to land—for the fair-haired and reckless young knight of the nozzle was none other than his gracious majesty, Charles the Twelfth of Sweden.

"Truly it is one thing to be brave and another to be skilful," said the king, as he stood soaked and dripping on the shore. "But for you, friend Arvid, I had almost gone."

"You are very wet, sire, and may take cold," said Arvid; "let us hasten at once to yonder house for warmth and dry clothes."

"Not so, Arvid; I do not fear the water—on land," said the king. "I am no such milksop as to need to dry off before a kitchen fire. See, this is the better way"; and catching up a stout hazel-stick, he bade Arvid stand on his guard. Nothing loath, Arvid Horn accepted the kingly challenge, and picking up a similar hazel-stick, he rapped King Charles' weapon smartly, and the two boys went at each other "hammer and tongs" in a lively bout at "single-stick."

They were soon thoroughly warmed up by this vigorous exercise, and forgot their recent bath and the king's danger. It was a drawn battle, however, and, as they paused for breath, King Charles said: "Trust that to drive away cold and ague, Arvid. Faith, 'tis a rare good sport."

"Could it be done on horseback, think you?" queried Arvid, always on the lookout for sensation.

"And why not? 'Tis well thought," said the king. "Let us straight to the palace yard and try it for ourselves."

But ere they reached the palace the idea had developed into still greater proportions.

The king's guards were summoned, and divided into two parties. Their horses were unsaddled, and, riding "bareback" and armed with nothing but hazel-sticks, the two forces were pitted against each other in a great cavalry duel of "single-stick."

King Charles commanded one side, and young Arvid Horn the other. At it they went, now one side and now the other having the advantage, the two leaders fighting with especial vigor.

Arvid pressed the king closely, and both lads were full of the excitement of the fray when Charles, careless of his aim and with his customary recklessness, brought his hazel-stick with a terrible thwack upon poor Arvid's face. Now Arvid Horn had a boil on his cheek, and if any of my boy readers know what a tender piece of property a boil is, they will know that King Charles's hazel-stick was not a welcome poultice.

With a cry of pain Arvid fell fainting from his horse, and the cavalry battle at "single-stick" came to a sudden stop. But the heat and the pain brought on so fierce a fever that the lad was soon as near to death's door as his friend King Charles had been in the sea fight of the squirt-guns.

The king was deeply concerned during young Arvid's illness, and when the lad at last recovered he made him a present of two thousand thalers, laughingly promising to repeat the prescription whenever Arvid was again wounded at "single-stick." He was greatly pleased to have his friend with him once more, and, when Arvid was strong enough to join in his vigorous sports again, one of the first things he proposed was a great bear-hunt up among the snow-filled forests that skirted the Maelar Lake.

A day's ride from Stockholm, the hunting-lodge of the kings of Sweden lay upon the heavily drifted hill-slopes just beyond the lake shore, and through the forests and marshes two hundred years ago the big brown bear of Northern Europe, the noble elk, the now almost extinct auroch, or bison, and the great gray wolf roamed in fierce and savage strength, affording exciting and dangerous sport for daring hunters.

And among these hunters none excelled young Charles of Sweden. Reckless in the face of danger, and brave as he was reckless, he was ever on the alert for any novelty in the manner of hunting that should make the sport even more dangerous and exciting. So young Arvid Horn was not surprised when the king said to him:

"I have a new way for hunting the bear, Arvid, and a rarely good one, too."

"Of that I'll be bound, sire," young Arvid responded; "but—how may it be?"

"You shall know anon," King Charles replied; "but this much will I say: I do hold it but a coward's part to fight the poor brute with firearms. Give the fellow a chance for his life, say I, and a fair fight in open field—and then let the best man win."

Here was a new idea. Not hunt the bear with musket, carbine, or wheel-lock? What then— did King Charles reckon to have a wrestling bout

or a turn at "single-stick" with the *Jarl* Bruin?
So wondered Arvid Horn, but he said nothing,
waiting the king's own pleasure, as became a shrewd
young courtier.

And soon enough he learned the boy-hunter's
new manner of bear-hunting, when, on the very
day of their arrival at the Maelar lodge, they
tracked a big brown bear beneath the great pines
and spruces of the almost boundless forest, armed
only with strong wooden pitchforks. Arvid was
not at all anxious for this fighting at close quarters,
but when he saw King Charles boldly advance upon
the growling bear, when he saw the great brute
rise on his hind legs and threaten to hug Sweden's
monarch to death, he would have sprung forward
to aid his king. But a huntsman near at hand held
him back.

"Wait," said the man; "let the 'little father' play
his part."

And even as he spoke Arvid saw the king walk
deliberately up to the towering bear, and, with a
quick thrust of his long-handled fork, catch the
brute's neck between the pointed wooden prongs,
and with a mighty shove force the bear backward
in the snow.

Then, answering his cry of "Holo, all!" the
huntsmen sprang to his side, flung a stout net over
the struggling bear, and held it thus, a floundering
prisoner, while the intrepid king coolly cut its
throat with his sharp hunting-knife.

Arvid learned to do this, too, in time, but it required some extra courage even for his steady
young head and hand.

One day when each of the lads had thus trans-fixed and killed his bear, and as, in high spirits, they were returning to the hunting-lodge, a courserman dashed hurriedly across their path, recognized the king, and reining in his horse, dismounted hastily, saluted, and handed the king a packet.

"From the council, sire," he said.

Up to this day the young king had taken but little interest in the affairs of state, save as he directed the review or drill, leaving the matters of treaty and of state policy to his trusted councillors. He received the courserman's despatch with evident unconcern, and read it carelessly. But his face changed as he read it a second time; first clouding darkly, and then lighting up with the gleam of a new determination and purpose.

"What says Count Piper?" he exclaimed half aloud; "Holstein laid waste by Denmark, Gottorp Castle taken, and the duke a fugitive? And my council dares to temper and negotiate? *Ack; so!* Arvid Horn, we must be in Stockholm ere night-fall."

"But, sire, how can you?" exclaimed Arvid. "The roads are heavy with snow, and no horse could stand the strain or hope to make the city ere morning."

"No horse!" cried King Charles; "then three shall do it. Hasten; bid Hord the equerry har-ness the triple team to the strongest sledge, and be you ready to ride with me in a half hour's time. For we shall be in Stockholm by nightfall."

And ere the half hour was up they were off.

Careless of roadway, straight for Stockholm they headed, the triple team of plunging Ukraine horses, driven abreast by the old equerry Hord, dashing down the slopes and across the Maelar ice, narrowly escaping collision, overturn, and death. With many a plunge and many a ducking, straight on they rode, and ere the Stockholm clocks had struck the hour of six the city gates were passed, and the spent and foaming steeds dashed panting into the great yard of the Parliament House.

The council was still in session, and the grave old councillors started to their feet in amazement at this sudden apparition of the boy king, soiled and bespattered from head to foot, standing there in their midst.

"Gentlemen," he said, with earnestness and determination in his voice, "your despatch tells me of unfriendly acts on the part of the King of Denmark against our brother and ally of Holstein-Gottorp. I am resolved never to begin an unjust war, but never to finish an unjust one save with the destruction of mine enemies. My resolution is fixed. I will march and attack the first one who shall declare war; and when I shall have conquered him, I hope to strike terror into the rest."

These were ringing and, seemingly, reckless words for a boy of seventeen, and we do not wonder that, as the record states, "the old councillors, astonished at this declaration, looked at one another without daring to answer." The speech seemed all the more reckless when they considered, as we may here, the coalition against which the boy king spoke so confidently.

CHARLES XII OF SWEDEN

At that time—in the year 1699—the three neighbors of this young Swedish monarch were three kings of powerful northern nations—Frederick the Fourth, King of Denmark; Augustus, called the Strong, King of Poland and Elector of Saxony, and Peter, afterward known as the Great, Czar of Russia. Tempted by the large possessions of young King Charles, and thinking to take advantage of his youth, his inexperience, and his presumed indifference, these three monarchs concocted a fine scheme by which Sweden was to be overrun, conquered, and divided among the three members of this new copartnership of kings—from each of whom, or from their predecessors, this boy king's ancestors had wrested many a fair domain and wealthy city.

But these three kings—as has many and many another plotter in history before and since—reckoned without their host. They did not know the mettle that was in this grandnephew of the great Gustavus.

Once aroused to action, he was ready to move before even his would-be conquerors, in those slow-going days, imagined he had thought of resistance. Money and men were raised, the alliance of England and Holland was secretly obtained, a council of defence was appointed to govern Sweden during the absence of the king, and on April 23, 1700, two months before his eighteenth birthday, King Charles bade his grandmother and his sisters good-by and left Stockholm forever.

Even as he left, the news came that another member in this firm of hostile kings, Agustus of

258

Saxony and Poland, had invaded Sweden's tributary province of Livonia on the Gulf of Finland. Not to be drawn aside from his first object—the punishment of Denmark—Charles simply said, "We will make King Augustus go back the way he came," and hurried on to join his army in southern Sweden.

By August 3, 1700, King Charles had grown tired of waiting for his reserves and new recruits, and so, with scarce six thousand men, he sailed away from Malmo—clear down at the most southerly point of Sweden—across the Sound, and steered for the Danish coast not twenty-five miles away.

Young Arvid Horn, still the king's fast friend, and now one of his aids, following his leader, leaped into the first of the small barges or rowboats that were to take the troops from the frigates to the Danish shore. His young general and king, impatient at the slowness of the clumsy barges, while yet three hundred yards from shore, stood upright in the stern, drew his sword, and exclaimed: "I am wearied with this pace. All you who are for Denmark follow me!" And then, sword in hand, he sprang over into the sea.

Arvid Horn quickly followed his royal friend. The next moment generals and ministers, ambassadors and belaced officials, with the troops that filled the boats, were wading waist-deep through the shallow water of the Sound, struggling toward the Danish shore, and fully as enthusiastic as their hasty young leader and king.

The Danish musket-balls fell thick around them

as the Danish troops sought from their trenches to repel the invaders.

"What strange whizzing noise is this in the air?" asked the young king, now for the first time in action.

" 'Tis the noise of the musket-balls they fire upon you," was the reply.

"*Ack,* say you so," said Charles; "good, good; from this time forward that shall be my music."

In the face of this "music" the shore was gained, the trenches were carried by fierce assault and King Charles's first battle was won. Two days later, Copenhagen submitted to its young conqueror, and King Frederick of Denmark hastened to the defence of his capital, only to find it in the possession of the enemy, and to sign a humiliating treaty of peace.

The boy conqueror's first campaign was over, and, as his biographer says, he had "at the age of eighteen begun and finished a war in less than six weeks." Accepting nothing for himself from this conquest, he spared the land from which his dearly remembered mother had come from the horrors of war and pillage which in those days were not only allowable but expected.

King Augustus of Poland, seeing the short work made of his ally the King of Denmark, by this boy king, whom they had all regarded with so much contempt, deemed discretion to be the better part of valor and, as the lad had prophesied, withdrew from Livonia, "going back by the way he came." Then the young conqueror, flushed with his successes, turned his army against his third and greatest enemy, Czar Peter, of Russia, who, with over eighty thousand men, was besieging the Swedish town of Narva.

A quaint old German-looking town, situated a few miles from the shores of the Gulf of Finland, in what is now the Baltic provinces of Russia, and near to the site of the czar's later capital of St. Petersburg, the stout-walled town of Narva was the chief defence of Sweden on its eastern borders, and a stronghold which the Russian monarch especially coveted for his own. Young Arvid Horn's uncle, the Count Horn, was in command of the Swedish forces in the town, which, with a thousand men, he held for the young king, his master, against all the host of the Czar Peter.

The boy who had conquered Denmark in less than six weeks, and forced a humiliating peace from Poland, was not the lad to consider for a moment the question of risk or of outnumbering forces. In the middle of November, when all that cold Northern land is locked in ice and snow, he flung out the eagle-flag of Sweden to the Baltic blasts, and crossed to the instant relief of Narva, with an army of barely twenty thousand men. Landing at Pernau with but a portion of his troops, he pushed straight on, and with scarce eight thousand men hurried forward to meet the enemy. With a courage as daring as his valor was headlong, he surprised and routed first one and then another advance detachment of the Russian force, and soon twenty-five thousand demoralized and defeated men were retreating before him into the Russian camp. In less than two days all the Russian outposts were carried, and on the noon of the thirtieth of November, 1700, the boy from Sweden appeared with his eight thousand victory-flushed though wearied troops before the fortified camp of his enemy, and, without a moment's hesitation, ordered instant battle.

"Sire," said one of his chief officers, the General Stenbock, "do you comprehend the greatness of our danger? The Muscovites outnumber us ten to one."

"What, then!" said the intrepid young king, "do you imagine that with my eight thousand brave Swedes I shall not be able to march over the bodies of eighty thousand Muscovites?" And then at the signal of two fusees and the watchword, "With the help of God," he ordered his cannon to open on the Russian trenches, and through a furious snow-storm charged straight upon the enemy.

Again valor and enthusiasm triumphed. The Russian line broke before the impetuosity of the Swedes, and, as one chronicler says, "ran about like a herd of cattle"; the bridge across the river broke under the weight of fugitives, panic followed, and when night fell, the great Russian army of eighty thousand men surrendered as prisoners of war to a boy of eighteen with but eight thousand tired soldiers at his back.

So the boy conqueror entered upon his career of victory. Space does not permit to detail his battles and his conquests. How he placed a new king on the throne of Poland, kept Denmark in submission, held the hosts of Russia at bay, humbled Austria, and made his name, ere yet he was twenty, at once a wonder and a terror in all the courts of Europe. How, at last, his ambition getting the better of his discretion, he thought to be a modern Alexander, to make Europe Protestant, subdue Rome, and carry his conquering eagles into Egypt and Turkey and Persia. How, by unwise measures and foolhardy endeavors, he lost all the fruits of his hundred victories and his nine years of conquest in the terrible defeat by the Russians at Pultowa, which sent him an exile into Turkey, kept him there a prisoner of state for over five years; and how, finally, when once again at the head of Swedish troops, instead of defending his own home-land of Sweden, he invaded Norway in the depth of winter, and was killed, when but thirty-six, by a cannon-shot from the enemy's batteries at Frederickshall on December 11, 1718.

Charles the Twelfth of Sweden was one of the most remarkable of the world's historic boys. Elevated to a throne founded on despotic power and victorious memories, at an age when most lads regard themselves as the especial salt of the earth, he found himself launched at once into a war with three powerful nations, only to become in turn the conqueror of each. A singularly good boy, so far as the customary temptations of power and high station are concerned—temperate, simple, and virtuous in tastes, dress, and habits—he was, as one of his biographers has remarked, "the only one among kings who had lived without a single frailty."

But this valorous boy, who had first bridled his own spirit, and then conquered the Northern world, "reared," as has been said, "under a father cold and stern, defectively educated, taught from childhood to value nothing but military glory," could not withstand the temptation of success. An ambition to be somebody and to do something is always a laudable one in boy or girl, until it supplants and overgrows the sweet, true, and manly boy and girl nature, and makes us regardless of the comfort or the welfare of others. A desire to excel the great conquerors of old, joined to an obstinacy as strong as his courage, caused young Charles of Sweden to miss the golden opportunity, and instead of seeking to rule his own country wisely, sent him abroad a homeless wanderer on a career of conquest, as romantic as it was, first, glorious, and at the last disastrous.

In the northern quarter of the beautiful city of Stockholm, surrounded by palaces and gardens, theatres, statues, and fountains, stands Molin's striking statue of the boy conqueror, Charles the Twelfth of Sweden. Guarded at the base by captured mortars, the outstretched hand and unsheathed sword seem to tell of conquests to be won and victories to be achieved. But to the boy and girl of this age of peace and good-fellowship, when wars are averted rather than sought, and wise statesmanship looks rather to the healing than to the opening of the world's wounds, one cannot but feel how much grander, nobler, and more helpful would have been the life of this young "Lion of the North," as his Turkish captors called him, had it been devoted to deeds of gentleness and charity rather than of blood and sorrow, and how much more enduring might have been his fame and his memory if he had been the lover and helper of his uncultivated and civilization-needing people, rather than the valorous, ambitious, head-strong, and obstinate boy conqueror of two centuries ago.

THE TRUE STORY OF A KID-NAPPED BOY AS TOLD BY HIMSELF

By Peter Williamson

I WAS born in Hirulay, in the county of Aberdeen, Scotland. My parents, though not rich, were respectable, and so long as I was under their care all went well with me. Unhappily, I was sent to stay with an aunt at Aberdeen, where, at eight years old, when playing on the quay, I was noticed as a strong, active little fellow by two men belonging to a vessel in the harbor. Now, this vessel was in the employ of certain merchants of Aberdeen, who used her for the villainous purpose of kidnapping—that is, stealing young children from their parents and selling them as slaves in the plantations abroad.

These impious monsters, marking me out for their prey, tempted me on board the ship, which I had no sooner entered than they led me between the decks to some other boys whom they had kidnapped in like manner. Not understanding what a fate was in store for me, I passed the time in childish amusement with the other lads in the steerage, for we were never allowed to go on deck while the vessel stayed in the harbor, which it did till they had imprisoned as many luckless boys as they needed.

Then the ship set sail for America. I cannot remember much of the voyage, being a mere child at the time, but I shall never forget what happened when it was nearly ended. We had reached the American coast, when a hard gale of wind sprang up from the southeast, and about midnight the ship struck on a sandbank off Cape May, near Delaware. To the terror of all on board, it was soon almost full of water. The boat was then hoisted out, and the captain and his fellow-villains, the crew, got into it, leaving me and my deluded companions, as they supposed, to perish. The cries, shrieks, and tears of a throng of children had no effect on these merciless wretches.

But happily for us the wind abated, and the ship being on a sandbank, which did not give way to let her deeper, we lay here till morning, when the captain, unwilling to lose all his cargo, sent some of the crew in a boat to the ship's side to bring us ashore. A sort of camp was made, and here we stayed till we were taken in by a vessel bound to Philadelphia.

At Philadelphia, people soon came to buy us. We were sold for £16 apiece. I never knew what became of my unhappy companions, but I was sold for seven years to one of my countrymen, Hugh Wilson, who in his youth had suffered the same fate as myself in being kidnapped from his home.

Happy was my lot in falling into his power, for

he was a humane, worthy man. Having no children of his own, and pitying my sad condition, he took great care of me till I was fit for business, and at twelve years old set me about little things till I could manage harder work. Meanwhile, seeing my fellow-servants often reading and writing, I felt a strong desire to learn, and told my master that I should be glad to serve a year longer than the bond obliged me if he would let me go to school. To this he readily agreed, and I went every winter for five years, also learning as much as I could from my fellow-servants.

With this good master I stayed till I was seventeen years old, when he died, leaving me a sum of money, about £120 sterling, his best horse, and all his wearing apparel.

I now maintained myself by working about the country, for any one who would employ me, for nearly seven years, when I determined to settle down. I applied to the daughter of a prosperous planter, and found my suit was acceptable both to her and her father, so we married. My father-in-law, wishing to establish us comfortably, gave me a tract of land which lay, unhappily for me, as it has since proved, on the frontiers of Pennsylvania. It contained about two hundred acres, with a good house and barn.

I was now happy in my home, with a good wife; but my peace did not last long, for about 1754 the Indians in the French interest, who had formerly been very troublesome in our province, began to renew their old practices. Even many of the Indians whom we supposed to be in the English interest joined the plundering bands; it was no wonder, for the French did their utmost to win them over, promising to pay £15 for every scalp of an Englishman!

Hardly a day passed but some unhappy family fell a victim to French bribery and savage cruelty. As for me, though now in comfortable circumstances, with an affectionate and amiable wife, it was not long before I suddenly became the most pitiable of mankind. I can never bear to think of the last time I saw my dear wife, on the fatal 2d of October, 1754. That day she had left home to visit some of her relations, and, no one being in the house but myself, I stayed up later than usual, expecting her return. How great was my terror when, at eleven o'clock at night, I heard the dismal warwhoop of the savages, and, flying to the window, saw a band of them outside, about twelve in number.

They made several attempts to get in, and I asked them what they wanted. They paid no attention, but went on beating at the door, trying to get it open. Then, having my gun loaded in my hand, I threatened them with death if they would not go away. But one of them, who could speak a little English, called out in return that if I did not come out they would burn me alive in the house. They told me further—what I had already found out—that they were no friends to the English, but that if I would surrender myself prisoner they would not kill me.

My horror was beyond all words. I could not depend on the promises of such creatures, but I must either accept their offer or be burned alive. Accordingly, I went out of my house with my gun in my hand, not knowing what I did or that I still held it. Immediately, like so many tigers, they rushed on me and disarmed me. Having me now completely in their power, the merciless villains bound me to a tree near the door, and then went into the house and plundered what they could. Numbers of things which they were unable to carry away were set fire to with the house and consumed before my eyes. Then they set fire to my barn, stable, and outhouses, where I had about two hundred bushels of wheat, and cows, sheep, and horses. My agony as I watched all this havoc it is impossible to describe.

When the terrible business was over, one of the monsters came to me, a tomahawk in his hand, threatening me with a cruel death if I would not consent to go with them. I was forced to agree, promising to do all that was in my power for them, and trusting to Providence to deliver me out of their hands. On this they untied me, and gave me a great load to carry on my back, under which I travelled all that night with them, full of the most terrible fear lest my unhappy wife should likewise have fallen into their clutches. At daybreak my master ordered me to lay down my load, tying my hands round a tree with a small cord. They then kindled a fire near the tree to which I was bound, which redoubled my agony, for I thought they were going to sacrifice me there.

When the fire was made, they danced round me after their manner, with all kinds of antics, whooping and crying out in the most horrible fashion. Then they took the burning coals and sticks, flaming with fire at the ends, and held them near my face, head, hands and feet, with fiendish delight, at the same time threatening to burn me entirely if I called out or made the least noise. So, tortured as I was, I could make no sign of distress but shedding silent tears, which, when they saw, they took fresh coals, and held them near my eyes, telling me my face was wet, and they would dry it for me. I have often wondered how I endured these tortures; but at last they were satisfied, and sat down round the fire and roasted the meat which they had brought from my dwelling!

When they had prepared it, they offered some to me, and though it may be imagined that I had not much heart to eat, I was forced to seem pleased, lest if I refused it they should again begin to torture me. What I could not eat I contrived to get between the bark and the tree—my foes having unbound my hands till they supposed I had eaten all they gave me. But then they bound me as before, and so I continued all day.

When the sun was set they put out the fire, and covered the ashes with leaves, as is their custom, that the white people may find no signs of their having been there.

Travelling thence, by the river, for about six miles, I being loaded heavily, we reached a spot near the Blue Hills, where the savages hid their plunder under logs of wood. Thence, shocking to relate, they went to a neighboring house, that of Jacob Snider, his wife, five children, and a young man, a servant. They soon forced their way into the unhappy man's dwelling, slew the whole family, and set fire to the house.

The servant's life was spared for a time, since they thought he might be of use to them, and forthwith loaded him with plunder. But he could not bear the cruel treatment that we suffered; and though I tried to console him with a hope of deliverance, he continued to sob and moan. One of the savages, seeing this, instantly came up, struck him to the ground, and slew him.

The family of John Adams next suffered. All were here put to death except Adams himself, a good old man, whom they loaded with plunder, and day after day continued to treat with the most shocking cruelty, painting him all over with various colors, plucking the white hairs from his beard, and telling him he was a fool for living so long, and many other tortures which he bore with wonderful composure, praying to God.

One night after he had been tortured, when he and I were sitting together, pitying each other's misfortunes, another party of Indians arrived, bringing twenty scalps and three prisoners, who gave us terrible accounts of what tragedies had passed in their parts, on which I cannot bear to dwell.

These three prisoners contrived to escape, but unhappily, not knowing the country, they were recaptured and brought back. They were then all put to death, with terrible tortures.

A great snow now falling, the savages began to be afraid that the white people would follow their tracks upon it and find out their skulking retreats, and this caused them to make their way to their winter quarters, about two hundred miles further from any plantations or English inhabitants. There, after a long and tedious journey, in which I was almost starved, I arrived with this villainous crew. The place where we had to stay, in their tongue, was called Alamingo, and there I found a number of wigwams full of Indian women and children. Dancing, singing, and shooting were their general amusements, and they told what successes they had had in their expeditions, in which I found myself part of their theme. The severity of the cold increasing, they stripped me of my own clothes and gave me what they usually wear themselves—a blanket, a piece of coarse cloth, and a pair of shoes made of deerskin.

The better sort of Indians have shirts of the finest linen they can get, and with these some wear ruffles, but they never put them on till they have painted them different colors, and do not take them off to wash, but wear them till they fall into pieces. They are very proud, and delight in trinkets, such as silver plates round their wrists and necks, with several strings of *wampum,* which is made of cotton, interwoven with pebbles, cockle-shells, etc. From their ears and noses they have rings and beads, which hang dangling an inch or two.

The hair of their heads is managed in different ways: some pluck out and destroy all except a lock hanging from the crown of the head, which they interweave with wampum and feathers. But the women wear it very long, twisted down their backs, with beads, feathers, and wampum, and on their heads they carry little coronets of brass or copper.

No people have a greater love of liberty or affection for their relations, yet they are the most revengeful race on earth, and inhumanly cruel. They generally avoid open fighting in war, yet they are brave when taken, enduring death or torture with wonderful courage. Nor would they at any time commit such outrages as they do if they were not tempted by drink and money by those who call themselves civilized.

At Alamingo I was kept nearly two months, till the snow was off the ground—a long time to be among such creatures! I was too far from any plantations or white people to try to escape; besides, the bitter cold made my limbs quite benumbed. But I contrived to defend myself more or less against the weather by building a little wigwam with the bark of the trees, covering it with earth, which made it resemble a cave, and keeping a good fire always near the door.

Seeing me outwardly submissive, the savages sometimes gave me a little meat, but my chief food was Indian corn.

Having liberty to go about was, indeed, more than I expected; but they knew well it was impossible for me to escape.

At length they prepared for another expedition against the planters and white people, but before they set out they were joined by many other Indians from Fort Duquesne, well stored with powder and ball that they had received from the French.

As soon as the snow was quite gone, so that no trace of their footsteps could be found, they set out on their journey toward Pennsylvania, to the number of nearly a hundred and fifty. Their wives and children were left behind in the wigwams. My duty was to carry whatever they intrusted to me; but they never gave me a gun. For several days we were almost famished for want of proper provisions: I had nothing but a few stalks of Indian corn, which I was glad to eat dry, and the Indians themselves did not fare much better.

When we again reached the Blue Hills, a council of war was held, and we agreed to divide into companies of about twenty men each, after which every captain marched with his party where he thought proper. I still belonged to my old masters, but was left behind on the mountains with ten Indians, to stay till the rest returned, as they did not think it safe to carry me nearer to the plantations.

Here being left, I began to meditate on my escape, for I knew the country round very well, having often hunted there. The third day after the great body of the Indians quitted us, my keepers visited the mountains in search of game, leaving me bound in such a way that I could not get free.

When they returned at night they unbound me, and we all sat down to supper together, feasting on two polecats which they had killed. Then, being greatly tired with their day's excursion, they lay down to rest as usual.

Seeing them apparently fast asleep, I tried different ways of finding out whether it was a pretence to see what I should do. But after making a noise and walking about, sometimes touching them with my feet, I found that they really slept. My heart exulted at the hope of freedom, but it sank again when I thought how easily I might be recaptured. I resolved, if possible, to get one of their guns, and if discovered to die in self-defence rather than be taken; and I tried several times to take one from under their heads, where they always secure them. But in vain; I could not have done so without rousing them.

So, trusting myself to the Divine protection, I set out defenceless. Such was my terror, however, that at first I halted every four or five yards, looking fearfully toward the spot where I had left the Indians, lest they should wake and miss me. But when I was about two hundred yards off I mended my pace and made all the haste I could to the foot of the mountains.

Suddenly I was struck with the greatest terror and dismay, hearing behind me the fearful cries and howlings of the savages, far worse than the roaring of lions or the shrieking of hyenas; and I knew that they had missed me. The more my dread increased, the faster I hurried, scarce knowing where I trod, sometimes falling and bruising myself, cutting my feet against the stones, yet, faint and maimed as I was, rushing on through the woods. I fled till daybreak, then crept into a hollow tree, where I lay concealed, thanking God for so far having favored my escape. I had nothing to eat but a little corn.

But my repose did not last long, for in a few

hours I heard the voices of the savages near the tree in which I was hid threatening me with what they would do if they caught me, which I already guessed too well. However, at last they left the spot where I heard them, and I stayed in my shelter the rest of that day without any fresh alarms.

At night I ventured out again, trembling at every bush I passed, and thinking each twig that touched me a savage. The next day I concealed myself in the same manner, and at night travelled forward, keeping off the main road, used by the Indians, as much as possible, which made my journey far longer, and more painful than I can express.

But how shall I describe my terror when, on the fourth night, a party of Indians lying round a small fire which I had not seen, hearing the rustling I made among the leaves, started from the ground, seizing their arms, and ran out into the wood? I did not know, in my agony of fear, whether to stand still or rush on. I expected nothing but a terrible death; but at that very moment a troop of swine made toward the place where the savages were. They, seeing the hogs, guessed that their alarm had been caused by them, and returned merrily to their fire and lay down to sleep again. As soon as this happened, I pursued my way more cautiously and silently, but in a cold perspiration of terror at the peril I had just escaped. Bruised, cut, and shaken, I still held on my path till break of day, when I lay down under a huge log, and slept undisturbed till noon. Then, getting up I climbed a great hill, and, scanning the country round, I saw, to my unspeakable joy, some habitations of white people, about ten miles distant.

My pleasure was somewhat damped by not being able to get among them that night. But they were too far off; therefore, when evening fell, I again commended myself to Heaven, and lay down, utterly exhausted. In the morning, as soon as I woke, I made toward the nearest of the cleared lands which I had seen the day before; and that afternoon I reached the house of John Bull, an old acquaintance.

I knocked at the door, and his wife, who opened it, seeing me in such a frightful condition, flew from me like lightning, screaming, into the house.

This alarmed the whole family, who immediately seized their arms, and I was soon greeted by the master with his gun in his hand. But when I made myself known—for at first he took me for an Indian—he and all his family welcomed me with great joy at finding me alive; since they had been told I was murdered by the savages some months ago.

No longer able to bear up, I fainted and fell to the ground. When they had recovered me, seeing my weak and famished state, they gave me some food, but let me at first partake of it very sparingly. Then for two days and nights they made me welcome, and did their utmost to bring back my strength, with the kindest hospitality. Finding myself once more able to ride, I borrowed a horse and some clothes of these good people, and set out for my father-in-law's house in Chester County, about a hundred and forty miles away. I reached it on January 4, 1755; but none of the family could believe their eyes when they saw me, having lost all hope on hearing that I had fallen a prey to the Indians.

They received me with great joy; but when I asked for my dear wife, I found she had been dead two months, and this fatal news greatly lessened the delight I felt at my deliverance.

THE PRISONER WHO WOULD NOT STAY IN PRISON

Anonymous

FEW people out of his own country would have heard of Baron Trenck had it not been for the wonderful skill and cunning with which he managed to cut through the stone walls and iron bars of all his many cages. He was born at Königsberg in Prussia in 1726, and entered the body-guard of Frederic II in 1742, when he was about sixteen. Trenck was a young man of good family, rich, well educated, and, according to his own account, fond of amusement. He confesses to having shirked his duties more than once for the sake of some pleasure, even after the War of Austrian Succession had broken out (September, 1744), and Frederic, strict though he was, had forgiven him. It is plain from this that the king must have considered that Trenck had been guilty of some deadly treachery toward him when after years he declined to par-

don him for crimes which after all the young man
had never committed.

Trenck's first confinement was in 1746, when he
was thrown into the Castle of Glatz, on a charge of
corresponding with his cousin and namesake, who
was in the service of the Empress Maria Theresa,
and of being an Austrian spy. At first he was
kindly treated and allowed to walk freely about the
fortifications, and he took advantage of the liberty
given him to arrange a plan of escape with one of
his fellow-prisoners. The plot was, however, betrayed by the other man, and a heavy punishment
fell on Trenck. By the king's orders, he was
promptly deprived of all his privileges and placed
in a cell in one of the towers, which overlooked the
ramparts lying ninety feet below, on the side nearest the town. This added a fresh difficulty to his
chances of escape, as, in passing from the castle to
the town, he was certain to be seen by many people.
But no obstacles mattered to Trenck. He had
money, and money could do a great deal. So he
began by bribing one of the officials about the
prison, and the official in his turn bribed a soap-
boiler, who lived not far from the castle gates, and
promised to conceal Trenck somewhere in his
house. Still, liberty must have seemed a long way
off, for Trenck had only one little knife with which
to cut through anything. By dint of incessant and
hard work, he managed to saw through three thick
steel bars, but even so, there were eight others left
to do. His friend the official then procured him a
file, but he was obliged to use it with great care,
lest the scraping sound should be heard by his

guards. Perhaps they wilfully closed their ears, for many of them were sorry for Trenck; but, at all events, the eleven bars were at last sawn through, and all that remained was to make a rope ladder. This he did by tearing his leather portmanteau into strips and plaiting them into a rope, and as this was not long enough, he added his sheets. The night was dark and rainy, which favored him, and he reached the bottom of the rampart in safety. Unluckily, he met here with an obstacle on which he had never counted. There was a large drain, opening into one of the trenches, which Trenck had neither seen nor heard of, and into this he fell. In spite of his struggles, he was held fast, and his strength being at last exhausted, he was forced to call the sentinel, and at midday, having been left in the drain for hours to make sport for the town, he was carried back to his cell.

Henceforth he was still more strictly watched than before, though, curiously enough, his money never seems to have been taken from him, and at this time he had about eighty louis left, which he always kept hidden. Eight days after his last attempt, Fouquet, the commandant of Glatz, who hated Trenck and all his family, sent a deputation consisting of the adjutant, an officer, and a certain Major Doo to speak to the unfortunate man and exhort him to patience and submission. Trenck entered into conversation with them for the purpose of throwing them off their guard, when suddenly he snatched away Doo's sword, rushed from his cell, knocked down the sentinel and lieutenant who were standing outside, and striking right and left at the soldiers who came flying to bar his progress, he dashed down the stairs and leaped from the ramparts. Though the height was great he fell into the fosse without injury, still grasping his sword. He scrambled quickly to his feet and jumped easily over the second rampart, which was much lower than the first, and then began to breathe freely, as he thought he was safe from being overtaken by the soldiers, who would have to come a long way round. At this moment, however, he saw a sentinel making for him, a short distance off, and he rushed for the palisades which divided the fortifications from the open country, from which the mountains and Bohemia were easily reached. In the act of scaling them, his foot was caught tight between the bars, and he was trapped till the sentinel came up, and after a sharp fight got him back to prison.

For some time poor Trenck was in a sad condition. In his struggle with the sentinel he had been wounded, while his right foot had got crushed in the palisades. Besides this, he was watched far more strictly than before, for an officer and two men remained always in his cell, and two sentinels were stationed outside. The reason of these precautions, of course, was to prevent his gaining over his guards singly, either by pity or bribery. His courage sank to its lowest ebb, as he was told on all sides that his imprisonment was for life, whereas long after he discovered the real truth, that the king's intention had been to keep him under arrest for a year only, and if he had had a little more patience, three weeks would have found him free.

His repeated attempts to escape naturally angered
Frederic, while on the other hand the king knew
nothing of the fact which excused Trenck's im-
patience—namely, the belief carefully instilled in
him by all around him that he was doomed to perpetual confinement.

It is impossible to describe in detail all the plans
made by Trenck to regain his freedom; first because they were endless, and secondly because several were nipped in the bud. Still, the unfortunate
man felt that as long as his money was not taken
from him his case was not hopeless, for the officers
in command were generally poor and in debt, and
were always sent to garrison work as a punishment.
After one wild effort to liberate all the prisoners in
the fortress, which was naturally discovered and
frustrated, Trenck made friends with an officer
named Schell, lately arrived at Glatz, who promised
not only his aid but his company in the new enterprise. As more money would be needed than
Trenck had in his possession, he contrived to apply
to his rich relations outside the prison, and by some
means—what we are not told—they managed to
convey a large sum to him. Suspicion, however,
got about that Trenck was on too familiar a footing
with the officers, and orders were given that his
door should always be kept locked. This occasioned
further delay, as false keys had secretly to be made
before anything else could be done.

Their flight was unexpectedly hastened by Schell
accidentally learning that he was in danger of
arrest. One night they crept unobserved through
the arsenal and over the inner palisade, but on

reaching the rampart they came face to face with two of the officers, and again a leap into the fosse was the only way of escape. Luckily, the wall at this point was not high, and Trenck arrived at the bottom without injury; but Schell was not so happy, and hurt his foot so badly that he called on his friend to kill him, and to make the best of his way alone. Trenck, however, declined to abandon him, and having dragged him over the outer palisade, took him on his back, and made for the frontier. Before they had gone five hundred yards, they heard the boom of the alarm guns from the fortress, while clearer still were the sounds of pursuit. As they knew that they would naturally be sought on the side toward Bohemia, they changed their course and pushed on to the river Neiss, at this season partly covered with ice. Trenck swam over slowly with his friend on his back, and found a boat on the other side. By means of this boat they evaded their enemies, and reached the mountains after some hours, very hungry, and almost frozen to death.

Here a new terror awaited them. Some peasants with whom they took refuge recognized Schell, and for a moment the fugitives gave themselves up for lost. But the peasants took pity on the two wretched objects, fed them and gave them shelter, till they could make up their minds what was best to be done. To their unspeakable dismay, they found that they were, after all, only seven miles from Glatz, and that in the neighboring town of Wunschelburg a hundred soldiers were quartered, with orders to capture all deserters from the fortress. This time, however, fortune favored the luckless Trenck, and though he and Schell were both in uniform, they rode unobserved through the village while the rest of the people were at church, and, skirting Wunschelburg, crossed the Bohemian frontier in the course of the day.

Then follows a period of comparative calm in Trenck's history. He travelled freely about Poland, Austria, Russia, Sweden, Denmark and Holland, and even ventured occasionally across the border into Prussia. Twelve years seem to have passed by in this manner, till, in 1758, his mother died, and Trenck asked leave of the council of war to go up to Dantzic to see his family and to arrange his affairs. Curiously enough, it appears never to have occurred to him that he was a deserter, and as such liable to be arrested at any moment. And this was what actually happened. By order of the king, Trenck was taken first to Berlin, where he was deprived of his money and some valuable rings, and then removed to Magdeburg, of which place Duke Ferdinand of Brunswick was the governor.

Here his quarters were worse than he had ever known them. His cell was only six feet by ten, and the window was high, with bars without as well as within. The wall was seven feet thick, and beyond it was a palisade, which rendered it impossible for the sentinels to approach the window. On the other side the prisoner was shut in by three doors, and his food (which was not only bad, but very scanty) was passed to him through an opening.

One thing only was in his favor. His cell was only entered once a week, so he could pursue any work to further his escape without much danger of being discovered. Notwithstanding the high window, the thick wall, and the palisade—notwithstanding, too, his want of money—he soon managed to open negotiations with the sentinels, and found, to his great joy, that the next cell was empty. If he could only contrive to burrow his way into that, he would be able to watch his opportunity to steal through the open door; once free, he could either swim the Elbe and cross into Saxony, which lay about six miles distant, or else float down the river in a boat till he was out of danger.

Small as the cell was, it contained a sort of cupboard, fixed into the floor by irons, and on these Trenck began to work. After frightful labor, he at last extracted the heavy nails which fastened the staples to the floor, and breaking off the heads (which he put back to avoid detection), he kept the rest to fashion for his own purposes. By this means he made instruments to raise the bricks.

On this side also the wall was seven feet thick, and formed of bricks and stones. Trenck numbered them as he went on with the greatest care, so that the cell might present its usual appearance before the Wednesday visit of his guards. To hide the joins, he scraped off some of the mortar, which he smeared over the place.

As may be supposed, all this took a very long time. He had nothing to work with but the tools he himself had made, which, of course, were very rough. But one day a friendly sentinel gave him a little iron rod and a small knife with a wooden handle. These were treasures indeed! And with their help he worked away for six months at his hole, as in some places the mortar had become so hard that it had to be pounded like a stone.

During this time he enlisted the compassion of some of the other sentinels, who not only described to him the lay of the country which he would have to traverse if he ever succeeded in getting out of prison, but interested in his behalf a Jewess named Esther Heymann, whose own father had been for two years a prisoner in Magdeburg. In this manner Trenck became the possessor of a file, a knife, and some writing paper, as the friendly Jewess had agreed to convey letters to some influential people, both at Vienna and Berlin, and also to his sister. But this step led to the ruin, not only of Trenck, but of several persons concerned, for they were betrayed by an imperial secretary of embassy called Weingarten, who was tempted by a bill for 20,000 florins. Many of those guilty of abetting Trenck in this fresh effort to escape were put to death, while his sister was ordered to build a new prison for him in the Fort de l'Etoile, and he himself was destined to pass nine more years in chains.

In spite of his fetters, Trenck was able in some miraculous way to get on with his hole, but his long labor was rendered useless by the circumstance that his new prison was finished sooner than he expected, and he was removed into it hastily, being only able to conceal his knife. He was now chained even more heavily than before, his two feet being attached to a heavy ring fixed in the wall, another ring being fastened round his body. From this ring was suspended a chain with a thick iron bar, two feet long at the bottom, and to this his hands were fastened. An iron collar was afterward added to his instruments of torture.

Besides torments of body, nothing was wanting which could work on his mind. His prison was built between the trenches of the principal rampart, and was of course very dark. It was likewise very damp, and, to crown all, the name of "Trenck" had been printed in red bricks on the wall, above a tomb whose place was indicated by a death's-head.

Here again, he tells us, he excited the pity of his guards, who gave him a bed and coverlet, and as much bread as he chose to eat; and, wonderful as it may seem, his health did not suffer from all these horrors. As soon as he got a little accustomed to his cramped position, he began to use the knife he had left, and to cut through his chains. He next burst the iron band, and after a long time severed his leg fetters, but in such a way that he could put them on again and no one be any the wiser. Nothing is more common in the history of prisoners than this exploit, and nothing is more astonishing, yet we meet with the fact again and again in their memoirs and biographies. Trenck at any rate appears to have accomplished the feat without much difficulty, though he found it very hard to get his hand back into his handcuffs. After he had disposed of his bonds, he began to saw at the doors leading to the gallery. These were four in number, and all of wood, but when he arrived at the fourth, his knife broke in two, and the courage that had upheld him for so many years gave away. He opened his veins and lay down to die, when in his despair he heard the voice of Gefhardt, the friendly sentinel from the other prison. Hearing of Trenck's sad plight, he scaled the palisade, and, we are told expressly, bound up his wounds, though we are *not* told how he managed to enter the cell. Be that as it may, the next day, when the guards came to open the door, they found Trenck ready to meet them, armed with a brick in one hand, and a knife, doubtless obtained from Gefhardt, in the other. The first man that approached him, he stretched wounded at his feet, and thinking it dangerous to irritate further a desperate man, they made a compromise with him. The governor took off his chains for a time, and gave him strong soup and fresh linen. Then, after a while, new doors were put to his cell, the inner door being lined with plates of iron, and he himself was fastened with stronger chains than those he had burst through.

For all this the watch must have been very lax, as Gefhardt soon contrived to open communication with him again, and letters were passed through the window (to which the prisoner had made a false and movable frame) and forwarded to Trenck's rich friends. His appeal was always answered promptly and amply. More valuable than money were two files, also procured from Gefhardt, and by their means the new chains were speedily cut through, though, as before, without any apparent break. Having freed his limbs, he began to saw through the floor of his cell, which was of wood. Underneath, instead of hard rock, there was sand. which Trenck scooped out with his hands. This earth was passed through the window to Gefhardt, who removed it when he was on guard, and gave his friend pistols, a bayonet, and knives to assist him when he had finally made his escape.

All seemed going smoothly. The foundations of the prison were only four feet deep, and Trenck's tunnel had reached a considerable distance when everything was again spoiled. A letter written by Trenck to Vienna fell into the hands of the governor, owing to some stupidity on the part of Gefhardt's wife, who had been intrusted to deliver it. The letter does not seem to have contained any special disclosure of his plan of escape, as the governor, who was still Duke Ferdinand of Brunswick, could find nothing wrong in Trenck's cell except the false window-frame. The cut chains, though examined, somehow escaped detection, from which we gather either that the officials were very careless, or the carpenter very stupid. Perhaps both may have been the case, for as the Seven Years' War (against Austria) was at this time raging, sentinels and officers were frequently changed, and prison discipline insensibly relaxed. Had this not been so, Trenck could never have been able to labor unseen, but as it was, he was merely deprived of his bed, as a punishment for tampering with the window.

As soon as he had recovered from his fright and an illness which followed, he returned to his digging.

It was necessary for him to bore under the subterranean gallery of the principal rampart, which was a distance of thirty-seven feet, and to get outside the foundation of the rampart. Beyond that was a door leading to the second rampart. Trenck was forced to work almost naked, for fear of raising the suspicions of the officials by his dirty clothes, but in spite of all his precautions and the wilful blindness of his guards, who as usual were on his side, all was at length discovered. His hole was filled up, and a year's work lost.

The next torture invented for him was worse than any that had gone before. He was visited and awakened every quarter of an hour, in order that he might not set to work in the night. This lasted for four years, during part of which time Trenck employed himself in writing verses and making drawings on his tin cups, after the manner of all prisoners, and in writing books with his blood, as ink was forbidden. We are again left in ignorance as to how he got paper. He also began to scoop out another hole, but was discovered afresh, though nothing particular seems to have been done to him, partly owing to the kindness of the new governor, who soon afterward died.

It had been arranged by his friends that for the space of one year horses should be ready for him at a certain place on the first and fifteenth of every month. Inspired by this thought, he turned to his burrowing with renewed vigor, and worked away at every moment when he thought he could do so unseen. One day, however, when he had reached some distance, he dislodged a large stone which blocked up the opening toward his cell. His terror was frightful. Not only was the air suffocating, and the darkness dreadful, but he knew that if any of the guards were unexpectedly to come into his cell, the opening must be discovered, and all his toil again lost. For eight hours he stayed in the tunnel paralyzed by fear. Then he roused himself, and by dint of superhuman struggles managed to open a passage on one side of the stone, and to reach his cell, which for once appeared to him as a haven of rest.

Soon after this the war ended with the Peace of Paris (1763), and Trenck's hopes of release seemed likely to be realized. He procured money from his friends, and bribed the Austrian ambassador in Berlin to open negotiations on his behalf, and while these were impending he rested from his labors for three whole months. Suddenly he was possessed by an idea which was little less than madness. He bribed a major to ask for a visit from Duke Ferdinand of Brunswick, again Governor of Magdeburg, offering to disclose his passage, and to reveal all his plans of escape, on condition that the duke would promise to plead for him with the king. This message never reached the duke himself, but some officers arrived ostensibly sent by him, but in reality tools of the major's. They listened to all he had to say, and saw all he had to show, then broke their word, filled up the passage, and redoubled the chains and the watch.

Notwithstanding this terrible blow, Trenck's trials were drawing to an end. Whether Frederic's heart was softened by his brilliant victories, or whether Trenck's influential friends succeeded in making themselves heard, we do not know, but six months later he was set free, on condition that he never tried to revenge himself on any one, and that he never again should cross the frontiers of Saxony or Prussia.

A WHITE BOY AMONG THE INDIANS, AS TOLD BY HIMSELF

By John Tanner

THE earliest event of my life which I distinctly remember (says John Tanner) is the death of my mother. This happened when I was two years old, and many of the attending circumstances made so deep an impression that they are still fresh in my memory. I cannot recollect the name of the settlement at which we lived, but I have since learned it was on the Kentucky River, at a considerable distance from the Ohio.

My father, whose name was John Tanner, was an emigrant from Virginia, and had been a clergyman.

When about to start one morning to a village at some distance, he gave, as it appeared, a strict charge to my sisters, Agatha and Lucy, to send me to school; but this they neglected to do until afternoon, and then, as the weather was rainy and unpleasant, I insisted on remaining at home. When my father returned at night, and found that I had been at home all day, he sent me for a parcel of small canes, and flogged me much more severely than I could suppose the offence merited. I was displeased with my sisters for attributing all the blame to me, when they had neglected even to tell me to go to school in the forenoon. From that time, my father's house was less like home to me, and I often thought and said, "I wish I could go and live among the Indians."

One day we went from Cincinnati to the mouth of the Big Miami, opposite which we were to settle. Here was some cleared land, and one or two log cabins, but they had been deserted on account of the Indians. My father rebuilt the cabins, and inclosed them with a strong picket. It was early in the spring when we arrived at the mouth of the Big Miami, and we were soon engaged in preparing a field to plant corn. I think it was not more than ten days after our arrival, when my father told us in the morning that, from the actions of the horses, he perceived there were Indians lurking about in the woods, and he said to me, "John, you must not go out of the house to-day." After giving strict charge to my stepmother to let none of the little children go out, he went to the field, with the negroes, and my elder brother, to sow corn.

Three little children, besides myself, were left in the house with my stepmother. To prevent me from going out, my stepmother required me to take care of the little child, then not more than a few months old; but as I soon became impatient of confinement I began to pinch my little brother, to make him cry. My mother, perceiving his uneasiness, told me to take him in my arms and walk about the house; I did so, but continued to pinch him. My mother at length took him from me to nurse him. I watched my opportunity and escaped into the yard;

thence through a small door in the large gate of the wall into the open field. There was a walnut-tree at some distance from the house, and near the side of the field where I had been in the habit of finding some of last year's nuts. To gain this tree without being seen by my father and those in the field, I had to use some precaution. I remember perfectly well having seen my father as I skulked toward to the tree; he stood in the middle of the field, with his gun in his hand, to watch for Indians, while the others were sowing corn. As I came near the tree, I thought to myself, "I wish I could see these Indians." I had partly filled with nuts a straw hat which I wore, when I heard a crackling noise behind me; I looked round, and saw the Indians; almost at the same instant, I was seized by both hands, and dragged off between two. One of them took my straw hat, emptied the nuts on the ground, and put it on my head. The Indians who seized me were an old and a young one; these, as I learned subsequently, were Manito-o-geezhik, and his son Kish-kau-ko.

After I saw myself firmly seized by both wrists by the two Indians, I was not conscious of anything that passed for a considerable time. I must have fainted, as I did not cry out, and I can remember nothing that happened to me until they threw me over a large log, which must have been at a considerable distance from the house. The old man I did not now see; I was dragged along between Kish-kau-ko and a very short thick man. I had probably made some resistance, or done something to irritate this latter, for he took me a little to one side, and drawing his tomahawk, motioned to me to look up. This I plainly understood, from the expression of his face, and his manner, to be a direction for me to look up for the last time, as he was about to kill me. I did as he directed, but Kish-kau-ko caught his hand as the tomahawk was descending, and prevented him from burying it in my brains. Loud talking ensued between the two. Kish-kau-ko presently raised a yell: the old man and four others answered it by a similar yell, and come running up. I have since understood that Kish-kau-ko complained to his father that the short man had made an attempt to kill his little brother, as he called me. The old chief, after reproving the short man, took me by one hand, and Kish-kau-ko took me by the other and thus they dragged me between them, the man who threatened to kill me, and who was now an object of terror to me, being kept at some distance. I could perceive, as I retarded them somewhat in their retreat, that they were apprehensive of being overtaken; some of them were always at some distance from us.

It was about one mile from my father's house to the place where they threw me into a hickory-bark canoe, which was concealed under the bushes, on the bank of the river. Into this they all seven jumped, and immediately crossed the Ohio, landing at the mouth of the Big Miami, and on the south side of that river. Here they abandoned their canoe, and stuck their paddles in the ground, so that they could be seen from the river. At a little distance in the woods they had some blankets and provisions concealed; they offered me some dry venison and bear's grease, but I could not eat. My father's house was plainly to be seen from the place where we stood; they pointed at it, looked at me, and laughed, but I have never known what they said.

After they had eaten a little, they began to ascend the Miami, dragging me along as before.

It must have been early in the spring when we arrived at Sau-ge-nong, for I can remember that at this time the leaves were small, and the Indians were about planting their corn. They managed to make me assist at their labors, partly by signs, and partly by the few words of English old Manito-o-geezhik could speak. After planting, they all left the village, and went out to hunt and dry meat. When they came to their hunting-grounds, they chose a place where many deer resorted, and here they began to build a long screen like a fence; this they made of green boughs and small trees. When they had built a part of it, they showed me how to remove the leaves and dry brush from that side of it to which the Indians were to come to shoot the deer. In this labor I was sometimes assisted by the squaws and children, but at other times I was left alone. It now began to be warm weather, and it happened one day that, having been left alone, as I was tired and thirsty, I fell asleep. I cannot tell how long I slept, but when I began to awake, I thought I heard someone crying a great way off. Then I tried to raise up my head, but could not. Being now more awake, I saw my Indian mother and sister standing by me, and perceived that my face and head were wet. The old woman and her daughter were crying bitterly, but it was some time before I perceived that my head was badly cut and bruised. It appears that, after I had fallen asleep, Manito-o-geezhik, passing that way, had perceived me, had tomahawked me, and thrown me in the bushes; and that when he came to his camp he had said to his wife, "Old woman, the boy I brought you is good for nothing; I have killed him; you will find him in such a place." The old woman and her daughter having found me, discovered still some signs of life, and had stood over me a long time, crying, and pouring cold water on my head, when I waked. In a few days I recovered in some measure from this hurt, and was again set to work at the screen, but I was more careful not to fall asleep; I endeavored to assist them at their labors, and to comply in all instances with their directions, but I was notwithstanding treated with great harshness, particularly by the old man and his two sons She-mung and Kwo-tash-e. While we remained at the hunting camp, one of them put a bridle in my hand, and pointing in a certain direction motioned me to go. I went accordingly, supposing he wished me to bring a horse: I went and caught the first I could find, and in this way I learned to discharge such services as they required of me.

I had been about two years at Sau-ge-nong, when a great council was called by the British agents at Mackinac. This council was attended by the Sioux, the Winnebagoes, the Menomonees, and many remote tribes, as well as by the Ojibbeways, Ottaw-waws, etc. When old Manito-o-geezhik returned from this council, I soon learned that he had met there his kinswoman, Net-no-kwa, who, notwith-standing her sex, was then regarded as principal chief of the Ottawwaws. This woman had lost her son, of about my age, by death; and, having heard of me, she wished to purchase me to supply his place. My old Indian mother, the Otter woman, when she heard of this, protested vehemently against it. I heard her say, "My son has been dead once, and has been restored to me; I cannot lose him again." But these remonstrances had little in-fluence when Net-no-kwa arrived with plenty of presents. She brought to the lodge first blankets, tobacco, and other articles of great value. She was perfectly acquainted with the dispositions of those with whom she had to negotiate. Objections were made to the exchange until a few more pres-ents completed the bargain, and I was transferred to Net-no-kwa. This woman, who was then ad-vanced in years, was of a more pleasing aspect than my former mother. She took me by the hand, after she had completed the negotiation with my former possessors, and led me to her own lodge, which stood near. Here I soon found I was to be treated more indulgently than I had been. She gave me plenty of food, put good clothes upon me, and told me to go and play with her own sons. We remained but a short time at Sau-ge-nong. She would not stop with me at Mackinac, which we passed in the night, but ran along at Point St. Ignace, where she hired some Indians to take care of me, while she returned to Mackinac by herself, or with one or two of her young men. After finishing her business at Mackinac, she returned, and, continuing on our journey, we arrived in a few days at Shab-a-wy-wy-a-gun.

The husband of Net-no-kwa was an Ojibbeway of Red River, called Taw-ga-we-ninne, the hunter. He was always indulgent and kind to me, treating me like an equal, rather than as a dependent. When speaking to me, he always called me his son. Indeed, he himself was but of secondary importance in the family, as everything belonged to Net-no-kwa, and she had the direction in all affairs of any moment. She imposed on me, for the first year, some tasks. She made me cut wood, bring home game, bring water, and perform other services not commonly required of boys of my age; but she treated me invariably with so much kindness that I was far more happy and content than I had been in the family of Manito-o-geezhik. She sometimes whipped me, as she did her own children: but I was not so severely and frequently beaten as I had been before.

Early in the spring, Net-no-kwa and her husband, with their family, started to go to Mackinac. They left me, as they had done before, at Point St. Ignace, as they would not run the risk of losing me by suffering me to be seen at Mackinac. On our return, after we had gone twenty-five or thirty miles from Point St. Ignace, we were detained by contrary winds at a place called Me-nau-ko-king, a point running out into the lake. Here we encamped with some other Indians, and a party of traders. Pigeons were very numerous in the woods, and the boys of my age, and the traders, were busy shooting them. I had never killed any game, and, indeed, had never in my life discharged a gun. My mother had purchased at Mackinac a keg of powder, which, as they thought it a little damp, was here spread out to dry. Taw-ga-we-ninne had a large horseman's pistol; and, finding myself somewhat emboldened by his indulgent manner toward me, I requested permission to go and try to kill some pigeons with the pistol. My request was seconded by Net-no-kwa, who said, "It is time for our son to begin to learn to be a hunter." Accordingly, my father, as I called Taw-ga-we-ninne, loaded the pistol and gave it to me, saying, "Go, my son, and if you kill anything with this, you shall immediately have a gun and learn to hunt." Since I have been a man, I have been placed in difficult stations; but my anxiety for success was never greater than in this, my first essay as a hunter. I had not gone far from the camp before I met with pigeons, and some of them alighted in the bushes very near me. I cocked my pistol, and raised it to my face, bringing the breech almost in contact with my nose. Having brought the sight to bear upon the pigeon, I pulled trigger, and was in the next instant sensible of a humming noise, like that of a stone sent swiftly through the air. I found the pistol at the distance of some paces behind me, and the pigeon under the tree on which he had been sitting. My face was much bruised, and covered with blood. I ran home, carrying my pigeon in triumph. My face was speedily bound up; my pistol exchanged for a fowling-piece; I was accoutred with a powder-horn, and furnished with shot, and allowed to go out after birds. One of the young Indians went with me, to observe my manner of shooting. I killed three more pigeons in the course of the afternoon, and did not discharge my gun once without killing. Henceforth I began to be treated with more consideration, and was allowed to hunt often, that I might become expert.

Game began to be scarce, and we all suffered from hunger. The chief man of our band was called As-sin-ne-boi-nainse (the Little Assinneboin), and he now proposed to us all to move, as the country where we were was exhausted. The day on which we were to commence our removal was fixed upon, but before it arrived our necessities became extreme. The evening before the day on which we intended to move my mother talked much of all our misfortunes and losses, as well as of the urgent distress under which we were then laboring. At the usual hour I went to sleep, as did all the younger part of the family; but I was wakened again by the loud praying and singing of the old woman, who continued her devotion through a great part of the night. Very early on the following morning she called us all to get up, and put on our moccasins, and be ready to move. She then called Wa-me-gon-a-biew to her, and said to him in rather a low voice: "My son, last night I sung and prayed to the Great Spirit, and when I slept there came to me one like a man, and said to me, 'Net-no-kwa, to-morrow you shall eat a bear. There is, at a distance from the path you are to travel to-morrow, and in such a direction' (which she described to him), 'a small round meadow, with something like a path leading from it; in that path there is a bear.'

Now, my son, I wish you to go to that place, without mentioning to any one what I have said, and you will certainly find the bear, as I have described to you." But the young man, who was not particularly dutiful, or apt to regard what his mother said, going out of the lodge, spoke sneeringly to the other Indians of the dream. "The old woman," said he, "tells me we are to eat a bear to-day; but I do not know who is to kill it." The old woman, hearing him, called him in, and reproved him; but she could not prevail upon him to go to hunt.

I had my gun with me, and I continued to think of the conversation I had heard between my mother and Wa-me-gon-a-biew respecting her dream. At length I resolved to go in search of the place she had spoken of, and without mentioning to any one my design, I loaded my gun as for a bear, and set off on our back track. I soon met a woman belonging to one of the brothers of Taw-ga-we-ninne, and of course my aunt. This woman had shown little friendship for us, considering us as a burden upon her husband, who sometimes gave something for our support; she had also often ridiculed me. She asked me immediately what I was doing on the path, and whether I expected to kill Indians, that I came there with my gun. I made her no answer; and thinking I must be not far from the place where my mother had told Wa-me-gon-a-biew to leave the path, I turned off, continuing carefully to regard all the directions she had given. At length I found what appeared at some former time to have been a pond. It was a small, round, open place in the woods, now grown up with grass and small bushes. This I thought must be the meadow my mother had spoken of; and examining around it, I came to an open space in the bushes, where, it is probable, a small brook ran from the meadow; but the snow was now so deep that I could see nothing of it. My mother had mentioned that, when she saw the bear in her dream, she had, at the same time, seen a smoke rising from the ground. I was confident this was the place she had indicated, and I watched long, expecting to see the smoke; but, wearied at length with waiting, I walked a few paces into the open place, resembling a path, when I unexpectedly fell up to my middle in the snow. I extricated myself without difficulty, and walked on; but, remembering that I had heard the Indians speak of killing bears in their holes, it occurred to me that it might be a bear's hole into which I had fallen and, looking down into it, I saw the head of a bear lying close to the bottom of the hole. I placed the muzzle of my gun nearly between his eyes and discharged it. As soon as the smoke cleared away, I took a piece of stick and thrust it into the eyes and into the wound in the head of the bear, and, being satisfied that he was dead, I endeavored to lift him out of the hole; but being unable to do this, I returned home, following the track I had made in coming out. As I came near the camp, where the squaws had by this time set up the lodges, I met the same woman I had seen in going out, and she immediately began again to ridicule me. "Have you killed a bear, that you come back so soon, and walk so fast?" I thought to myself, "How does she know that I have killed a bear?" But I passed by her without saying anything, and went into my mother's lodge. After a few minutes, the old woman said, "My son, look in that kettle, and you will find a mouthful of beaver meat, which a man gave me since you left us in the morning. You must leave half of it for Wame-gon-a-biew, who has not yet returned from hunting, and has eaten nothing to-day." I accordingly ate the beaver meat, and when I had finished it, observing an opportunity when she stood by herself, I stepped up to her, and whispered in her ear, "My mother, I have killed a bear." "What do you say, my son?" said she. "I have killed a bear." "Are you sure you have killed him?" "Yes." "Is he quite dead?" "Yes." She watched my face for a moment, and then caught me in her arms, hugging and kissing me with great earnestness, and for a long time. I then told her what my aunt had said to me, both going and returning, and this being told to her husband when he returned, he not only reproved her for it, but gave her a severe flogging. The bear was sent for, and, as being the first I had killed, was cooked all together, and the hunters of the whole band invited to feast with us, according to the custom of the Indians. The same day one of the Crees killed a bear and a moose, and gave a large share of the meat to my mother.

One winter I hunted for a trader called by the Indians Aneeb, which means an elm tree. As the winter advanced, and the weather became more and more cold, I found it difficult to procure as much game as I had been in the habit of supplying, and as was wanted by the trader. Early one morning, about mid-winter, I started an elk. I pursued until night, and had almost overtaken him; but hope and strength failed me at the same time. What clothing I had on me, notwithstanding the extreme coldness of the weather, was drenched with sweat. It was not long after I turned toward home that I felt it stiffening about me. My leggings were of cloth, and were torn in pieces in running through the bush. I was conscious I was somewhat frozen before I arrived at the place where I had left our lodge standing in the morning, and it was now midnight. I knew it had been the old woman's intention to move, and I knew where she would go; but I had not been informed she would go on that day. As I followed on their path, I soon ceased to suffer from cold, and felt that sleepy sensation which I knew preceded the last stage of weakness in such as die of cold. I redoubled my efforts, but with an entire consciousness of the danger of my situation; it was with no small difficulty that I could prevent myself from lying down. At length I lost all consciousness for some time, how long I cannot tell, and, awaking as from a dream, I found I had been walking round and round in a small circle not more than twenty or twenty-five yards over. After the return of my senses, I looked about to try to discover my path, as I had missed it; but, while I was looking, I discovered a light at a distance, by which I directed my course. Once more, before I reached the lodge, I lost my senses; but I did not fall down; if I had, I should never have gotten up again; but I ran round and round in a circle as before. When I at last came into the lodge, I immediately fell down, but I did not lose myself as before. I can remember seeing the thick and sparkling coat of frost on the inside of the pukkwi lodge, and hearing my mother say that she had kept a large fire in expectation of my arrival; and that she had not thought I should have been so long gone in the morning, but that I should have known long before night of her having moved. It was a month before I was able to go out again, my face, hands, and legs having been much frozen.

After many dangerous and disagreeable experiences, John Tanner, when almost an old man, came back to the whites to tell his history, which, as he could not write, was taken down at his dictation.

EVANGELINE OF ACADIA

By Henry W. Longfellow

MORE than two hundred years ago there lived in Acadia, as Nova Scotia was then called, a beautiful maiden named Evangeline. Benedict Bellefontaine, Evangeline's father, was the wealthiest farmer in the neighborhood. His goodly acres were somewhat apart from the little village of Grand-Pré, but near enough for Evangeline not to feel lonely.

The people of Grand-Pré were simple and kindly, and dwelt together in the love of God and man. They had neither locks to their doors nor bars to their windows; visitors were always welcome, and all gave of their best to whoever might come.

The house of Benedict Bellefontaine, firmly builded with rafters of oak, was on a hill commanding the sea. The barns stood toward the north, shielding the house from storms. They were bursting with hay and corn, and were so numerous as to form almost a village by themselves. The horses, the cattle, the sheep and the poultry were all well-fed and well cared for. At Benedict Bellefontaine's there was comfort and plenty. The men and the maids never grumbled. All men were equal, all were brothers and sisters. In Acadia the richest man was poor, but the poorest lived in abundance.

Evangeline was her father's housekeeper; her mother was dead. Benedict was seventy years old, but he was hale and hearty and managed his prosperous farm himself. His hair was as white as snow and his face was as brown as oak leaves. Evangeline's hair was dark brown and her eyes were black. She was the loveliest girl in Grand-Pré and many a lad was in love with her.

Among all Evangeline's suitors only one was welcome, and he was Gabriel Lajeunesse, son of Basil the blacksmith. Gabriel and Evangeline had grown up together like brother and sister. The priest had taught them their letters out of the self-same book, and together they had learned their hymns and their verses. Together they had watched Basil at his forge and with wondering eyes had seen him handle the hoof of a horse as easily as a plaything, taking it into his lap and nailing on the shoe. Together they had ridden on sledges in winter and hunted birds' nests in summer, seeking eagerly that marvellous stone which the swallow is said to bring from the shore of the sea to restore the sight of its fledglings. Lucky is he who finds that stone!

And now they were man and woman. Benedict and Basil were old friends and they desired the marriage of the children. They were ready to marry. The young men of the village had built them a house and a barn. The barn was filled with hay and the house was stored with food enough to last a year.

One beautiful evening in Indian summer Evangeline and Gabriel were betrothed.

Benedict was sitting in-doors by the wide-mouthed fireplace singing fragments of songs such as his fathers before him had sung in their orchards in sunny France, and Evangeline was close beside him at her wheel industriously spinning flax for her loom. Up-stairs there was a chest filled with strong white linen which Evangeline would take to her new home. Every thread of it had been spun and woven by the maiden.

As they sat by the fireside, footsteps were heard, and the wooden latch was suddenly lifted. Benedict knew by the hob-nailed shoes that it was Basil the blacksmith, and Evangeline knew by her beating heart that Gabriel was with him.

"Welcome," said Benedict the farmer, "welcome, Basil, my friend. Come and take thy place on the settle close by the chimney-side. Take thy pipe and the box of tobacco from the shelf overhead. Never art thou so much thyself as when through the curling smoke of the pipe or the forge thy friendly and jovial face gleams as round and red as the harvest moon through the mist of the marshes."

"Benedict Bellefontaine, thou art always joking. Thou art cheerful even when others are grave and anxious," answered Basil.

He paused to take the pipe which Evangeline was handing him, and lighted it with a coal from the embers.

"For four days the English ships have ridden at their anchors in the Gaspereau's mouth, and their cannon are pointed against us. What they are here for we do not know, but we are all commanded to meet in church to-morrow to hear his Majesty's will proclaimed as law in the land. Alas! in the meantime the hearts of the people are full of fears of evil," continued the blacksmith.

"Perhaps some friendly purpose brings these ships to our shores," replied the farmer. "Perhaps the harvests in England have been blighted and they have come to buy our grain and hay."

"The people in the village do not think so," said Basil, gravely shaking his head. "They remember that the English are our enemies. Some have fled already to the forest, and lurk on its outskirts waiting anxiously to hear to-morrow's news. If the news is not to be bad why have our weapons been taken from us? Only the blacksmith's sledge and the scythes of the mowers have been left."

"We are safer unarmed," answered the cheerful farmer, who, as usual made the best of everything. "What can harm us here in the midst of our flocks and our corn-fields? Fear no evil, my friend, and above all, may no shadow fall on this house and hearth to-night. It is the night of the contract. René Leblanc will be here presently with his papers and inkhorn. Shall we not be glad and rejoice in the happiness of our children?"

Evangeline and her lover were standing by the window. They heard the words of the farmer and the maiden blushed. Hardly had he spoken when the worthy notary entered the room.

René Leblanc was bent with age. His hair was yellow, his forehead was high, and he looked very wise, with his great spectacles sitting astride on his nose. He was the father of twenty children, and more than a hundred grandchildren rode on his knee. All children loved him for he could tell them wonderful fairy tales and strange stories of the forest. He told them of the goblins that came at night to water the horses, of how the oxen talked in their stalls on Christmas Eve, of how a spider shut up in a nutshell could cure the fever, and of the marvellous powers possessed by horse shoes and four-leaved clover. He knew more strange things than twenty other men.

As soon as Basil saw the notary he asked him about the English ships.

"Father Leblanc, thou hast heard the talk of the village. Perhaps, thou canst tell us something about the ships and their errand."

"I have heard enough talk," answered the notary, "but I am none the wiser. Yet I am not one of those who think that the ships are here to do us evil. We are at peace and, why then, should they harm us?"

"Must we in all things look for the how and the why and wherefore?" shouted the hasty and somewhat excitable blacksmith. "Injustice is often done and might is the right of the strongest."

"Man is unjust," replied the notary, "but God is just, and finally justice triumphs. I remember a story that has often consoled me when things have seemed to be going wrong.

"Once in an ancient city, whose name I have forgotten, there stood high on a marble column, in the public square, a brazen statue of Justice holding her scales in her left hand and a sword in her right. This meant that justice reigned over the land and in the hearts and homes of the people. Yet in the course of time the laws of the land were corrupted and might took the place of right, the weak were oppressed, and the mighty ruled with a rod of iron. By and by, birds built their nests in the scales of Justice; they were not afraid of the sword that flashed in the sunshine above them.

"It happened that in the palace of a wealthy nobleman a necklace of pearls disappeared. Suspicion fell on a poor orphan girl, who was arrested and sentenced to be hanged right at the foot of the statue of Justice.

"The girl was put to death, but as her innocent spirit ascended to heaven a great storm arose and lightning struck the statue, angrily hurling the scales from the left hand of the figure of Justice. They fell to the pavement with a clatter and in one of the shattered nests was found the pearl necklace.

It had been stolen by a magpie who had cunningly woven the string of pearls into the clay wall of her babies' cradle. So the poor girl was proven innocent and the people of that city were taught to be more careful of justice."

This story silenced the blacksmith but did not drive away his forebodings of evil. Evangeline lighted the brazen lamp on the table and filled the great pewter tankard with home-brewed nut brown ale. The notary drew from his pocket his papers and his inkhorn and began to write the contract of marriage. In spite of his age his hand was steady. He set down the names and the ages of the parties and the amount of Evangeline's dowry in flocks of sheep and in cattle. All was done in accordance with the law and the paper was signed and sealed. Benedict took from his leathern pouch three times the notary's fee in solid pieces of silver. The old man arose and blessed the bride and the bridegroom, and then lifted aloft the tankard of ale and drank to their health. Then wiping the foam from his lip, he bowed solemnly and went away.

The others sat quietly by the fireside until Evangeline brought the draught-board to her father and Basil and arranged the pieces for them. They were soon deep in the game, while Evangeline and her lover sat apart in the embrasure of a window and whispered together as they watched the moon rise over the sea. Their hearts were full of happiness as they looked into the future, believing that they would be together.

At nine o'clock the guests rose to depart, but Gabriel lingered on the doorstep with many farewell words and sweet good-nights. When he was gone Evangeline carefully covered the fire and noiselessly followed her father up-stairs. Out in the orchard Gabriel waited and watched for the gleam of her lamp and her shadow as she moved about behind her snowy curtains. She did not know that he was so near, yet her thoughts were of him.

The next day the betrothal feast was held in Benedict's house and the orchard. There were good Benedict and sturdy Basil the blacksmith and there were the priest and the notary. Beautiful Evangeline welcomed the guests with a smiling face and words of gladness. Then Michael the fiddler took a seat under the trees and he sang and played for the company to dance, sometimes beating time to the music with his wooden shoes.

Merrily, merrily whirled the dancers, old and young together, and the children among them. Fairest of all the maidens was Evangeline, and Gabriel was the noblest of all the youths.

So the morning passed away. A loud summons sounded from the church tower and from the drums of the soldiers. The men thronged to the church leaving the women outside in the church yard.

The church doors were closed, and the crowd silently awaited the will of the soldiers. Then the commander arose and spoke from the steps of the altar.

How dreadful were the words spoken from that holy place! The lands and dwellings and the cattle of all kinds, of the people were to be given up to the

King of England whom they had to obey for he had conquered the French. They were to be driven from their homes and Englishmen were to be allowed to take possession of Acadia.

The commander declared the men prisoners, but overcome with sorrow and anger, they rushed to the door-way. Basil, the hot-headed blacksmith, cried out, "Down with the tyrants of England!" but a soldier struck him on the mouth and dragged him down to the pavement.

Then Father Felician, the priest, spoke to his people and tried to quiet them. His words were few, but they sank deep in the hearts of his flock.

"O Father, forgive them," they cried, as the crucified Christ had cried centuries before them.

The evening service followed and the people fell on their knees and were comforted.

Evangeline waited for her father at his door. She had set the table and his supper was ready for him. On the white cloth were the wheaten bread, the fragrant honey, the tankard of ale, and fresh cheese just brought from the dairy, but Benedict did not come. At last the girl went back to the church and called aloud the names of her father and Gabriel. There was no answer. Back to the empty house she went, feeling desolate. It began to rain; then the lightning flashed and it thundered, but Evangeline was not frightened, for she remembered that God was in Heaven and that He governs the world that He created. She thought of the story that she had heard the night before of the justice of Heaven and, trusting in God, she went to bed and slept peacefully until morning.

The men were kept prisoners in the church for four days and nights. On the fifth day the women and the children were bidden to take their household goods to the seashore and there they were joined by the long-imprisoned but patient Acadian farmers.

When Evangeline saw Gabriel she ran to him and whispered, "Gabriel, be of good cheer, for if we love each other nothing can harm us, whatever mischances may happen."

Then she saw her father. He was sadly changed; the fire was gone from his eyes and his footstep was heavy and slow. With a full heart she embraced him, feeling that words of comfort would do no good.

The Acadians were hurried on board the ships and in the confusion families were separated. Mothers were torn from their children and wives from their husbands. Basil was put on one ship and Gabriel on another, while Evangeline stood on the shore with her father. When night came not half the work of embarking was done. The people on shore camped on the beach in the midst of their household goods and their wagons.

None could escape, for the soldiers were watching them.

The priest moved about in the moonlight trying to comfort the people. He laid his hand on Evangeline's head and blessed her. Suddenly columns of shining smoke arose and flashes of flame were seen in the direction of Grand-Pré. The village was on fire. The people felt that they could never return to their homes and their hearts were swelled with anguish. Evangeline and the priest turned to Benedict. He was motionless, his soul had gone to Heaven.

There on the beach, with the light of the burning village for a torch, they buried the farmer of Grand-Pré, and the priest repeated the burial service to the accompaniment of the roaring sea.

In the morning the work of embarking was finished and toward night the ships sailed out of the harbor leaving the dead on the shore and the village in ruins.

The Acadians were scattered all over the land from north to south and from the bleak shores of the ocean even to the banks of the Mississippi River. Evangeline wandered from place to place looking for Gabriel Lajeunesse, and Gabriel sought Evangeline as earnestly. Sometimes they heard of one another but through long years they never met.

Evangeline was growing old and her hair showed faint streaks of gray when at last she made her home in Philadelphia. She became a Sister of Mercy and by day and by night ministered to the sick and the dying.

A pestilence fell on the city, carrying away rich and poor alike.

Evangeline lovingly tended the very poorest, and each day she went to the almshouse on her errand of mercy.

On morning she came to a pallet on which lay an old man, thin and gray. As she looked at him his face seemed to assume the form of earlier manhood. With a cry she fell on her knees.

"Gabriel, my beloved!"

JABEZ ROCKWELL

The old man heard the voice and it carried him back to the home of his childhood, to happiness and Evangeline. He opened his eyes. Evangeline was kneeling beside him. At last they were together.

JABEZ ROCKWELL'S POWDER-HORN

By Ralph D. Paine

"POOH, you are not tall enough to carry a musket! Go with the drums, and tootle on the fife you blew at the Battle of Saratoga. Away with you, little Jabez, crying for a powder-horn when grown men like me have not a pouch amongst them for a single charge of powder!"

A tall, gaunt Vermonter, whose uniform was a woolen bedcover draped to his knees, laughed loudly from the doorway of his log hut as he flung these taunts at the stripling soldier.

A little way down the snowy street of these rude cabins a group of ragged comrades was crowding at the heels of a man who hugged a leather apron to his chest with both arms. Jabez Rockwell was in hot haste to join the chase; nevertheless he halted to cry back at his critic:

"It's a lie! I put my fife in my pocket at Saratoga, and I fought with a musket as long and ugly as yourself. And a redcoat shot me through the arm. If the camp butcher has powder-horns to give away, I deserve one more than those raw militia recruits, so wait until you are a veteran of the Connecticut line before you laugh at us old soldiers."

The youngster stooped to tighten the clumsy wrappings of rags which served him for shoes, and hurried on after the little, shouting mob which had followed the butcher down to the steep hillside of Valley Forge, where he stood at bay with his back to the cliff.

"There are thirty of you desperate villains," puffed the fat fugitive, "and I have only ten horns, which have been saved from the choicest of all the cattle I've killed these two months gone. I would I had my maul and skinning-knife here to defend myself. Take me to headquarters, if there is no other way to end this riot. I want no pay for the horns. They are my gift to the troops, but, Heaven help me! who is to decide how to divide them amongst so many?"

"Stand him on his bald head, and loose the horns from the apron. As they fall, he who finds keeps!" roared one of the boisterous party.

"Toss them all in the air and let us fight for them," was another suggestion.

The hapless butcher glared round him with growing dismay.

At this rate half the American army would soon be clamoring round him, drawn by the chance to add to their poor equipment.

By this time Jabez Rockwell had wriggled under the arms of the shouting soldiers, twisting like an uncommonly active eel, until he was close to the red-faced butcher. With ready wit the youngster piped up a plan for breaking the deadlock:

"There are thirty of us, you say, that put you to rout, Master Ritter. Let us divide the ten horns by lot. Then you can return to your cow-pens with a whole skin and a clean conscience."

"There is more sense in that little carcass of yours than in all those big, hulking troopers, that could spit you on a bayonet like a sparrow!" rumbled Master Ritter. "How shall the lots be drawn?"

"Away with your lottery!" cried a burly rifleman, whose long hunting-shirt whipped in the bitter wind. "The road up the valley is well beaten down. The old forge is half a mile away. Do you mark a line, old beef-killing Jack, and we will run for our lives. The first ten to touch the stone wall of the smithy will take the ten prizes."

Some yelled approval, others fiercely opposed, and the wrangling was louder than before. Master Ritter, who had plucked up heart, began to steal warily from the hillside, hoping to escape in the confusion.

A dozen hands clutched his collar and leather apron, and jerked him headlong back into the argument.

Young Jabez scrambled to the top of the nearest boulder, and ruffled with importance like a turkey-cock as he waved his arms to command attention.

"The guard will be turned out and we shall end this fray by cooling our heels in the prison huts on the hill," he declaimed. "If we run a foot-race, who is to say which of us first reaches the forge? Again—and I say I never served with such thick-witted troops when I fought under General Arnold at Saratoga—those with shoes to their feet have the advantage over those that are bound up in bits

319

of cloth and clumsy patches of hide. Draw lots, I say, before the picket is down upon us!"

The good-natured crowd cheered the boy orator, and hauled him from his perch with such hearty thumps that he feared they would break him in two.

Suddenly the noise was hushed as if the wranglers had been stricken dumb. Fur-capped heads turned to face down the winding valley, and without need of an order, the company spread itself along the roadside in a rude, uneven line. Every man stood at attention, his head up, his shoulders thrown back, hands at his sides. Thus they stood while they watched a little group of horsemen trot toward them.

In front rode a commanding figure in buff and blue. The tall, lithe frame sat the saddle with the graceful ease of the hard-riding Virginia fox-hunter. The stern, smooth-shaven face, reddened and roughened by exposure to all weathers, lighted with an amiable curiosity at sight of this motley and expectant party, the central figure of which was the butcher, Master Ritter, who had dropped to his knees, as if praying for his life.

General Washington turned to a sprightly-looking, red-haired youth who rode at his side, as if calling his attention to this singular tableau. The Marquis de Lafayette shrugged his shoulders after the French manner, and said, laughingly:

"It ees vat you t'ink? Vill they make ready to kill 'im? Vat they do?"

Just behind them pounded General Mühlenberg, the clergyman who had doffed his gown for the uniform of a brigadier, stalwart, swarthy, laughter in his piercing eyes as he commented:

"To the rescue! The victim is a worthy member of my old Pennsylvania flock. This doth savor of a soldier's court martial for honest Jacob Ritter."

The cavalcade halted, and the soldiers saluted, tongue-tied and embarrassed, scuffling, and prodding one another's ribs in an attempt to urge a spokesman forward, while General Washington gazed down at them as if demanding an explanation.

The butcher was about to make a stammering attempt when the string of his apron parted, and the ten cow-horns were scattered in the snow. He dived in pursuit of them, and his speech was never made.

Because Jabez Rockwell was too light and slender to make much resistance, he was first to be pushed into the foreground, and found himself nearest the commander-in-chief. He made the best of a bad matter, and his frank young face flushed hotly as he doffed his battered cap and bowed low.

"May it please the general, we were in a good-natured dispute touching the matter of those ten cow-horns which the butcher brought amongst us to his peril. There are more muskets than pouches in our street, and we are debating a fair way to divide them. It is—it is exceedingly bold, sir, but dare we ask you to suggest a way out of the trouble which preys sorely on the butcher's mind and body?"

A fleeting frown troubled the noble face of the chief, and his mouth twitched, not with anger but in pain, for the incident brought home to him **anew** that his soldiers, these brave, cheerful, half-clothed, freezing followers were without even the simplest tools of warfare.

The cloud cleared and he smiled, such a proud, affectionate smile as a father shows to sons of his who have deemed no sacrifice too great for duty's sake. His eyes softened as he looked down at the straight stripling at his bridle-rein, and replied:

"You have asked my advice as a third party, and it is meet that I share in the distribution. Follow me to the nearest hut."

His officers wheeled and rode after him, while the bewildered soldiers trailed behind, two and two, down the narrow road, greatly wondering whether reward or punishment was to be their lot.

As for Jabez Rockwell, he strode proudly in the van as guide to the log cabin, and felt his heart flutter as he jumped to the head of the charger, while the general dismounted with the agility of a boy.

Turning to the soldiers, who hung abashed in the road, Washington called:

"Come in, as many of you as can find room!"

The company filled the hut, and made room for those behind by climbing into the tiers of bunks filled with boughs to soften the rough-hewn planks.

In one corner a wood-fire smoldered in a rough stone fireplace, whose smoke made even the general cough and sneeze. He stood behind a bench of barked logs, and took from his pocket a folded document. Then he picked up from the hearth a bit of charcoal, and announced:

"I will write down a number between fifteen hun-

THE PEOPLE OF GRAND-PRÉ DWELT TOGETHER
IN THE LOVE OF GOD AND MAN
—page 306
From the drawing by Frank Dicksee A. R. A.

dred and two thousand, and the ten that guess nearest this number shall be declared the winners of the ten horns."

He carefully tore the document into strips, and then into small squares, which were passed along the delighted audience. There was a busy whispering and scratching of heads. Over in one corner, jammed against the wall until he gasped for breath, Jabez Rockwell said to himself:

"I must guess shrewdly. Methinks he will choose a number half-way between fifteen hundred and two thousand. I will write down seventeen hundred and fifty. But, stay! Seventeen seventy-six may come first into his mind, the glorious year when the independence of the colonies was declared. But he will surely take it that we, too, are thinking of that number, wherefore I will pass it by."

As if reading his thoughts, a comrade curled up in a bunk at Rockwell's elbow muttered, "Seventeen seventy-six, I haven't a doubt of it!"

Alas for the cunning surmise of Jabez, the chief did write down the Independence year, "1776," and when this verdict was read aloud the boy felt deep disappointment. This was turned to joy, however, when his guess of "1750" was found to be among the ten nearest the fateful choice, and one of the powder-horns fell to him.

The soldiers pressed back to make way for General Washington as he went out of the hut, stooping low that his head might escape the roof-beams. Before the party mounted, the boyish Lafayette swung his hat round his head and shouted:

"A huzza for ze wise general!"

The soldiers cheered lustily, and General Mühlenberg followed with:

"Now a cheer for the Declaration of Independence and for the soldier who wrote down 'Seventeen seventy-six.'"

General Washington bowed in his saddle, and the shouting followed his clattering train up the valley on his daily tour of inspection. He left behind him a new-fledged hero in the person of Jabez Rockwell, whose bold tactics had won him a powder-horn and given his comrades the rarest hour of the dreary winter at Valley Forge.

In his leisure time he scraped and polished the horn, fitted it with a wooden stopper and cord, and with greatest care and labor scratched upon its gleaming surface these words:

Jabez Rockwell, Ridgeway, Conn.—His Horn.
Made in Camp at Valley Forge.

Thin and pale, but with unbroken spirit, this sixteen-year-old veteran drilled and marched and braved picket duty in zero weather, often without a scrap of meat to brace his ration for a week on end; but he survived with no worse damage than sundry frost-bites. In early spring he was assigned to duty as a sentinel of the company which guarded the path that led up the hill to the headquarters of the commander-in-chief. Here he learned much to make the condition of his comrades seem more hopeless and forlorn than ever.

Hard-riding scouting parties came into camp with reports of forays as far as the suburbs of

Philadelphia, twenty miles away. Spies, disguised as farmers, returned with stories of visits into the heart of the capital city held by the enemy. This gossip and information, which the young sentinel picked up bit by bit, he pieced together to make a picture of an invincible, veteran British army, waiting to fall upon the huddled mob of "rebels" at Valley Forge, and sweep them away like chaff. He heard it over and over again, that the Hessians, with their tall and gleaming brass hats and fierce mustaches, "were dreadful to look upon," that the British Grenadiers, who tramped the Philadelphia streets in legions, "were like moving ranks of stone wall."

Then Jabez would look out across the valley, and perhaps see an American regiment at drill, without uniforms, ranks half-filled, looking like an array of scarecrows. His heart would sink, despite his memories of Saratoga; and in such dark hours he could not believe it possible even for General Washington to win a battle in the coming summer campaign.

It was on a bright day of June that Capt. Allan McLane, the leader of scouts, galloped past the huts of the sentinels, and shouted as he rode:

"The British have marched out of Philadelphia! I have just cut my way through their skirmishers over in New Jersey!"

A little later orderlies were buzzing out of the old stone house at headquarters like bees from a hive, with orders for the troops to be ready to march. As Jabez Rockwell hurried to rejoin his regiment, men were shouting the glad news along the green valley, with songs and cheers and laughter. They fell in as a fighting army, and left behind them the tragic story of their winter at Valley Forge, as the trailing columns swept beyond the Schuylkill into the wide and smiling farm lands of Pennsylvania.

Summer heat now blistered the dusty faces that had been for so long blue and pinched with hunger and cold. A week of glad marching and full rations carried Washington's awakened army into New Jersey, by which time the troops knew their chief was leading them to block the British retreat from Philadelphia.

Jabez Rockwell, marching with the Connecticut Brigade, had forgotten his fears of the brass-capped Hessians and the stone-wall Grenadiers. One night they camped near Monmouth village, and scouts brought in the tidings that the British were within sight. In the long summer twilight Jabez climbed a little knoll hard by, and caught a glimpse of the white tents of the Queen's Rangers, hardly beyond musket-shot. Before daybreak a rattle of firing woke him, and he scrambled out to find that the pickets were already exchanging shots.

He picked up his old musket, and chewing a hunk of dry bread for breakfast, joined his company drawn up in a pasture. Knapsacks were piled near Freehold meeting-house, and the troops marched ahead, not knowing where they were sent.

Across the wooded fields Jabez saw the lines of red splotches which gleamed in the early sunlight, and he knew these were British troops. The rattling musket-fire became a grinding roar, and the deeper note of artillery boomed into the tumult. A battle had begun, yet the Connecticut Brigade was stewing in the heat hour after hour, impatient, troubled, wondering why they had no part to play. As the forenoon dragged along the men became sullen and weary.

When at last an order came it was not to advance, but to retreat. Falling back, they found themselves near their camping place. Valley Forge had not quenched the faith of Jabez Rockwell in General Washington's power to conquer any odds, but now he felt such dismay as brought hot tears to his eyes. On both sides of his regiment American troops were streaming to the rear, their columns broken and straggling. It seemed as if the whole army was fleeing from the veterans of Clinton and Cornwallis.

Jabez flung himself into a cornfield, and hid his face in his arms. Round him his comrades were muttering their anger and despair. He fumbled for his canteen, and his fingers closed round his powder-horn. "General Washington did not give you to me to run away with," he whispered; and then his parched lips moved in a little prayer:

"Dear Lord, help us to beat the British this day, and give me a chance to empty my powder-horn before night. Thou hast been with General Washington and me ever since last year. Please don't desert us now."

Nor was he surprised when, as if in direct answer to his petition, he rose to see the chief riding through the troop lines, but such a chief as he had never known before. The kindly face was aflame with anger, and streaked with dust and sweat. The powerful horse he rode was lathered, and its heaving flanks were scarred from hard-driven spurs.

As the commander passed the regiment, his staff in a whirlwind at his heels, Jabez heard him shout in a great voice vibrant with rage and grief:

"I cannot believe the army is retreating. I ordered a general advance. Who dared to give such an order? Advance those lines—"

"It was General Lee's order to retreat," Jabez heard an officer stammer in reply.

Washington vanished in a moment, with a storm of cheers in his wake. Jabez was content to wait for orders now. He believed the Battle of Monmouth as good as won.

His recollection of the next few hours was jumbled and hazy. He knew that the regiment went forward, and then the white smoke of musket-fire closed down before him. Now and then the summer breeze made rifts in this stifling cloud, and he saw it streaked with spouting fire. He aimed his old musket at that other foggy line beyond the rail fence, whose top was lined with men in coats of red and green and black.

Suddenly his officers began running to and fro, and a shout ran down the thin line:

"Stand steady, Connecticut! Save your fire! Aim low! Here comes a charge!"

A tidal wave of red and brass broke through the gaps in the rail fence, and the sunlight rippled along a wavering line of British bayonets. They crept nearer, nearer, until Jabez could see the grim ferocity, the bared teeth, the staring eyes of the dreaded Grenadiers.

At the command to fire he pulled the trigger, and the kick of his musket made him grunt with pain. Pulling the stopper from his powder-horn with his teeth, Jabez poured in a charge, and was ramming the bullet home when he felt his right leg double under him and burn as if red-hot iron had seared it.

Then the charging tide of Grenadiers swept over him. He felt their hobnailed heels bite into his back; then his head felt queer, and he closed his eyes. When he found himself trying to rise, he saw, as through a mist, his regiment falling back, driven from their ground by the first shock of the charge. He groaned in agony of spirit. What would General Washington say?

Jabez was now behind the headlong British column, which heeded him not. He was in a little part of the field cleared of fighting for the moment, except for the wounded who dotted the trampled grass. The smoke had drifted away, for the swaying lines in front of him were locked in the frightful embrace of cold steel.

The boy staggered to his feet, with his musket as a crutch, and his wound was forgotten. He was given strength to his need by the spirit of a great purpose.

Alone he stood and reeled, while he beckoned, passionately, imploringly, his arm outstretched toward his broken regiment. The lull in the firing made a moment of strange quiet, broken only by groans and the hard, gasping curses of men locked in the death-grip. Therefore the shrill young voice carried far, as he shouted:

"Come back, Connecticut! I'm waiting for you!"

His captain heard the boy, and waved his sword with hoarse cries to his men. They caught sight of the lonely little figure in the background, and his cry went to their hearts, and a great wave of rage and shame swept the line like a prairie fire. Like a landslide the men of Connecticut swept forward to recapture the ground they had yielded. Back fell the British before a countercharge they could not withstand, back beyond the rail fence. Nor was there refuge even there, for, shattered and spent, they were smashed to fragments in a flank attack driven home in the nick of time by the American reserves.

From a low hill to the right of this action General Washington had paused to view the charge just when his line gave way. He sent an officer in hot haste for reserves, and waited for them where he was.

Thus it happened that his eyes swept the littered field from which Jabez Rockwell rose, as one from the dead, to rally his comrades, alone, undaunted, pathetic beyond words. A little later two privates were carrying to the rear the wounded lad who had been picked up alive and conscious. They halted to salute their commander-in-chief, and laid their burden down as the general drew rein and said:

"Take this man to my quarters, and see to it that he has every possible attention. I saw him save a regiment and retake a position."

JABEZ ROCKWELL

The limp figure on the litter of boughs raised itself on an elbow, and said very feebly:

"I didn't want to see that powder-horn disgraced, sir."

With a smile of recognition General Washington responded:

"The powder-horn? I remember. *You* are the lad who led the powder-horn rebellion at Valley Forge. And I wrote down 'Seventeen seventy-six.' You have used it well, my boy. I will not forget."

When Jabez Rockwell was able to rejoin his company he scratched upon the powder-horn this addition to the legend he had carved at Valley Forge:

First Used at Monmouth
June 28, 1778

A hundred years later the grandson of Jabez Rockwell hung the powder-horn in the old stone house at Valley Forge which had been General Washington's headquarters. And if you should chance to see it there you will find that the young soldier added one more line to the rough inscription:

Last Used at Yorktown, 1781.

A MAN WHO COVETED WASH-INGTON'S SHOES

By Frank R. Stockton

THE person whose story we are now about to tell was not a Jerseyman; but, as most of the incidents which make him interesting to us occurred in this State, we will give him the benefit of a few years' residence here.

This was General Charles Lee, who might well have been called a soldier of fortune. He was born in England, but the British Isles were entirely too small to satisfy his wild ambitions and his roving disposition. There are few heroes of romance who have had such a wide and varied experience, and who have engaged in so many strange enterprises. He was a brave man and very able, but he had a fault which prevented him from being a high-class soldier; and that fault was, that he could not bear restraint, and was always restive under command of another, and, while always ready to tell other people what they ought to do, was never willing to be told what he ought to do.

He joined the British army when he was a young man; and he first came to this country in 1757, when General Abercrombie brought over an army to fight the French. For three years, Lee was engaged in the wilds and forests, doing battle with the Indians and French, and no doubt he had all the adventures an ordinary person would desire. But this experience was far from satisfactory.

When he left America, he went to Portugal with

another British army, and there he fought the
Spanish with as much impetuosity as he had
fought the French and Indians. Life was absolutely tasteless to Lee without a very strong
sprinkle of variety. Consequently he now tried
fighting in an entirely different field, and went
into politics. He became a Liberal, and with his
voice fought the government for whom he had been
previously fighting with his sword.

But a few years of this satisfied him; and then
he went to Poland, where he became a member of
the king's staff, and as a Polish officer disported
himself for two years.

It is very likely that in Turkey a high-spirited
man would find more opportunities for lively adventure than even in Poland. At any rate,
Charles Lee thought so; and to Turkey he went,
and entered into the service of the sultan. Here
he distinguished himself in a company of Turks
who were guarding a great treasure in its trans-
portation from Moldavia to Constantinople. No
doubt he wore a turban and baggy trousers, and
carried a great scimitar, for a man of that sort is
not likely to do things by halves when he does them
at all.

Having had such peculiar experiences in various
armies and various parts of the world, Lee thought
himself qualified to occupy a position of rank in
the British army, and, coming back to England,
he endeavored to obtain military promotion. But
the government there did not seem to think he had
learned enough in Poland and Turkey to enable
him to take precedence of English officers accus-

tomed to command English troops, and it declined to put him above such officers, and to give him the place he desired. Lee was not a man of mild temper. He became very angry at the treatment he received, and, abandoning his native country again, he went to Russia, where the czar gave him command of a company of wild Cossacks. But he did not remain long with the Cossacks. Perhaps they were not wild and daring enough to suit his fancy, although there are very few fancies which would not be satisfied with the reckless and furious demeanor generally attributed to these savage horsemen.

He threw up his command and went to Hungary, and there he did some fighting in an entirely different fashion. Not having any opportunity to distinguish himself upon a battlefield, he engaged in a duel; and of course, as he was acting the part of a hero of romance, he killed his man.

Hungary was not a suitable residence for him after the duel, and he went back to England, and there he found the country in a state of excitement in regard to the American Colonies. Now, if there was anything that Lee liked, it was a state of excitement, and in the midst of this political hubbub he felt as much at home as if he had been charging the ranks of an enemy. Of course, he took part against the government, for, as far as we know, he had always been against it, and he became a violent supporter of the rights of the colonists.

He was so much in earnest in this matter, that in 1773 he came to America to see for himself how matters stood. When he got over here, he became more strongly in favor of the colonists than he had been at home, and everywhere proclaimed that the Americans were right in resisting the unjust taxation claims of Great Britain. As he had always been ready to lay aside his British birthright and become some sort of a foreigner, he now determined to become an American; and to show that he was in earnest, he went down to Virginia and bought a farm there.

Lee soon became acquainted with people in high places in American politics; and when the first Congress assembled, he was ready to talk with its members, urging them to stand up for their rights, and draw their swords and load their guns in defense of independence. It was quite natural, that, when the Revolution really began, a man who was so strongly in favor of the patriots, and had had so much military experience in so many different lands, should be allowed to take part in the war, and Charles Lee was appointed major general.

This was a high military position—much higher, in fact, than he could ever have obtained in his own country—but it did not satisfy him. The position he wanted was that of commander-in-chief of the American army; and he was surprised and angry that it was not offered to him, and that a man of his ability should be passed over, and that high place given to a person like George Washington, who knew but little of war, and had no idea whatever how the thing was done in Portugal, Poland, Russia and Turkey, and who was, in fact, no more than a country gentleman.

All this showed that these Americans were fools, who did not understand their best interests. But as there was a good chance for a fight, and, in fact, a good many fights, and as a major generalship was not to be sneered at, he accepted it, and resigned the commission which he held in the English army.

He was doubtless in earnest in his desire to assist the Americans to obtain their independence, for he was always in earnest when he was doing anything that he was inclined to do. But he did not propose to sacrifice his own interests to the cause he had undertaken; and as, by entering the American army, he risked the loss of his estate in England, he arranged with Congress for compensation for such a loss.

But, although General Lee was now a very ardent American soldier, he could not forgive Mr. Washington for taking command above him. If that Virginia gentleman had had the courtesy and good sense which were generally attributed to him, he would have resigned the supreme command, and, modestly stepping aside, would have asked General Lee to accept it.

At least, that was the opinion of General Charles Lee.

As this high and mighty soldier was so unwilling to submit to the orders of incompetent people, he never liked to be under the direct command of Washington, and, if it were possible to do so, he managed to be concerned in operations not under the immediate eye of the commander-in-chief. In fact, he was very jealous indeed of Washington, and did not hesitate to express his opinion about him whenever he had a chance.

The American army was not very successful in Long Island, and there was a time when it fared very badly in New Jersey; and Lee was not slow to declare that these misfortunes were owing entirely to the ignorance of the man who was in command. Moreover, if there was any one who wanted to know if there was another man in the Colonies who could command the army better, and lead it more certainly and speedily to victory, General Lee was always ready to mention an experienced leader who would be able to perform that duty most admirably.

If it had not been for this unfortunate and jealous disposition, Charles Lee—a very different man from "Light Horse Harry" Lee—would have been one of the most useful officers in the American army. But he had such a jealousy of Washington, and hoped so continually that something would happen which would give him the place then occupied by the Virginia country gentleman, that, although he was at heart an honest patriot, he allowed himself to do things which were not at all patriotic. He wanted to see the Americans successful in the country, but he did not want to see all that happen under the leadership of Washington; and if he could put an obstacle in the way of that incompetent person, he would do it, and be glad to see him stumble over it.

In the winter of 1776, when the American army was taking its way across New Jersey towards the Delaware River with Cornwallis in pursuit,

Washington was anxiously looking for the troops under the command of General Lee, who had been ordered to come to his assistance; and if ever assistance was needed, it was needed then. But Lee liked to do his own ordering, and, instead of hurrying to help Washington, he thought it would be a great deal better to do something on his own account; and so he endeavored to get into the rear of Cornwallis's army, thinking that, if he should attack the enemy in that way, he might possibly win a startling victory which would cover him with glory, and show how much better a soldier he was than that poor Washington who was retreating across the country, instead of boldly turning and showing fight.

If Lee had been a true soldier, and had conscientiously obeyed the commands of his superior, he would have joined Washington and his army without delay and a short time afterward would have had an opportunity of taking part in the battle of Trenton, in which the Virginia country gentleman defeated the British, and gained one of the most important victories of the war.

Lee pressed slowly onward—ready to strike a great blow for himself, and unwilling to help anybody else strike a blow—until he came to Morristown; and, after staying there one night, he proceeded in the direction of Basking Ridge, a pretty village not far away. Lee left his army at Bernardsville, which was then known as Vealtown, and rode on to Basking Ridge, accompanied only by a small guard. There he took lodgings at an inn, and made himself comfortable. The next morning he did not go and put himself at the head of his army and move on, because there were various affairs which occupied his attention.

Several of his guard wished to speak to him, some of them being men from Connecticut, who appeared before him in full-bottomed wigs, showing plainly that they considered themselves people who were important enough to have their complaints attended to. One of them wanted his horse shod, another asked for some money on account of his pay, and a third had something to say about rations. But General Lee cut them all off very shortly with, "You want a great deal, but you have not mentioned what you want most. You want to go home, and I should be glad to let you go, for you are no good here." Then his adjutant general asked to see him; and he had a visit from a Major Wilkinson, who arrived that morning with a letter from General Gates.

All these things occupied him very much, and he did not sit down to breakfast till ten o'clock. Shortly after they had finished their meal, and Lee was writing a letter to General Gates, in which he expressed a very contemptible opinion of General Washington, Major Wilkinson saw, at the end of the lane which led from the house down to the main road, a party of British cavalry who dashed round the corner toward the house. The major immediately called out to General Lee that the redcoats were coming; but Lee, who was a man not to be frightened by sudden reports, finished signing the letter, and then jumped up to see what was the matter.

By this time the dragoons had surrounded the house; and when he perceived this, General Lee naturally wanted to know where the guards were, and why they did not fire on these fellows. But there was no firing, and apparently there were no guards, and when Wilkinson went to look for them, he found their arms in the room which had been their quarters, but the men were gone. These private soldiers had evidently been quite as free and easy, and as bent upon making themselves comfortable, as had been the general, and they had had no thought that such a thing as a British soldier was anywhere in the neighborhood. When Wilkinson looked out of the door, he saw the guards running in every direction, with dragoons chasing them.

What all this meant, nobody knew at first; and Wilkinson supposed that it was merely a band of marauders of the British army, who were making a raid into the country to get what they could in the way of plunder. It was not long before this was found to be a great mistake; for the officer in command of the dragoons called from the outside, and demanded that General Lee should surrender himself, and that, if he did not do so in five minutes, the house would be set on fire.

Now, it was plain to everybody that the British had heard of the leisurely advance of this American general, and that he had left his command and come to Basking Ridge to take his ease at an inn, and so they had sent a detachment to capture him. Soon the women of the house came to General Lee, and urged him to hide himself under a feather bed.

They declare that they would cover him up so that nobody would suspect that he was in the bed; then they would tell the soldiers that he was not there, and that they might come and search the house if they chose.

But although Lee was a jealous man and a hasty man, he had a soul above such behavior as this, and would not hide himself in a feather bed; but, as there was no honorable way of escape, he boldly came forward and surrendered himself.

The British gave him no time to make any preparations for departure. They did not know but that his army might be on the way to Basking Ridge; and the sooner they were off, the better. So they made him jump on Major Wilkinson's horse, which was tied by the door; and in his slippers and dressing gown, and without a hat, this bold soldier of wide experience, who thought he should be commander-in-chief of the American army, was hurried away at full gallop. He was taken to New York, where he was put into prison. It is said that Lee plotted against America during his imprisonment; but General Washington did not know that, and used every exertion to have him exchanged, so that his aspiring rival soon again joined the American army.

But his misfortune had no effect upon General Charles Lee, who came back to his command with as high an opinion of himself, and as low an opinion of certain other people, as he had had when he involuntarily left it. It was some time after this, at the battle of Monmouth Court House, that Charles Lee showed what sort of a man he really was. He

341

had now become so jealous that he positively determined that he would not obey orders, and would act as he thought best. He had command of a body of troops numbering five thousand, a good-sized army for those days, and he was ordered to advance to Monmouth Court House and attack the enemy who were there, while Washington, with another force, would hasten to his assistance as rapidly as possible.

Washington carried out his part of the plan; but when he had nearly reached Monmouth, he found, to his amazement, that Lee had gone there, but had done no fighting at all, and was now actually retreating, and coming in his direction. As it would be demoralizing in the highest degree to his own command, if Lee's armed forces in full retreat should come upon them, Washington hurried forward to prevent anything of the sort, and soon met Lee. When the latter was asked what was the meaning of this strange proceeding, he could give no good reason, except that he thought it better not to risk an engagement at that time.

Then the Virginia country gentleman blazed out at the soldier of fortune, and it is said that no one ever heard George Washington speak to any other man as he spoke to General Lee on that day. He was told to go back to his command and to obey orders, and together the American forces moved on. In the battle which followed, the enemy was repulsed; but the victory was not so complete as it should have been, for the British departed in the night and went where they intended to go, without being cut off by the American army, as would have been the case if Lee had obeyed the orders which were given him.

General Lee was very angry at the charges which Washington had made against him, and demanded that he should be tried by court-martial. His wish was granted. He was tried, and found guilty of every charge made against him, and in consequence was suspended from the army for one year.

But Charles Lee never went back into the American army. Perhaps he had enough of it. In any event, it had had enough of him; and seven years afterwards, when he died of a fever, his ambition to stand in Washington's shoes died with him. While he lived on his Virginia farm, he was as impetuous and eccentric as when he had been in the army, and he must have been a very unpleasant neighbor. In fact, the people there thought he was crazy. This opinion was not changed when his will was read, for in that document he said:

"I desire most earnestly that I may not be buried in any church or churchyard, or within a mile of any Presbyterian or Anabaptist meeting house; for since I have resided in this country I have kept so much bad company when living, that I do not choose to continue it when dead."

A FAMOUS FIGHT BETWEEN AN ENGLISH AND A FRENCH FRIGATE

By Rev. W. H. Fitchett, LL. D.

ONE of the most famous frigate fights in British history is that between the *Arethusa* and *La Belle Poule*, fought off Brest on June 17, 1778. Who is not familiar with the name and fame of "the saucy *Arethusa*"? Yet there is a curious absence of detail as to the fight. The combat, indeed, owes its enduring fame to two somewhat irrelevant circumstances — first, that it was fought when France and England were not actually at war, but were trembling on the verge of it. The sound of the *Arethusa's* guns, indeed, was the signal of war between the two nations. The other fact is that an ingenious rhymster—scarcely a poet—crystallised the fight into a set of verses in which there is something of the true smack of the sea, and an echo, if not of the cannon's roar, yet of the rough-voiced mirth of the forecastle; and the sea-fight lies embalmed, so to speak, and made immortal in the sea-song. The *Arethusa* was a stumpy little frigate, scanty in crew, light in guns, attached to the fleet of Admiral Keppel, then cruising off Brest. Keppel had as perplexed and delicate a charge as was ever entrusted to a British admiral. Great Britain was at war with her American colonies, and there was every sign that France intended to add herself to the fight. No fewer than thirty-two sail of the line and twelve frigates were gathered in Brest roads, and another fleet of almost equal strength in Toulon. Spain, too, was slowly collecting a mighty armament. What would happen to England if the Toulon and Brest fleets united, were joined by a third fleet from Spain, and the mighty array of ships thus collected swept up the British Channel? On June 13, 1778, Keppel, with twenty-one ships of the line and three frigates, was despatched to keep watch over the Brest fleet. War had not been proclaimed, but Keppel was to prevent a junction of the Brest and Toulon fleets, by persuasion if he could, but by gunpowder in the last resort.

Keppel's force was much inferior to that of the Brest fleet, and as soon as the topsails of the British ships were visible from the French coast, two French frigates, the *Licorne* and *La Belle Poule*, with two lighter craft, bore down upon them to reconnoiter. But Keppel could not afford to let the French admiral know his exact force, and signalled to his own outlying ships to bring the French frigates under his lee.

At nine o'clock at night the *Licorne* was overtaken by the *Milford*, and with some rough sailorly persuasion, and a hint of broadsides, her head was turned towards the British fleet. The next morning, in the grey dawn, the Frenchman, having meditated on affairs during the night, made a wild dash for freedom. The *America*, an English 64— double, that is, the *Licorne's* size—overtook her, and fired a shot across her bow to bring her to. Longford, the captain of the *America*, stood on the gunwale of his own ship politely urging the captain of the *Licorne* to return with him. With a burst of Celtic passion the French captain fired his whole broadside into the big Englishman, and then instantly hauled down his flag so as to escape any answering broadside!

Meanwhile the *Arethusa* was in eager pursuit of the *Belle Poule;* a fox-terrier chasing a mastiff! The *Belle Poule* was a splendid ship, with heavy metal, and a crew more than twice as numerous as that of the tiny *Arethusa*. But Marshall, its captain, was a singularly gallant sailor, and not the man to count odds. The song tells the story of the fight in an amusing fashion:

> "Come all ye jolly sailors bold,
> Whose hearts are cast in honor's mould,
> While England's glory I unfold.
> Huzza to the *Arethusa!*
> She is a frigate tight and brave
> As ever stemmed the dashing wave;
> Her men are staunch
> To their fav'rite launch,
> And when the foe shall meet our fire,
> Sooner than strike we'll all expire
> On board the *Arethusa.*
>
> On deck five hundred men did dance,
> The stoutest they could find in France;
> We, with two hundred, did advance
> On board the *Arethusa.*
> Our captain hailed the Frenchman, 'Ho!'
> The Frenchman then cried out, 'Hallo!'
> 'Bear down, d'ye see,
> To our Admiral's lee.'
> 'No, no,' says the Frenchman, 'that can't be.'
> 'Then I must lug you along with me,'
> Says the saucy *Arethusa!*"

As a matter of fact Marshall hung doggedly on the Frenchman's quarter for two long hours, fighting a ship twice as big as his own. The *Belle Poule* was eager to escape; Marshall was resolute that it should not escape, and, try as he might, the Frenchman, during that fierce two hours' wrestle, failed to shake off his tiny but dogged antagonist. The *Arethusa's* masts were shot away, its jib-boom hung a tangled wreck over its bows, its bulwarks were shattered, half its guns were dismounted, and nearly every third man in its crew struck down. But still it hung, with quenchless and obstinate courage, on the *Belle Poule's* quarter, and by its perfect seamanship and the quickness and the deadly precision with which its lighter guns worked, reduced its towering foe to a condition of wreck almost as complete as its own. The terrier, in fact, was proving too much for the mastiff.

Suddenly the wind fell. With topmasts hanging over the side, and canvas torn to ribbons, the *Arethusa* lay shattered and moveless on the sea. The shot-torn but loftier sails of the *Belle Poule,* however, yet held wind enough to drift her out of the reach of the *Arethusa's* fire. Both ships were close under the French cliffs; but the *Belle Poule,* like a broken-winged bird, struggled into a tiny cove in the rocks, and nothing remained for the *Arethusa* but to cut away her wreckage, hoist what sail she could, and drag herself sullenly back under jury-masts to the British fleet. But the story of that two hours' heroic fight maintained against such odds sent a thrill of grim exultation through Great Britain. Menaced by the combination of so many mighty states, while her sea-dogs were of this fighting temper, what had Great Britain to fear? In the streets of many a British seaport, and in many a British forecastle, the story of how the *Arethusa* fought was sung in deep-throated chorus:

> "The fight was off the Frenchman's land;
> We forced them back upon their strand;
> For we fought till not a stick would stand
> Of the gallant *Arethusa!*"

THE TRICK OF AN INDIAN SPY

By Arthur Quiller-Couch

IT was in 1779, when America was struggling with England for her Independence, and a division of the English redcoats were encamped on the banks of the Potomac. So admirably fortified was their position by river and steep woods, that no ordinary text-book of warfare would admit the possibility of surprising it. But Washington and his men did not conduct their campaigns by the book. "If you fight with art," said that general once to his soldiery, "you are sure to be defeated. Acquire discipline enough for retreat and the uniformity of combined attack, and your country will prove the best of engineers."

In fact, it was with a guerilla warfare, and little else, that the British had to contend. The Americans had enrolled whole tribes of Indians in their ranks and made full use of the Indian habits of warfare. The braves would steal like snakes about

the pathless forests, and dashing unexpectedly on
the outposted redcoats, kill a handful in one fierce
charge, and then retreat pell-mell back into their
shelter, whither to follow them was to court certain
death. The injuries thus inflicted were not overwhelming, but they were teasing for all that. Day
by day the waste went on — loss of sentinels, of
stragglers, sometimes of whole detachments, and
all this was more galling from the impossibility of
revenge. In order to limit the depredations it was
the custom of the British commanders to throw
forward their outposts to a great distance from
the main body, to station sentinels far into the
woods, and cover the main body with a constant
guard.

One regiment was suffering from little less than
a panic. Perpetually and day after day sentinels
had been missing. Worse than this, they had been
surprised, apparently, and carried off without giving any alarm or having time to utter a sound.
It would happen that a sentinel went forward to
his post with finger upon his trigger, while his comrades searched the woods around and found them
empty. When the relief came, the man would just
be missing. That was all. There was never a
trace left to show the manner in which he had been
conveyed away: only, now and then, a few drops
of blood splashed on the leaves where he had been
standing.

The men grew more and more uneasy. Most
suspected treachery. It was unreasonable, they
argued, to believe that man after man could be
surprised without having time even to fire his mus-

ket. Others talked of magic, and grew gloomy with strange suspicions of the Indian medicine-men. At any rate, here was a mystery. Time would clear it up, no doubt; but meanwhile the sentry despatched to his post felt like a man marked out for death. It was worse. Many men who would have marched with firm step to death in any familiar shape would go with pale cheeks and bowed knees to this fate of which nothing was known except that nothing was left of the victim.

Matters at length grew intolerable. One morning, the sentinels having been set as usual overnight, the guard went as soon as dawn began to break to relieve a post that extended far into the woods. The sentinel was gone! They searched about, found his footprints here and there on the trodden leaves, but no blood—no trace of struggle, no marks of surrounding enemies. It was the old story, however, and they had almost given up the problem by this time. They left another man at the post, and went their way back, wishing him better luck.

"No need to be afraid," he called after them, "I will not desert."

They looked back. He was standing with his musket ready to fly up to his shoulder at the slightest sound, his eyes searching the glades before him. There was nothing faint about Tom, they determined, and returned to the guard-house.

The sentinels were replaced every four hours, and at the regular time the guard again marched to relieve the post. The man was gone!

They rubbed their eyes, and searched again. But

this one had disappeared as mysteriously as his fellows. Again there was no single trace. But it was all the more necessary that the post should not remain unguarded. They were forced to leave a third man and return, promising him that the colonel should be told of his danger as soon as they got back.

It was panic indeed that filled the regiment when they returned to the guard-house and told the news. The colonel was informed at once. He promised to go in person to the spot when the man was relieved, and search the woods round about. This gave them some confidence, but they went nevertheless with the gloomiest forebodings as to their comrade's fate. As they drew near the spot they advanced at a run. Their fears were justified. The post was vacant—the man gone without a sound.

In the blank astonishment that followed, the colonel hesitated. Should he station a whole company at the post? This would doubtless prevent further loss; but then it was little likely to explain the mystery; for the hands that had carried off three sentinels, would, it was reasonable to believe, make no attempt to spirit away a whole company of men. And for future action as well as to put an end to the superstitious terror of the soldiery, the vital necessity was to clear up the mystery. He had no belief in the theory that these men deserted. He knew them too well. He prided himself that he was thoroughly acquainted with his own regiment, and had well-grounded reasons for pride in his men. For this reason he was more chary of ex-

posing a fourth brave man where three had already
been lost. However, it had to be done. The poor
fellow whose turn it was to take the post, though a
soldier of proved courage and even recklessness in
action, positively shook from head to foot.

"I must do my duty," he said to the colonel. "I
know that well enough; but for all that I should
like to lose my life with a bit of credit."

There was no higher bravery than facing an in-
definite terror such as this, as the colonel was at
pains to point out, but he added—

"I will leave no man here against his will."

Immediately a soldier stepped out of the ranks.
"Give me the post," he said quietly.

The colonel looked at the volunteer admiringly,
and spoke some words in praise of his courage.

"No," said the man; "I have an idea, that is all.
What I promise you is that I will not be taken
alive. I shall give you a deal of trouble; because
you will hear of me on the least alarm. If I am
given this post, I propose to fire my piece if I hear
the slightest noise. If a bird chatters or a leaf
falls, my musket shall go off. Of course you may be
alarmed when nothing is the matter: but that's my
condition, and you must take the chance."

"Take the chance!" said the colonel. "It's the
very wisest thing you can do. You're a fellow of
courage, and what's more, you're a fellow with a
head."

He shook hands with him, as did the rest of the
soldiers, with faces full of foreboding. "Come,"
said the man, "don't look so glum; cheer up, and I
shall have a story to tell you when we meet again."

They left him and went back to the guard-room again. An hour passed away in suspense. It seemed as though every ear in the regiment were on the rack for the discharge of that musket. Hardly a man spoke, but as the minutes dragged along the conviction gained ground that already the brave man had followed the fate of the other three. The colonel paced up and down in the guard-room, as anxious as any of the men. He looked at his watch for the twentieth time. An hour and twenty minutes had gone.

Suddenly, down in the woods, the report of a musket rang out.

Colonel, officers, and men poured out of the guard-room, almost without a word, and advanced at a double through the woods. The mystery was going to be solved at last. Until quite close to the spot, they were forced, by the thickness of the forest, to remain in ignorance of what had happened, and whether their comrade was dead or alive. But they shouted, and an answering "Halloa!" at last came back. As they turned into the glade where the sentinel had been posted, they beheld him advancing towards them and dragging another man along the ground by the hair of the head.

He flung the body down. It was an Indian, stone-dead, with a musket-wound in his side.

"How did it happen?" panted the colonel, beside himself with joy.

"Well," said the soldier, saluting, "I gave your honor notice that I should fire if I heard the least noise. That's what I did, and it saved my life; and it just happened in this way.

"I hadn't been long standing here, peering round till my eyes ached, when I heard a rustling about fifty yards away. I looked and saw an American hog, of the sort that are common enough in these parts, coming down the glade opposite, crawling along the ground and sniffing to right and left—just as if he'd no business in life but to sniff about for nuts under the fallen leaves and all about the roots of the trees. Boars are common enough, so I gave him a glance and didn't take much notice for some minutes.

"But after a while, thinks I to myself—'No doubt the others kept their eyes about them sharp enough, and was only took in by neglecting something that seemed of no account;' so being on the alarm and having no idea what was to be feared and what was not, I woke up after some minutes and determined to keep my eyes on it and watch how it passed in and out among the trees. For I thought, if it comes on an Indian skulking about yonder, I may be able to learn something from its movements. Indians are thick enough here and to spare: but they're not so thick as nuts, for all that.

"So I kept glancing at the hog, and then looking round and glancing again. Not another creature was in sight; not a leaf rustling. And then, all of a sudden—I can't tell why—it struck me as queer that the animal was snuffling around among the trees and making off to the right, seemingly for the thick coppice just behind my post. I didn't want anything behind me, you may be sure, not even a hog, and as it was now only a few yards from my coppice I kept my eye more constantly on it, and cast up in my mind whether I should fire or not.

"It seemed foolish enough to rouse you all up by shooting a pig! I fingered my trigger, and couldn't for the life of me make up my mind what to do. I looked and looked, and the more I looked the bigger fool I thought myself for being alarmed at it. It would be a rare jest against me that I mistook a pig for an Indian; and this was a hog sure enough. You've all seen scores of them, and know how they move. Well, this one was for all the world like any other, and I was almost saying to myself that 'twas more like the average hog than any hog I'd ever seen, when just as it got close to the thicket I fancied it gave an unusual spring.

"At any rate, fancy or no, I didn't hesitate. I took cool aim, and directly I did so, felt sure I was right. The beast stopped in a hesitating sort of way, and by that I knew it saw what I was about, though up to the moment it had never seemed to be noticing me. 'An Indian's trick, for a sovereign,' thought I, and pulled the trigger.

"It dropped over like a stone; and then, as I stood there, still doubting if it were a trap that I should fall into by running to look, I heard a groan—and the groan of a man, too. I loaded my musket and ran up to it. I had shot an Indian, sure enough, and that groan was his last.

"He had wrapped himself in the hog's skin so completely, and his hands and feet were so neatly hid, and he imitated the animal's walk and noise so cleverly, that I swear, if you saw the trick played again, here before you, your honor would doubt

your honor's eyes. And seeing him at a distance,
in the shadow of the trees, no man who had not
lost three comrades before him, as I had, would
ever have guessed. Here's the knife and tomahawk
the villain had about him. You see, once in the
coppice he had only to watch his moment for throwing off the skin and jumping on me from behind; a
dig in the back before a man had time to fire his
piece was easy work enough. After that it's easier
still to drag the body off and hide it under a heap
of leaves. The rebels pay these devils by the scalp,
and no doubt if your honor looks about, you'll find
the collection our friend here has already made
to-day."

THE MAN IN THE "AUGER HOLE"

By Frank R. Stockton

WHEN we consider the American Revolution,
we are apt to think of it as a great war in
which all the inhabitants of the Colonies rose up
against Great Britain, determined, no matter what
might be the hardships and privations, no matter
what the cost in blood and money, to achieve their
independence and the right to govern themselves.

But this was not the case. A great majority
of the people of the Colonies were ardently in
favor of independence; but there were also a great
many people, and we have no right to say that
some of them were not very good people, who were
as well satisfied that their country should be a
colony of Great Britain as the Canadians are now

satisfied with that state of things, and who were earnestly and honestly opposed to any separation from the mother country.

This difference of opinion was the cause of great trouble and bloodshed among the colonists themselves, and the contests between the Tories and the Whigs were nowhere more bitter than in New Jersey. In some parts of the Colony, families were divided against themselves; and not only did this result in quarrels and separations, but fathers and sons, and brothers and brothers, fought against each other. At one time the Tories, or, as they came to be called, "refugees," were in such numbers that they took possession of the town of Freehold, and held it for more than a week; and when at last the town was retaken by the patriotic forces, most of them being neighbors and friends of the refugees, several prominent Tories were hanged, and many others sent to prison.

The feeling between the Americans of the two different parties was more violent than that between the patriots and the British troops, and before long it became entirely unsafe for any Tory to remain in his own home in New Jersey. Many of them went to New York, where the patriotic feeling was not so strong at that time, and there they formed themselves into a regular military company called the "Associated Loyalists"; and this company was commanded by William Temple Franklin, son of the great Benjamin Franklin, who had been appointed Governor of New Jersey by the British Crown. He was now regarded with great hatred by the patriots of New Jersey, because he was a strong Tory. This difference of opinion between William Franklin and his father was the most noted instance of this state of feeling which occurred in those days.

It will be interesting to look upon this great contest from a different point of view than that from which we are accustomed to regard it; and some extracts from the journal of a New Jersey lady who was a decided Tory, will give us an idea of the feeling and condition of the people who were opposed to the Revolution.

This lady was Mrs. Margaret Hill Morris, who lived in Burlington. She was a Quaker lady, and must have been a person of considerable wealth; for she had purchased the house on Green Bank, one of the prettiest parts of Burlington, overlooking the river, in which Governor Franklin had formerly resided. This was a fine house and contained the room which afterwards became celebrated under the name of the "Auger Hole." This had been built, for what reason is not known, as a place of concealment. It was a small room, entirely dark, but said to be otherwise quite comfortable, which could be approached only through a linen closet. In order to get at it, the linen had to be taken from the shelves, the shelves drawn out, and a small door opened at the back of the closet, quite low down, so that the dark room could only be entered by stooping.

In this "Auger Hole," Mrs. Morris, who was a strong Tory, but a very good woman, had concealed a refugee who at the time was sought for by the adherents of the patriotic side, and who probably would have had a hard time of it if he had been caught, for he was a person of considerable importance.

The name of the refugee was Jonathan Odell, and he was rector of St. Mary's Church in Burlington. He was a learned man, being a doctor as well as a clergyman, and a very strong Tory. He had been of much service to the people of Burlington; for when the Hessians had attacked the town, he had come forward and interceded with their commander, and had done his work so well that the soldiers were forbidden to pillage the town. But when the Hessians left, the American authorities began a vigorous search for Tories; and Parson Odell was obliged to conceal himself in good Mrs. Morris's "Auger Hole."

Mrs. Morris was apparently a widow who lived alone with her two boys, and, having this refugee in her house, she was naturally very nervous about the movements of the American troops and the actions of her neighbors of the opposite party.

She kept a journal of the things that happened about her in those eventful days, and from this we will give some extracts. It must be understood that in writing her journal, the people designated as the "enemy" were the soldiers under Washington, and that "gondolas" were American gunboats.

"From the 13th to the 16th we had various reports of the advancing and retiring of the enemy; parties of armed men rudely entered the town and diligent search was made for tories. Some of the gondola gentry broke into and pillaged Red Smith's house on the bank. About noon this day (16th) a very terrible account of thousands coming into the town, and now actually to be seen on Gallows Hill: my incautious son caught up the spyglass, and was running towards the hill to look at them. I told him it would be liable to misconstruction."

The journal states that the boy went out with the spyglass, but could get no good place from which he could see Gallows Hill, or any troops upon it, and so went down to the river, and thought he would take a view of the boats in which were the American troops. He rested his spyglass on the low limb of a tree, and with a boyish curiosity inspected the various boats of the little fleet, not suspecting that any one would object to such a harmless proceeding.

But the people on the boats saw him, and did object very much; and the consequence was that not long after he reached his mother's house, a small boat from one of the vessels came to shore. A party of men went to the front door of the house in which they had seen the boy enter, and began loudly to knock upon it. Poor Mrs. Morris was half frightened to death, and she made as much delay as possible in order to compose her features and act as if she had never heard of a refugee who wished to hide himself from his pursuers. In the mild manner in which Quaker women are always supposed to speak, she asked them what they wanted. They quickly told her that they had heard that there was a refugee, to whom they applied some very strong language, who was hiding somewhere about here, and that they had seen him spying at them with a glass from behind a tree, and afterwards watched him as he entered this house.

Mrs. Morris declared that they were entirely mistaken; that the person they had seen was no one but her son, who had gone out to look at them as any boy might do, and who was perfectly innocent of any designs against them. The men may have been satisfied with this explanation with regard to her son; but they asserted that they knew that there was a refugee concealed somewhere in that neighborhood, and they believed that he was in an empty house near by, of which they were told she had the key. Mrs. Morris, who had given a signal, previously agreed upon, to the man in the "Auger Hole," to keep very quiet, wished to gain as much time as possible, and exclaimed:

"Bless me! I hope you are not Hessians."

"Do we look like Hessians?" asked one of them rudely.

"Indeed, I don't know."

"Did you ever see a Hessian?"

"No, never in my life; but they are men, and you are men, and may be Hessians, for anything I know. But I will go with you into Colonel Cox's house, though indeed it was my son at the mill; he is but a boy, and meant no harm; he wanted to see the troops."

So she took the key of the empty house referred to, and went in ahead of the men, who searched the place thoroughly, and, after finding no place where anybody could be, they searched one or two of the houses adjoining; but for some reason they did not think it worth while to go through Mrs. Morris's own house. Had they done so, it is not probable that the good lady could have retained her composure, especially if they had entered the room in which was the linen closet; for, even had they been completely deceived by the piles of sheets and pillowcases, there is no knowing but that the unfortunate man in the "Auger Hole" might have been inclined to sneeze.

But although she was a brave woman and very humanely inclined, Mrs. Morris felt she could not any longer take the risk of a refugee in her house. And so that night, after dark, she went up to the parson in the "Auger Hole," and made him come out; and she took him into the town, where he was concealed by some of the Tory citizens, who were better adapted to take care of the refugee than this lone Quaker woman with her two inquisitive boys. It is believed that soon after this he took refuge in New York, which was then in the hands of the British.

Further on in the journal Mrs. Morris indulges in some moral reflections in regard to the war in which her countrymen were engaged, and no one of right feeling will object to her sentiments.

"Jan. 14. I hear Gen. Howe sent a request to Washington desiring three days' cessation of arms to take care of the wounded and bury the dead, which was refused; what a woeful tendency war has to harden the human heart against the tender feelings of humanity. Well may it be called a *horrid art* thus to change the nature of man. I thought that even barbarous nations had a sort of religious regard for their dead."

After this the journal contains many references to warlike scenes on the river and warlike sounds from the country around. Numbers of gondolas

filled with soldiers went up and down the river, at
times cannon from distant points firing alarms.
At other times the roaring of great guns from a
distance, showing that a battle was going on, kept
the people of Burlington in a continual excitement; and Mrs. Morris, who was entirely cut off
from her relatives and friends, several of whom
were living in Philadelphia, was naturally very
anxious and disturbed in regard to events, of which
she heard but little, and perhaps understood less.

One day she saw a number of gunboats, with
flags flying and drums beating, that were going,
she was told, to attend a court-martial at which a
number of refugees, men of her party, were to be
tried by General Putnam; and it was believed that
if they were found guilty they would be executed.

After a time, Mrs. Morris found an opportunity
of showing, that, although in principle she might be
a Tory, she was at heart a good, kind Quaker lady
ready to give help to suffering people, no matter
whether they belonged to the side she favored or
to that which she opposed.

Some of the people who came up the river in the
gunboats—and in many cases the soldiers brought
their wives with them, probably as cooks—were
taken sick during that summer; and some of these
invalids stopped at Burlington, being unable to
proceed farther.

Here, to their surprise, they found no doctors;
for all the patriots of that profession had gone to
the army, and the Tory physician had departed to
the British lines.   But, as is well known, the
women in the early days of New Jersey were often

obliged to be physicians; and among the good housewives of Burlington, who knew all about herb teas, homemade plasters, and potions, Mrs. Morris held a high position. The sick Continentals were told that she was just as good as a doctor, and, besides, was a very kind woman, always ready to help the sick and suffering.

So some of the sick soldiers came to her; and from what Mrs. Morris wrote, one or two of them must have been the same men who had previously come to her house and threatened the life of her boy, who had been looking at them with a spyglass. But now they very meekly and humbly asked her to come and attend their poor comrades who were unable to move. At first Mrs. Morris thought this was some sort of a trick, and that they wanted to get her on board of one of the gunboats, and carry her away. But when she found that the sick people were in a house in the town, she consented to go and do what she could. So she took her bottles with her, and her boxes and her herbs, and visited the sick people, several of whom she found were women.

They were all afflicted with some sort of a fever, probably of a malarial kind, contracted from living day and night on board of boats without proper protection; and, knowing just what to do with such cases, she, to use her own expression, "treated them according to art," and it was not long before they all recovered.

What happened in consequence of this hospital work for those whom she considered her enemies, is thus related by Mrs. Morris:

"I thought I had received all my pay when they thankfully acknowledged all my kindness, but lo! in a short time afterwards, a very rough, ill-looking man came to the door and asked for me. When I went to him, he drew me aside and asked me if I had any friends in Philadelphia. The question alarmed me, supposing that there was some mischief meditated against that poor city; however, I calmly said, 'I have an ancient father-in-law, some sisters, and other near friends there.' 'Well,' said the man, 'do you wish to hear from them, or send anything by way of refreshment to them? If you do, I will take charge of it and bring you back anything you may send for.' I was very much surprised, to be sure, and thought he only wanted to get provisions to take to the gondolas, when he told me his wife was one I had given medicine to, and this was the only thing he could do to pay me for my kindness. My heart leaped for joy, and I set about preparing something for my dear absent friends. A quarter of beef, some veal, fowls, and flour, were soon put up, and about midnight the man came and took them away in his boat."

Mrs. Morris was not mistaken in trusting to the good intentions of this grateful Continental soldier, for, as she says, two nights later there came a loud knocking at the door:

"Opening the chamber window, we heard a man's voice saying, 'Come down softly and open the door, but bring no light.' There was something mysterious in such a call, and we concluded to go down and set the candle in the kitchen. When we got to the front door we asked, 'Who are you?' The man replied, 'A friend; open quickly': so the door was opened, and who should it be but our honest gondola man with a letter, a bushel of salt, a jug of molasses, a bag of rice, some tea, coffee, and sugar, and some cloth for a coat for my poor boys—all sent by my kind sisters. How did our hearts and eyes overflow with love to them and thanks to our Heavenly Father for such seasonable supplies. May we never forget it. Being now so rich, we thought it our duty to hand out a little to the poor around us, who were mourning for want of salt, so we divided the bushel and gave a pint to every poor person who came for it, and had a great plenty for our own use."

As the war drew to its close and it became plain to every one that the cause of the patriots must triumph, the feeling between the two parties of Americans became less bitter; and the Tories, in many cases, saw that it would be wise for them to accept the situation, and become loyal citizens of the United States of America, as before they had been loyal subjects of Great Britain.

When peace was at last proclaimed, those Tories who were prisoners were released, and almost all of them who had owned farms or estates had them returned to them, and Mrs. Morris could visit her "ancient father-in-law" and her sisters in Philadelphia, or they could come up the river and visit her in her house on the beautiful Green Bank at Burlington, without fear or thought of those fellow-countrymen who had been their bitter enemies.

THE REMARKABLE VOYAGE OF THE BOUNTY

Anonymous

THIS is a story of a man who, when in command of his ships and when everything went prosperously with him, was so overbearing and cruel that some of his men, in desperation at the treatment they received, mutinied against him.

But the story shows another side of his character in adversity, which it is impossible not to admire.

In 1787, Captain Bligh was sent from England to Otaheite in charge of the *Bounty,* a ship which had been especially fitted out to carry young plants of the breadfruit tree for transplantation in the West Indies.

"The breadfruit grows on a spreading tree about the size of a large apple tree; the fruit is round, and has a thick, tough rind. It is gathered when it is full-grown, and while it is still green and hard; it is then baked in an oven until the rind is black and scorched. This is scraped off, and the inside is soft and white, like the crumb of a penny loaf."

The Otaheitans use no other bread but the fruit kind. It is, therefore, little wonder that the West Indian planters were anxious to grow this valuable fruit in their own islands, as, if it flourished there, food would be provided with little trouble for their servants and slaves.

In the passage to Otaheite, Captain Bligh had several disturbances with his men. He had an extremely irritable temper, and would often fly into a passion and make most terrible accusations, and use most terrible language to his officers and sailors.

On one occasion he ordered the crew to eat some decayed pumpkins, instead of their allowance of cheese, which he said they had stolen from the ship's stores.

The pumpkin was to be given to the men at the rate of one pound of pumpkin to two pounds of biscuits.

The men did not like accepting the substitute on

these terms. When the captain heard this, he was
infuriated, and ordered the first man of each mess
to be called by name, at the same time saying to
them, "I'll see who will dare refuse the pumpkin
or anything else I may order to be served out."
Then, after swearing at them in a shocking way, he
ended by saying, "I'll make you eat grass, or anything else you can catch, before I have done with
you," and threatened to flog the first man who dared
to complain again.

While they were at Otaheite, several of the
sailors were flogged for small offences, or without
reason, and on the other hand, during the seven
months they stayed at the island, both officers and
men were allowed to spend a great deal of time on
shore, and were given the greatest possible liberty.

Therefore, when the breadfruit plants were collected, and they weighed anchor on April 4, in 1787,
it is not unlikely they were loath to return to the
strict discipline of the ship, and to leave an island
so lovely, and where it was possible to live in the
greatest luxury without any kind of labor.

From the time they sailed until April 27, Christian, the third officer, had been in constant hot water
with Captain Bligh. On the afternoon of that day,
when the captain came on deck, he missed some
cocoanuts that had been heaped up between the
guns. He said at once that they had been stolen,
and that it could not have happened without the
officers knowing of it. When they told him they
had not seen any of the crew touch them, he cried,
"Then you must have taken them yourselves!"
After this he questioned them separately; when

he came to Christian, the latter answered, "I do not know, sir, but I hope you do not think me so mean as to be guilty of stealing yours."

The captain swore terribly, and said, "You must have stolen them from me, or you would be able to give a better account of them!" He turned to the others with much more abuse, saying, "You scoundrels, you are all thieves alike, and combine with the men to rob me! I suppose you'll steal my yams next, but I'll sweat you for it, you rascals! I'll make half of you jump overboard before you get through Endeavor Straits!"

Then he turned to the clerk, giving the order to "give them but half a pound of yams to-morrow: if they steal *them,* I'll reduce them to a quarter."

That night, Christian, who was hardly less passionate and resentful than the captain, told two of the midshipmen, Stewart and Hayward, that he intended to leave the ship on a raft, as he could no longer endure the captain's suspicion and insults. He was very angry and excited, and made some preparations for carrying out his plan, though these had to be done with the greatest secrecy and care.

It was his duty to take the morning watch, which is from four to eight o'clock, and this time he thought would be a good opportunity to make his escape. He had only just fallen into a restless slumber when he was called to take his turn.

He got up with his brain still alert with the sense of injury and wrong, and most curiously alive to seize any opportunity which might lead to an escape from so galling a service.

On reaching the deck, he found the mate of the watch had fallen asleep, and that the other midshipman was not to be seen.

Then he made a sudden determination to seize the ship, and rushing down the gangway ladder, whispered his intention to Matthew Quintal and Isaac Martin, seamen, both of whom had been flogged. They readily agreed to join him, and several others of the watch were found to be quite as willing.

Some one went to the armorer for the keys of the arm chest, telling him they wanted to fire at a shark alongside.

Christian then armed those men whom he thought he could trust, and putting a guard at the officers' cabins, went himself with three other men to the captain's cabin.

It was just before sunrise when they dragged him from his bed, and tying his hands behind his back, threatened him with instant death if he should call for help or offer any kind of resistance. He was taken up to the quarter-deck in his nightclothes, and made to stand against the mizzen-mast with four men to guard him.

Christian then gave orders to lower the boat in which he intended to cast them adrift, and one by one the men were allowed to come up the hatchways, and made to go over the side of the ship into it. Meanwhile, no heed was given to the remonstrances, reasoning, and prayers of the captain, saving threats of death unless he was quiet.

Some twine, canvas, sails, a small cask of water, and a quadrant and compass were put into the boat, also some bread and a small quantity of rum and wines. When this was done the officers were brought up one by one and forced over the side. There was a great deal of rough joking at the captain's expense, who was still made to stand by the mizzen-mast, and much bad language was used by everybody.

When all the officers were out of the ship, Christian said, "Come, Captain Bligh, your officers and men are now in the boat, and you must go with them; if you make the least resistance you will be instantly put to death."

He was lowered over the side with his hands still fastened behind his back, and directly after the boat was veered astern with a rope.

Some one with a little pity for them threw in some pieces of pork and some clothes, as well as two or three cutlasses; these were the only arms given.

There were altogether nineteen men in this pitiful strait. Although much of the conduct of the mutineers is easily understood with regard to the captain, the wholesale crime of thrusting so many innocent persons out to the mercy of the winds and waves, or to the death from hunger and thirst which they must have believed would inevitably overtake them, is incomprehensible.

As the *Bounty* sailed away, leaving them to their fate, those in the boat cast anxious looks to the captain, wondering what should be done. At a time when his mind must have been full of the injury he had received, and the loss of his ship at a moment when his plans were so flourishing and he had every reason to congratulate himself as to the ultimate success of the undertaking, it is much in his favor that he seems to have realized their unfortunate position and to have been determined to make the best of it.

His first care was to see how much food they had. On examining it, they found there was a hundred and fifty pounds of bread, thirty-two pounds of pork, six quarts of rum, six bottles of wine, and twenty-eight gallons of water.

As they were so near Tofoa they determined to put in there for a supply of breadfruit and water, so that they might keep their other provisions. But after rowing along the coast for some time, they only discovered some cocoanut trees on the top of a stony cliff, against which the sea beat furiously. After several attempts they succeeded in getting about twenty nuts. The second day they failed to get anything at all.

However, some natives came down to the boat and made inquiries about the ship; but the captain unfortunately told the men to say she had been lost, and that only they were saved.

This proved most disastrous; for the treacherous natives, finding they were defenceless, at first brought them presents of breadfruit, plantains and cocoanuts, rendering them all more hopeful and cheerful by their kindness. But toward night their numbers increased in a most alarming manner, and soon the whole beach was lined with them.

Presently they began knocking stones together, by which the men knew they intended to make an attack upon them. They made haste to get all the things into the boat, and all but one, named John Norton, succeeded in reaching it. The natives rushed upon this poor man and stoned him to death.

Those in the boat put to sea with all haste, but were again terribly alarmed to find themselves followed by natives in canoes from which they renewed the attack.

Many of the sailors were a good deal hurt by stones, and they had no means at all with which to protect themselves. At last they threw some clothes overboard; these tempted the enemy to stop to pick them up, and as soon as night came on they gave up the chase and returned to the shore.

All the men now begged Captain Bligh to take them toward England; but he told them there could be no hope of relief until they reached Timor, a distance of full twelve hundred leagues; and that, if they wished to reach it, they would have to content themselves with one ounce of bread and a quarter of a pint of water a day. They all readily agreed to this allowance of food, and made a most solemn oath not to depart from their promise to be satisfied with the small quantity. This was about May 2.

After the compact was made, the boat was put in order, the men divided into watches, and they bore away under a reefed lug-foresail.

A fiery sun rose on the 3d, which is commonly a sign of rough weather, and filled the almost hopeless derelicts with a new terror.

In an hour or two it blew very hard, and the sea ran so high that their sail was becalmed between the waves; they did not dare to set it when on the top of the sea, for the water rushed in over the stern of the boat, and they were obliged to bale with all their might.

The bread was in bags, and in the greatest danger of being spoiled by the wet. They were obliged to throw some rope and the spare sails overboard, as well as all the clothes but what they wore, to lighten the boat; then the carpenter's tool-chest was cleared and the bread put into it.

They were all very wet and cold, and a teaspoonful of rum was served to each man, with a quarter of a breadfruit which was so bad that it could hardly be eaten; but the captain was determined at all risks to keep to the compact they had entered into, and to make their provisions last eight weeks.

In the afternoon the sea ran even higher, and at night it became very cold; but still they did not dare to leave off baling for an instant, though their legs and arms were numb with fatigue and wet.

In the morning a teaspoonful of rum was served to all, and five small cocoanuts divided for their dinner, and every one was satisfied.

When the gale had subsided they examined the bread, and found a great deal of it had become mouldy and rotten; but even this was carefully kept and used. The boat was now near some islands, but they were afraid to go on shore, as the natives might attack them; while being in sight of land, where they might replenish their poor stock of provisions and rest themselves, added to their misery. One morning they hooked a fish, and were overjoyed at their good fortune; but in trying to get it into the boat it was lost, and again they had to content themselves with the damaged bread and small allowance of water for their supper.

They were dreadfully cramped for room, and were obliged to manage so that half their number should lie down in the bottom of the boat or upon a chest, while the others sat up and kept watch; their limbs became so stiff from being constantly wet, and from want of space to stretch them in, that after a few hours' sleep they were hardly able to move.

About May 7, they passed what the captain supposed must be the Fiji Islands, and two large canoes put off and followed them for some time, but in the afternoon they gave up the chase. It rained heavily that day, and every one in the boat did his best to catch some water, and they succeeded in increasing their stock to thirty-four gallons, besides having had enough to drink for the first time since they had been cast adrift; but the rain made them very cold and miserable, as they had no dry clothes.

The next morning they had an ounce and a half of pork, a teaspoonful of rum, half a pint of cocoa-nut milk and an ounce of bread for breakfast, which was quite a large meal for them.

Through fifteen weary days and nights of ceaseless rain they toiled, sometimes through fierce storms of thunder and lightning, and before terrific seas lashed into foam and fury by swift and sudden squalls, with only their miserable pittance of bread and water to keep body and soul together.

In this rain and storm the little sleep they got only added to their discomfort, save for the brief forgetfulness it brought; for they had to lie down in water in the bottom of the boat, and with no covering but the streaming clouds above them.

The captain then advised them to wring their clothes through sea-water, which they found made them feel much warmer for a time.

On May 17 every one was ill and complaining of great pain, and begging for more food; but the captain refused to increase their allowance, though he gave them all a small quantity of rum.

Until the 24th they flew before the wild seas that swept over stem and stern of their boat and kept them constantly baling.

Some of them now looked more than half dead from starvation, but no one suffered from thirst, as they had absorbed so much water through the skin.

A fine morning dawned on the 25th, when they saw the sun for the first time for fifteen days, and were able to eat their scanty allowance in more comfort and warmth. In the afternoon there were numbers of birds called boobies and noddies near, which are never seen far from land.

The captain took this opportunity to look at the state of their bread, and found if they did not exceed their allowance there was enough to last for twenty-nine days, when they hoped to reach Timor.

That afternoon some noddies came so near the boat that one was caught. These birds are about the size of a small pigeon; it was divided into eighteen parts and given by lot. The men were much amused when they saw the beak and claws fall to the lot of the captain. The bird was eaten, bones and all, with bread and water, for dinner.

Now they were in calmer seas, they were overtaken by a new trouble. The heat of the sun became so great that many of them were overcome by faintness, and lay in the bottom of the boat in an apathetic state all day, only rousing themselves toward evening, when the catching of birds was attempted.

On the morning of the 28th the sound of breakers could be heard plainly; they had reached the Great Barrier Reef, which runs up much of the east coast of Australia.

After some little time a passage nearly a quarter of a mile in width was discovered through the reef, and they were carried by a strong current into the peaceful waters which lie within the Barrier.

For a little time they were so overjoyed that their past troubles were forgotten. The dull blue-gray lines of the mainland, with its white patches of glaring sandhills, could be seen in the distance, and that afternoon they landed on an island.

They found the rocks around it were covered with oysters and huge clams, which could easily be got at low tide. Some of their party sent out to reconnoitre returned greatly pleased at having found plenty of fresh water.

A fire was made by help of a small magnifying-glass. Among the things thrown into the boat from the ship was a small copper pot; and thus with a mixture of oysters, bread, and pork a stew was made, and every one had plenty to eat.

The day after they landed was the 29th of May, the anniversary of the restoration of King Charles II, and as the captain thought it applied to their own renewed health and strength, he named it Restoration Island.

After a few days' rest, which did much to revive the men, and when they had filled all their vessels with water and had gathered a large supply of oysters, they were ready to go on again.

As they were about to start, everybody was ordered to attend prayers, and as they were embarking about twenty naked savages came running and shouting toward them, each carrying a long barbed spear, but the English made all haste to put to sea.

For several days they sailed over the lakelike stillness of the Barrier reef-bound waters, and past the bold desolations of the Queensland coast, every headland and bay there bearing the names Cook gave them only a few years before, and which still tell us by that nomenclature each its own story of disappointment and hope.

Still making way to the north, they passed many more islands and keys, the onward passage growing hot and hotter, until on June 3, when they doubled Cape York, the peninsula which is all but unique in its northward bend, they were again in the open sea.

By this time many of them were ill with malaria; then for the first time some of the wine which they had with them was used.

But the little boat still bravely made its way with its crew, whose faces were so hollow and ghastly that they looked like a crew of specters, sailing beneath the scorching sun that beat down from the pale blue of the cloudless sky upon a sea hardly less blue in its greater depths. Only the hope that they would soon reach Timor seemed to rouse them from a state of babbling delirium or fitful slumber.

On the 11th the captain told them they had passed the meridian of the east of Timor; and at three o'clock on the next morning they sighted the land.

It was on Sunday, June 14, when they arrived at Company Bay, and were received with every kindness by the people.

Thus ended one of the most remarkable voyages that have ever been made. They had been sent out with provisions only sufficient for their number for *five* days, and Captain Bligh had, by his careful calculation and determination to give each man only that equal portion they had agreed to accept, made it last for *fifty* days, during which time they had come three thousand six hundred and eighteen nautical miles.

There had been days when the men were so hunger-driven that they had besought him with pitiful prayers for more to eat, and when it was his painful duty to refuse it; and times, as they passed those islands where plentiful food could be got, when he had to turn a deaf ear to their longings to land. He had to endure the need of food, the cramped position, the uneasy slumber, as did his men; as well as the more perfect knowledge of their dangers. There had been days and nights while he worked out their bearings when he had to be propped up as he took the stars or sun.

It was, therefore, Captain Bligh's good seamanship, his strict discipline and fairness in the method

of giving food and wine to those who were sick,
that enabled them to land at Timor with the whole
of their number alive, with the exception of the one
man who was stoned to death by the savages at
Tofoa.

THE TWO BOY HOSTAGES AT THE SIEGE OF SERINGAPATAM

Anonymous

IN the year 1791, Lord Cornwallis, then Gov-
ernor-General of India, made preparations for
a final and decisive campaign against Tippoo. He
had not proved himself a successful commander in
America, where he was compelled to surrender himself and army to Washington; but this time fortune
was to follow his arms. His great object was to
capture the principal stronghold of the tyrant,
Seringapatam; with this in view he proceeded to
reduce all the intermediate fortresses, and in February, 1792, appeared in sight of the famous city,
in the dungeons of which many a British soldier
had suffered both a weary imprisonment and a
cruel death.

The army gazed with admiration and wonder on
this magnificent Oriental city, its vast extent of
embattled walls bristling with cannon, on the domes
of its mosques which rose above them, on the cupo-
las of its splendid palaces and the lofty façades
of the great square pagodas. It was garrisoned
by no less than 45,000 men, while beneath its
walls were encamped the troops of the sultan. To

attempt the capture of so strong a place seemed an impossibility.

Great indeed would be the issue of the contest between the two hostile armies. Should the British and their allies be defeated there was nothing before them but a disastrous retreat over hundreds of miles of country already laid waste by sword and fire; while if Tippoo suffered a reverse nothing remained for him but a humiliating surrender. The ardor of Cornwallis's troops had been kindled by the stories of the frightful tortures which the despot had practiced upon his helpless prisoners, and they were passionately desirous of avenging them.

Although his forces were far inferior in number, Lord Cornwallis decided upon an immediate attack on the enemy's camp in three divisions. The evening was calm and beautiful, the moon just rising to shed her silvery light over the scene, as the troops moved on in silence, but with hearts beating high with courage and hopes of success.

Lord Cornwallis himself led the center division, sword in hand, and headed several bayonet charges, during which he received a wound in the hand. The attack took Tippoo by complete surprise. On the first alarm he rushed from his gorgeous tent and sprang on to his horse, and as he did so a mass of fugitives thronged past him, conveying the intelligence that his center had been penetrated, and a column was marching to cut off his retreat from the great ford leading across the river Cauvery to Seringapatam. He had only just time to make good his escape.

All night the fighting raged, and by morning

Tippoo reckoned he had lost, in killed, wounded, and missing, no less than 23,000 men. Being unable to recapture his largest—the sultan's—redoubt, he abandoned all the others, and, in a fit of despair, withdrew his forces to the island and fortress of Seringapatam, there to make a last stand.

The besiegers pressed forward with vigor, and on its two principal sides the city was completely invested. The pioneers and working-parties were actively at work, and soon turned Tippoo's wonderful garden into a scene of desolation. The sultan saw that his situation was becoming desperate, and made an attempt to negotiate, but at the same time thought to paralyse the efforts of the English and end the war, by procuring the assassination of their chief. A number of horsemen, drugged and maddened by *bhang,* vowed to bring to the sultan the head of his foe, and lay it at his feet as an offering. They made the dash into the British camp, but before they could secure their trophy were routed, and most of them slain.

It is impossible to enumerate all the deeds of heroism performed during the battle and the progress of the siege—the bravery of Captain Hugh Sibbald, who, with a hundred Highlanders, captured and defended the sultan's redoubt against innumerable odds; of the courage of Major Dalrymple, with his Highlanders and Bengal infantry, who, to draw attention from the working-parties, crossed the Cauvery, and fell furiously upon Tippoo's cavalry camp. Every British soldier seemed animated with a dauntless courage. Meantime a trench had been opened within 800 yards of the walls, and the advances carried on with spirit and energy. The anger of the Oriental despot manifested itself by a continual discharge of cannon.

Eighteen days after the battle everything was ready for a grand attack upon the citadel of Seringapatam. The British soldiers, flushed with success, and burning to avenge the cruel sufferings and murders of their countrymen, were eager to commence the assault. The besieged, crushed, despairing, expected every minute to hear the roar of the breaching batteries, and to see their stately mosques in flames. At this moment, so full of anticipation, orders were issued to cease all acts of hostility. Tippoo had sued for peace; but at the very instant the order for cessation of firing was issued, every gun that could be brought to bear upon the trenches, and the musketry from all available points, were ordered by the sultan to be fired.

In the treaty which was now drawn up Tippoo not only agreed to release all his prisoners, but to pay the equivalent of $16,500,000, yield up half his possessions, and to place in the hands of the British his two eldest sons, to be retained as hostages till the due performance of his pledges.

Never before had Indian history presented so touching a spectacle as that seen on the day when the young princes were delivered into the hands of their father's conquerors. On the morning of the 26th of February, twenty days only after the appearance of the British before the walls, the two youthful hostages, each mounted on a richly-caparisoned elephant, left the fort. Soldiers and citizens, stirred by deep sympathy, thronged the ram-

parts to take one last look at the two boys. Even
the stern and cruel Tippoo himself was moved, and
found it difficult to repress his emotion as, standing
on the bastion above the great entrance, he watched
the procession.

When the youthful hostages issued from the
fortress the guns of Seringapatam thundered forth
a salute; and as they approached the British lines
they were received with similar honors. Accompanied by the English negotiator of the terms of
peace and a guard of honor, they were met at the
outposts and conveyed to the camp. "Each was
seated in a howdah of chased silver. They were
arrayed in robes of white, with red turbans in which
a spray of pearls was fastened, while jewels and
diamonds of great value were around and suspended
from their necks. *Harcarrahs,* or Brahmin messengers of trust, headed the procession, and seven
standard-bearers, each carrying a small green banner displayed on a rocket-pole. After these
marched 100 pikemen, whose weapons were inlaid
with silver. Their escort was a squadron of cavalry,
with 200 sepoy soldiers. They were received by
the troops in line, with presented arms, drums beating, and officers in front saluting."

Being conducted to the tent of Lord Cornwallis,
who stood at the entrance surrounded by his staff
and the various colonels of the regiments, they descended from their howdahs and approached him.
Embracing them both, he took them by the hand
and led them inside. Although of the respective
ages of ten and twelve years, the children appeared
to possess all the politeness and reserve of man-

hood. The principal officer of Tippoo, after having
formally surrendered them to the general, said—
"These children were this morning the sons of my
master, the sultan. Their situation is now changed;
they must look up to your lordship as their father."

Early in the year 1794, Tippoo having fulfilled
all the terms of the treaty, the two youthful hostages were restored to their father. They were
conducted by an officer to Deonhully, on a plain
near which the sultan had pitched his tent. The
two boys knelt to their father, placing their heads
at his feet. He received them apparently unmoved,
touched their necks, and when they arose pointed
to their seats; and this was all the welcome they
publicly received.

THE MAN WHO SPOILED NAPO-
LEON'S "DESTINY"

By Rev. W. H. Fitchett, LL. D.

FROM March 18 to May 20, 1799—for more
than sixty days and nights, that is—a little
half-forgotten, and more than half-ruined Syrian
town was the scene of one of the fiercest and most
dramatic sieges recorded in military history. And
rarely has there been a struggle so apparently one-
sided.

A handful of British sailors and Turkish irregulars were holding Acre, a town without regular defences, against Napoleon, the most brilliant
military genius of his generation, with an army of

10,000 war-hardened veterans, the "Army of Italy" —soldiers who had dared the snows of the Alps and conquered Italy, and to whom victory was a familiar experience. In their ranks military daring had reached, perhaps, its very highest point. And yet the sailors inside that ring of crumbling wall won! At Acre Napoleon experienced his first defeat; and, years after, at St. Helena, he said of Sir Sidney Smith, the gallant sailor who baffled him, "That man made me miss my destiny." It is a curious fact that one Englishman thwarted Napoleon's career in the East, and another ended his career in the West, and it may be doubted which of the two Napoleon hated most—Wellington, who finally overthrew him at Waterloo, or Sidney Smith, who, to use Napoleon's own words, made him "miss his destiny," and exchange the empire of the East for a lonely pinnacle of rock in the Atlantic.

Sidney Smith was a sailor of the school of Nelson and of Dundonald—a man, that is, with a spark of that warlike genius which begins where mechanical rules end. He was a man of singular physical beauty, with a certain magnetism and fire about him which made men willing to die for him. He became a middy at the tender age of eleven years; went through fierce sea-fights, and was actually mate of the watch when fourteen years old. He was a fellow-middy with William IV in the fight off Cape St. Vincent, became commander when he was eighteen years of age, and captain before he was quite nineteen. But the British marine, even in those tumultuous days, scarcely yielded

THEY FOUND THE ROCKS WERE COVERED WITH
OYSTERS AND HUGE CLAMS
—page 377

From the drawing by Alec Ball

enough of the rapture of fighting to this post-captain in his teens. He took service under the Swedish flag, saw hard fighting against the Russians, became the close personal friend of the king, and was knighted by him. One of the feats at this period of his life with which tradition, with more or less of plausibility, credits Sidney Smith, is that of swimming by night through the Russian fleet, a distance of two miles, carrying a letter enclosed in a bladder to the Swedish admiral.

Sidney Smith afterwards entered the Turkish service. When war broke out betwixt France and England in 1790, he purchased a tiny craft at Smyrna, picked up in that port a mixed crew, and hurried to join Lord Hood, who was then holding Toulon. When the British abandoned the port—and it is curious to recollect that the duel between Sidney Smith and Napoleon, which reached its climax at Acre, began here—Sidney Smith volunteered to burn the French fleet, a task which he performed with an audacity and skill worthy of Nelson, and for which the French never forgave him.

Sidney Smith was given the command of an English frigate, and fought a dozen brilliant fights in the Channel. He carried with his boats a famous French privateer off Havre de Grace; but during the fight on the deck of the captured ship it drifted into the mouth of the Seine above the forts. The wind dropped, the tide was too strong to be stemmed, and Sidney Smith himself was captured. He had so harried the French coast that the French refused to treat him as an ordinary prisoner of war, and threw him into that forbidding prison, the Temple, from whose iron-barred windows the unfortunate sailor watched for two years the horrors of the Reign of Terror in its last stages, the tossing crowds, the tumbrils rolling past, crowded with victims for the guillotine. Sidney Smith escaped at last by a singularly audacious trick. Two confederates, dressed in dashing uniform, one wearing the dress of an adjutant, and the other that of an officer of still higher rank, presented themselves at the Temple with forged orders for the transfer of Sidney Smith.

The governor surrendered his prisoner, but insisted on sending a guard of six men with him. The sham adjutant cheerfully acquiesced, but, after a moment's pause, turned to Sidney Smith and said, if he would give his parole as an officer not to attempt to escape, they would dispense with the escort. Sidney Smith, with due gravity, replied to his confederate, "Sir, I swear on the faith of an officer to accompany you wherever you choose to conduct me." The governor was satisfied, and the two sham officers proceeded to "conduct" their friend with the utmost possible despatch to the French coast. Another English officer who had escaped—Captain Wright—joined Sidney Smith outside Rouen, and the problem was how to get through the barriers without a passport. Smith sent Wright on first, and he was duly challenged for his passport by the sentinel; whereupon Sidney Smith, with a majestic air of official authority, marched up and said in faultless Parisian French, "I answer for this citizen, I know him"; whereupon

the deluded sentinel saluted and allowed them both
to pass!

Sidney Smith's escape from the Temple made
him a popular hero in England. He was known
to have great influence with the Turkish authorities, and he was sent to the East in the double office
of envoy-extraordinary to the Porte, and commander of the squadron at Alexandria. By one
of the curious coincidences which marked Sidney
Smith's career, he became acquainted while in the
Temple with a French Royalist officer named Philippeaux, an engineer of signal ability, and who had
been a schoolfellow and a close chum of Napoleon
himself at Brienne. Smith took his French friend
with him to the East, and he played a great part in
the defence of Acre. Napoleon had swept north
through the desert to Syria, had captured Gaza
and Jaffa, and was about to attack Acre, which lay
between him and his ultimate goal, Constantinople.
Here Sidney Smith resolved to bar his way, and
in his flagship the *Tigre,* with the *Theseus*, under
Captain Miller, and two gunboats, he sailed to
Acre to assist in its defence. Philippeaux took
charge of the fortifications, and thus, in the breaches
of a remote Syrian town, the former prisoner of
the Temple and the ancient school friend of Napoleon joined hands to wreck that dream of a great
Eastern empire which lurked in the cells of Napoleon's masterful intellect.

Acre looks like a blunted arrow-head jutting out
from a point in the Syrian coast. Napoleon could
only attack, so to speak, the *neck* of the arrow,
which was protected by a ditch and a weak wall,

and flanked by towers; but Sidney Smith, having
command of the sea, could sweep the four faces of
the town with the fire of his guns, as well as command all the sea-roads in its vicinity. He guessed,
from the delay of the French in opening fire, that
they were waiting for their siege-train to arrive
by sea. He kept vigilant watch, pounced on the
French flotilla as it rounded the promontory of
Mount Carmel, captured nine of the vessels, carried them with their guns and warlike material to
Acre, and mounted his thirty-four captured pieces
on the batteries of the town. Thus the disgusted
French saw the very guns which were intended to
batter down the defences of Acre—and which were
glorious with the memories of a dozen victories
in Italy—frowning at them, loaded with English
powder and shot, and manned by English sailors.

It is needless to say that a siege directed by Napoleon—the siege of what he looked upon as a contemptible and almost defenceless town, the single
barrier betwixt his ambition and its goal—was
urged with amazing fire and vehemence. The wall
was battered day and night, a breach fifty feet wide
made, and more than twelve assaults delivered, with
all the fire and daring of which French soldiers, gallantly led, are capable. So sustained was the fighting, that on one occasion the combat raged in the
ditch and on the breach for *twenty-five* successive
hours. So close and fierce was it that one half-
ruined tower was held by *both* besiegers and besieged for twelve hours in succession, and neither
would yield. At the breach, again, the two lines
of desperately fighting men on repeated occasions

clashed bayonets together, and wrestled and stabbed and died, till the survivors were parted by the barrier of the dead which grew beneath their feet.

Sidney Smith, however, fought like a sailor, and with all the cool ingenuity and resourcefulness of a sailor. His ships, drawn up on two faces of the town, smote the French stormers on either flank till they learned to build up a dreadful screen, made up partly of stones plucked from the breach, and partly of the dead bodies of their comrades. Smith, too, perched guns in all sorts of unexpected positions—a 24-pounder in the lighthouse, under the command of an exultant middy; two 68-pounders under the charge of "old Bray," the carpenter of the *Tigre*, and, as Sidney Smith himself reports, "one of the bravest and most intelligent men I ever served with"; and yet a third gun, a French brass 18-pounder, in one of the ravelins, under a master's mate. Bray dropped his shells with the nicest accuracy in the center of the French columns as they swept up the breach, and the middy perched aloft, and the master's mate from the ravelin, smote them on either flank with case-shot, while the *Theseus* and the *Tigre* added to the tumult the thunder of their broadsides, and the captured French gunboats contributed the yelp of their lighter pieces.

The great feature of the siege, however, was the fierceness and the number of the sorties. Sidney Smith's sorties actually exceeded in number and vehemence Napoleon's assaults. He broke the strength of Napoleon's attacks, that is, by anticipating them. A crowd of Turkish irregulars, with a few naval officers leading them, and a solid mass of Jack-tars in the center, would break from a sally-port, or rush vehemently down through the gap in the wall, and scour the French trenches, overturn the gabions, spike the guns, and slay the guards. The French reserves hurried fiercely up, always scourged, however, by the flank fire of the ships, and drove back the sortie. But the process was renewed the same night or the next day with unlessened fire and daring. The French engineers, despairing of success on the surface, betook themselves to mining; whereupon the besieged made a desperate sortie and reached the mouth of the mine. Lieutenant Wright, who led them, and who had already received two shots in his sword-arm, leaped down the mine followed by his sailors, slew the miners, destroyed their work, and safely regained the town.

The British sustained one startling disaster. Captain Miller of the *Theseus*, whose ammunition ran short, carefully collected such French shells as fell into the town without exploding, and duly returned them, alight, and supplied with better fuses, to their original senders. He had collected some seventy shells on the *Theseus*, and was preparing, them for use against the French. The carpenter of the ship was endeavoring to get the fuses out of the loaded shells with an auger, and a middy undertook to assist him, in characteristic middy fashion, with a mallet and a spike-nail. A huge shell under his treatment suddenly exploded on the quarter-deck of the *Theseus*, and the other sixty-nine shells followed suit. The too ingenious middy disappeared into space; forty seamen, with Captain Miller himself, were killed; and forty-seven, including the two lieutenants of the ship, the chaplain, and the surgeon, were seriously wounded. The whole of the poop was blown to pieces, and the ship was left a wreck with fire breaking out at half-a-dozen points. The fire was subdued, and the *Theseus* survived in a half-gutted condition, but the disaster was a severe blow to Sir Sidney's resources.

As evening fell on May 7, the white sails of a fleet became visible, and all firing ceased while besiegers and besieged watched the approaching ships. Was it a French fleet or a Turkish? Did it bring succor to the besieged or a triumph to the besiegers? The approaching ships flew the crescent. It was the Turkish fleet from Rhodes bringing reinforcements. But the wind was sinking, and Napoleon, who had watched the approach of the hostile ships with feelings which may be guessed, calculated that there remained six hours before they could cast anchor in the bay. Eleven assaults had been already made, in which eight French generals and the best officers in every branch of the service had perished. There remained time for a twelfth assault. He might yet pluck victory from the very edge of defeat. At ten o'clock that night the French artillery was brought up close to the counterscarp to batter down the curtain, and a new breach was made. Lannes led his division against the shot-wrecked tower, and General Rimbaud took his grenadiers with a resistless rush through the new breach. All night the combat raged, the men fighting desperately hand to hand. When the rays of the level morning sun broke through the pall of smoke which hung sullenly over the combatants, the tricolor flew on the outer angle of the tower, and still the ships bringing reinforcements had not reached the harbor! Sidney Smith, at this crisis, landed every man from the English ships, and led them, pike in hand, to the breach, and the shouting and madness of the conflict awoke once more. To use Sidney Smith's own words, "the muzzles of the muskets touched each other—the spear-heads were locked together." But Sidney Smith's sailors, with the brave Turks who rallied to their help, were not to be denied.

Lanne's grenadiers were tumbled headlong from the tower, Lannes himself being wounded, while Rimbaud's brave men, who were actually past the breach, were swept into ruin, their general killed, and the French soldiers within the breach all captured or slain.

One of the dramatic incidents of the siege was the assault made by Kleber's troops. They had not taken part in the siege hitherto, but had won a brilliant victory over the Arabs at Mount Tabor, On reaching the camp, flushed with their triumph, and seeing how slight were the apparent defences of the town, they demanded clamorously to be led to the assault. Napoleon consented. Kleber, who was of gigantic stature, with a head of hair worthy of a German music-master or of a Soudan dervish, led his grenadiers to the edge of the breach and stood there, while with gesture and voice—a voice audible even above the fierce and sustained crackle of the musketry—he urged his men on. Napoleon, standing on a gun in the nearest French battery, watched the sight with eager eyes—the French grenadiers running furiously up the breach, the grim line of levelled muskets that barred it, the sudden roar of the English guns as from every side they smote the staggering French column. Vainly single officers struggled out of the torn mass, ran gesticulating up the breach, and died at the muzzles of the British muskets. The men could not follow, or only died as they leaped forward. The French grenadiers, still fighting, swearing, and screaming, were swept back past the point where Kleber stood, hoarse with shouting, black with gunpowder, furious with rage. The last assault on Acre had failed. The French sick, field artillery, and baggage silently defiled that night to the rear. The heavy guns were buried in the sand, and after sixty days of open trenches Napoleon, for the first time in his life, though not for the last, ordered a retreat.

Napoleon buried in the breaches of Acre not merely 3,000 of his bravest troops, but the golden dream of his life. "In that miserable fort," as he said, "lay the fate of the East." Napoleon expected to find in it the pasha's treasures, and arms for 300,000 men. "When I have captured it," he said to Bourrienne, "I shall march upon Damascus and Aleppo. I shall arm the tribes; I shall reach Constantinople; I shall overturn the Turkish Empire; I shall found in the East a new and grand empire. Perhaps I shall return to Paris by Adrianople and Vienna!" Napoleon was cheerfully willing to pay the price of what religion he had to accomplish this dream. He was willing, that is, to turn Turk. "Had I but captured Acre," Napoleon added, "I would have reached Constantinople and the Indies; I would have changed the face of the world. But that man made me miss my destiny."

A FIRE-FIGHTER'S RESCUE FROM THE FLAMES

By Arthur Quiller-Couch

ABOUT a hundred years ago, long before James Braidwood had arisen to organize the fire-brigades of Edinburgh and London and set the example which has since been followed by every town in the civilized world, late on a dark afternoon a young stableman, John Elliot by name, was sauntering carelessly homewards down Piccadilly, London, when a glare in the sky, the confused murmurs of a large crowd, and the hurrying footsteps of pedestrians who passed him, told of a not distant fire.

Following the footsteps of the passers-by, he found himself in one of the side streets leading off Piccadilly, and there at the end of the street, a large house was blazing furiously. He worked his way vigorously through the spectators, now so densely gathered as to form a living wedge in the narrow street and block it against all traffic, and at length found himself in a position to see clearly the ruin that had already been wrought on the burning pile.

As a matter of fact, all was pretty well over with

the house. How far the upper stories were intact he had little means of judging; but he saw that the ceilings of the first and second floors had given way, and also that the fire was running along the rafters of the floor above. Flames were pouring from half a dozen windows. He turned to a man who stood next him in the concourse.

"The house is nearly done for," he remarked.

"Quite," replied the man. "You see it is burned through, and it is only a question of minutes before the roof must tumble in. The firemen do not dare to make any further attempt. It is a dreadful business."

"What?"

"Why, don't you know? This is Lady Dover's house—poor old soul! and she is still there, in the top room. No one can save her now, but it is a hideous death all the same."

Elliot looked about him and now understood the pallor on the upturned faces of the crowd. He looked at the house again. The whole street was wrapped in a crimson mist; the falling streams of water which the firemen still continued to direct on the blaze were hissing impotently, and seemed only to feed the fire. In the crowd that watched there was hardly a sound; one could almost hear men's hearts beating as they waited for the conclusion of the tragedy which they knew to be inevitable. But further down the street, where it was not understood that human life was at stake in the midst of this spectacle, rose the sounds of girls laughing, men quarrelling and fighting, whistling, oaths, and merriment. Caps were flying about, and the mass

was jostling and swaying to and fro, as before
Newgate on a Monday morning.

"Do you mean to say," asked Elliot, after a moment, "that the poor old lady is up there and nobody is going to save her?"

"What's the use?" answered the man. "If you
think it possible, better try for yourself." But this
reply was not heard, for the young stableman had
already begun to push his way forward to the group
of firemen that stood watching the conflagration in
despair.

He was a man of extraordinary strength, and
now with a set purpose to inspire him still further,
he scattered the crowd to right and left, elbowing,
pushing, and thrusting, until he stood before the
firemen and repeated his question.

He met with the same answer. "It was impossible," they said. Everything had been done that
could be, and now there was nothing but to wait
for the end.

"But it is a question of human life," he objected.

In reply they merely pointed to the flame-points
now running along every yard of woodwork still
left in the building.

Elliot caught a ladder from their hands and, running forward with it, planted it firmly against the
house. He had to choose his place carefully, as
almost every one of the windows above was belch-
ing out an angry blaze.

"Which is the window where they were last
seen?" he asked.

The firemen pointed. The crowd at length finding that a brave man was going to risk his life,

raised a cheer as they caught sight of him, and standing on tiptoe, peered over each other's shoulders to get a better view of the work that was forward.

"Now then," said Elliot, "don't try to stop the flames, for that is useless, but keep the water playing on the ladder all the time."

He slipped off his shoes, and amid another cheer from the crowd, dashed up it as quick as thought. The window to which the fireman had pointed was clear of flames. On gaining it, Elliot sprang on to the sill and jumped down into the room.

It was lighted brilliantly enough by the glow from the street, and through the dense smoke that was already beginning to fill it he saw two figures.

Both were women, and for a moment the gallant man doubted that he had come in time; for so still and motionless were they that it seemed as if the smoke must have already stifled them, and left them in these startling attitudes. One—a very old lady—was kneeling by the bedside, her head bent forward in despair, her hands flung out over the counterpane. The other—a tall, heavy-looking woman—was standing bolt upright by the window. Neither spoke nor stirred, and the kneeling woman did not even raise her head at the noise of his entrance; the other, with eyes utterly expressionless and awful, supported herself with one hand against the wall, and gazed at him speechlessly. Awestruck by this sight, Elliot had to pause a moment before he found his speech.

"Which is Lady Dover?" he cried at last.

The kneeling woman lifted her head, saw him,

and with a cry, or rather a smothered exclamation
of hope, got upon her feet and ran forward to him.
He hurried her to the window. She obeyed him in
silence, for it was clear that terror had robbed her
tongue of all articulate speech. He clambered out,
turned on the topmost rung, and flinging an arm
round her waist, was lifting her out, when the other
figure stepped forward and set a hand on his
shoulder. The look on this woman's face was
now terrible. Something seemed working in her
throat and the muscles of her face: it was her
despair struggling with her paralyzed senses for
speech.

"Me to," she at length managed to mutter
hoarsely; but the sound when it came was, as Elliot afterwards declared, like nothing in heaven or
earth.

"If life is left in me, I will come back for you,"
he cried.

But his heart failed him when he saw the distance he should have to go, and still more when he
noted her size. For the ladder was slippery from
the water which the firemen kept throwing upon it,
and which alone saved it from catching on fire.
Moreover, the clouds of smoke in the room had
thickened considerably since his entrance, and it
could not be many minutes now before the floor
gave way, or the roof crashed in, or both. He had
felt his feet scorched through his stockings, when
he set foot on the boards.

Down in the street the crowd had increased
enormously; gentlemen from the clubs, waiters and
loungers from a distance had all gathered to look.

As Elliot descended the ladder with his burden a frantic storm of cheering broke forth—for every soul present understood the splendid action that had just been performed; and the crush around the foot of the ladder of those who pressed forward to express their admiration was terrific.

But they knew, of course, nothing of the stout lady still left in the bedroom; and when Elliot, heedless of the cheers and hand-shakes that met him, flung Lady Dover into the arms of the nearest bystander, and turned again towards the ladder, they were utterly at a loss to understand what he could be about.

But he kept his word. A dead hush fell again upon the spectators, as once more the brave man dashed up the ladder, upon which the firemen had ceased now to play. Half-way up he turned.

"Keep on at the pumps!" he called; and then again was up to the window and looked in. The lady had still preserved her former attitude, though leaning now further back against the wall and panting for breath in the stifling smoke. He put his hand out to her.

"Catch hold of my neck and hold tightly round it," he said.

But again she was speechless and helpless. Her eyes lit up as she saw him, but beyond this she hardly seemed to understand his words. Elliot groaned, and finding, after another trial, that she did not comprehend, boldly reached in and grasped her round the waist.

She was heavier even than he had imagined, and for one fearful moment, as he stood poised on the topmost rung, he thought that all was over. It seemed impossible that they should ever reach the ground except by tumbling off the ladder. By a superhuman effort, however, he managed to drag her out, and then clasping her waist with one arm, whilst with the other he held on like grim death, he hung breathless for a moment, and then began slowly to descend.

Up to this point there had been no sound in the street below. But now, as the watchers saw his feet moving down the ladder, their enthusiasm broke out in one deep sigh, followed by yells and shouts of admiration. As the young stableman slowly descended, and finally, by God's mercy, reached the ground with his burden, these feelings broke all bounds. Men rushed round him; guineas were poured by the handful into his pockets; and when these and his hands were full, the gold was even stuffed into his mouth.

But, in the midst of this excitement, a sudden crash caused the spectators to look upwards again. It was the roof of the house that had fallen in, only a minute after Elliot had set his foot upon the ground.

The lady whom he had saved by this second brave ascent was a relative of Lady Dover, by name Mlle. von Hompesch. It is pleasant to hear that her preserver was rewarded by the family of Lady Dover, who bestowed a pension upon him. At a later period he was in the service of the first Lord Braybrooke, and this narrative was preserved by a member of the family who had often heard Elliot relate it. Like all brave men, he never spoke vaingloriously of his exploit; but always professed great gratitude for his reward, which seemed to him considerably higher than his deserts.

HOW NAPOLEON REWARDED HIS MEN

By Lieutenant-General Baron de Marbot

AFTER crossing the Traun, burning the bridge at Mauthhausen, and passing the Enns, Napoleon's army advanced to Mölk, without knowing what had become of General Hiller. Some spies assured us that the archduke had crossed the Danube and joined him, and that we should on the morrow meet the whole Austrian army, strongly posted in front of Saint-Pölten. In that case, we must make ready to fight a great battle; but if it were otherwise, we had to march quickly on Vienna in order to get there before the enemy could reach it by the other bank. For want of positive information the emperor was very undecided. The question to be solved was, Had General Hiller crossed the Danube, or was he still in front of us, masked by a swarm of light cavalry, which, always flying, never let us get near enough to take a prisoner from whom one might get some enlightenment?

Still knowing nothing for certain, we reached, on May 7, the pretty little town of Mölk, standing on the bank of the Danube, and overhung by an immense rock, on the summit of which rises a Benedictine convent, said to be the finest and richest in Christendom. From the rooms of the monastery a wide view is obtained over both banks of the Danube. There the emperor and many marshals, including Lannes, took up their quarters, while our staff lodged with the parish priest. Much rain had fallen during the week, and it had not ceased for twenty-four hours and still was falling, so that the Danube and its tributaries were over their banks. That night, as my comrades and I, delivered at being sheltered from the bad weather, were having a merry supper with the parson, a jolly fellow, who gave us an excellent meal, the aide-de-camp on duty with the marshal came to tell me that I was wanted, and must go up to the convent that moment. I was so comfortable where I was that I found it annoying to have to leave a good supper and good quarters to go and get wet again, but I had to obey.

All the passages and lower rooms of the monastery were full of soldiers. On reaching the dwelling-rooms, I saw that I had been sent for about some serious matter, for generals, chamberlains, orderly officers, said to me repeatedly, "The emperor has sent for you." Some added, "It is probably to give you your commission as major." This I did not believe, for I did not think I was yet of sufficient importance to the sovereign for him to send for me at such an hour to give me my commission with his own hands. I was shown into a vast and handsome gallery, with a balcony looking over the Danube; there I found the emperor at dinner with several marshals and the abbot of the convent, who has the title of bishop. On seeing me, the emperor left the table, and went toward the balcony, followed by Lannes. I heard him say in a low tone, "The execution of this plan is almost impossible; it would be sending a brave officer for no purpose to almost certain death." "He will go, sir," replied the marshal; "I am certain he will go: at any rate we can but propose it to him."

Then, taking me by the hand, the marshal opened the window of the balcony over the Danube. The river at this moment, trebled in volume by the strong flood, was nearly a league wide; it was lashed by a fierce wind, and we could hear the waves roaring. It was pitch-dark, and the rain fell in torrents, but we could see on the other side a long line of bivouac fires. Napoleon, Marshal Lannes, and I being alone on the balcony, the marshal said, "On the other side of the river you see an Austrian camp. Now, the emperor is keenly desirous to know whether General Hiller's corps is there, or still on this bank. In order to make sure he wants a stout-hearted man, bold enough to cross the Danube, and bring away some soldier of the enemy's, and I have assured him that you will go." Then Napoleon said to me, "Take notice that I am not giving you an order; I am only expressing a wish. I am aware that the enterprise is as dangerous as it can be, and you can decline it without any fear of displeasing me. Go, and think it over for a few moments in the next room; come back and tell us frankly your decision."

I admit that when I heard Marshal Lanne's proposal I had broken out all over in a cold sweat; but at the same moment, a feeling which I cannot define, but in which a love of glory and of my country was mingled, perhaps, with a noble pride, raised my ardor to the highest point, and I said to myself, "The emperor has here an army of 150,000 devoted warriors, besides 25,000 men of his guard, all selected from the bravest. He is surrounded with aides-de-camp and orderly officers, and yet when an expedition is on foot, requiring intelligence no less than boldness, it is I whom the emperor and Marshal Lannes choose. "I will go, sir," I cried, without hesitation. "I will go; and if I perish, I leave my mother to your Majesty's care." The emperor pulled my ear to mark his satisfaction; the marshal shook my hand—"I was quite right to tell your Majesty that he would go. There's what you may call a brave soldier."

My expedition being thus decided on, I had to think about the means of executing it. The emperor called General Bertrand, his aide-de-camp, General Dorsenne, of the guard, and the commandant of the imperial headquarters, and ordered them to put at my disposal whatever I might require. At my request an infantry picket went into the town to find the burgomaster, the leader of the boatmen, and five of his best hands. A corporal and five grenadiers of the old guard who could all speak German, and had still to earn their decoration, were also summoned, and voluntarily agreed to go with me. The emperor had them brought in first, and promised that on their return they should receive the Cross at once. The brave men replied by a "Vive l'Empereur!" and went to get ready. As for the five boatmen, on its being explained to them through the interpreter that they had to take a boat across the Danube, they fell on their knees and began to weep. The leader declared that they might just as well be shot at once as sent to certain death. The expedition was absolutely impossible, not only from the strength of the current, but because the tributaries had brought into the Danube a great quantity of fir trees recently cut down in the mountains, which could not be avoided in the dark, and would certainly come against the boat and sink it. Besides, how could one land on the opposite bank among willows which would scuttle the boat, and with a flood of unknown extent? The leader concluded, then, that the operation was physically impossible. In vain did the emperor tempt them with an offer of 6,000 francs per man; even this could not persuade them, though, as they said, they were poor boatmen with families, and this sum would be a fortune to them. But, as I have already said, some lives must be sacrificed to save those of the greater number, and the knowledge of this makes commanders sometimes pitiless. The emperor was inflexible, and the grenadiers received orders to take the poor men, whether they would or not, and we went down to the town.

The corporal who had been assigned to me was an intelligent man. Taking him for my interpreter, I charged him as we went along to tell the leader of the boatmen that as he had to come along with us, he had better in his own interest show us his best boat, and point out everything that we should require for her fitting. The poor man obeyed; so we got an excellent vessel, and we took all that we wanted from the others. We had two anchors, but as I did not think we should be able to make use of them, I had sewn to the end of each cable a piece of canvas with a large stone wrapped in it. I had seen in the south of France the fishermen use an apparatus of this kind to hold their boats by throwing the cord over the willows at the water's edge. I put on a cap, the grenadiers took their forage caps, we had provisions, ropes, axes, saws, a ladder—everything, in short, which I could think of to take.

Our preparations ended, I was going to give the signal to start, when the five boatmen implored me with tears to let the soldiers escort them to their houses, to take perhaps the last farewell of their wives and children; but, fearing that a tender scene of this kind would further reduce their small stock of courage, I refused. Then the leader said, "Well, as we have only a short time to live, allow us five minutes to commend our souls to God, and do you do the same, for you also are going to your death." They all fell on their knees, the grenadiers and I following their example, which seemed to please the worthy people much. Then their prayer was over, I gave each man a glass of wine, and we pushed out into the stream.

I had bidden the grenadiers follow in silence all the orders of the syndic, or leader, who was steering; the current was too strong for us to cross over straight from Mölk: we went up, therefore, along the bank under sail for more than a league, and although the wind and the waves made the boat jump, this part was accomplished without accident.

But when the time came to take to our oars and row out from the land, the mast, on being lowered, fell over to one side, and the sail, dragging in the water, offered a strong resistance to the current and nearly capsized us. The master ordered the ropes to be cut and the masts to be sent overboard: but the boatmen, losing their heads, began to pray without stirring. Then the corporal, drawing his sword, said, "You can pray and work too; obey at once, or I will kill you." Compelled to choose between possible and certain death, the poor fellows took up their hatchets, and with the help of the grenadiers, the mast was promptly cut away and sent floating. It was high time, for hardly were we free from this dangerous burden when we felt a fearful shock. A pine-stem borne down by the stream had struck the boat. We all shuddered, but luckily the planks were not driven in this time. Would the boat, however, resist more shocks of this kind? We could not see the stems, and only knew that they were near by the heavier tumble of the waves. Several touched us, but no serious accident resulted. Meantime the current bore us along, and as our oars could make very little way against it to give us the necessary slant, I feared for a moment that it would sweep us below the enemy's camp, and that my expedition would fail. By dint of hard rowing, however, we had got three-quarters of the way over, when I saw an immense black mass looming over the water. Then a sharp scratching was heard, branches caught us in the face, and the boat stopped. To our questions the owner replied that we were on an island covered with willows and poplars, of which the flood had nearly reached the top. We had to grope about with our hatchets to clear a passage through the branches, and when we had succeeded in passing the obstacle, we found the stream much less furious than in the middle of the river, and finally reached the left bank in front of the Austrian camp. This shore was bordered with very thick trees, which, overhanging the bank like a dome, made the approach difficult, no doubt, but at the same time concealed our boat from the camp. The whole shore was lighted up by the bivouac fires, while we remained in the shadow thrown by the branches of the willows. I let the boat float downward, looking for a suitable landing-place. Presently I perceived that a sloping path had been made down the bank by the enemy to allow the men and horses to get to the water. The corporal adroitly threw into the willows one of the stones that I had made ready, the cord caught in a tree, and the boat brought up against the land a foot or two from the slope. It must have been just about midnight. The Austrians, having the swollen Danube between them and the French, felt themselves so secure that, except the sentry, the whole camp was asleep.

It is usual in war for the guns and the sentinels always to face toward the enemy, however far off he may be. A battery placed in advance of the camp was therefore turned toward the river, and sentries were walking on the top of the bank. The trees prevented them from seeing the extreme edge, while from the boat I could see through the branches a great part of the bivouac. So far my mission had been more successful than I had ventured to hope, but in order to make the success complete I had to bring away a prisoner, and to execute such an operation fifty paces away from several thousand enemies, whom a single cry would rouse, seemed very difficult. Still, I had to do something. I made the five sailors lie down at the bottom of the boat under guard of two grenadiers, another grenadier I posted at the bow of the boat, which was close to the bank, and myself disembarked, sword in hand, followed by the corporal and two grenadiers. The boat was a few feet from dry land; we had to walk in the water, but at last we were on the slope. We went up, and I was making ready to rush on the nearest sentry, disarm him, gag him, and drag him off to the boat, when the ring of metal and the sound of singing in a low voice fell on my ears. A man, carrying a great tin pail, was coming to draw water, humming a song as he went; we quickly went down again to the river to hide under the branches, and as the Austrian stooped to fill his pail, my grenadiers seized him by the throat, put a handkerchief full of wet sand over his mouth, and placing their sword-points against his body, threatened him with death if he resisted or uttered a sound. Utterly bewildered, the man obeyed, and let us take him to the boat; we hoisted him into the hands of the grenadiers posted there, who made him lie down beside the sailors. While this Austrian was lying captured, I saw by his clothes that he was not, strictly speaking, a soldier, but an officer's servant. I should have preferred to catch a combatant who could have given me more precise information; but I was going to content myself with this capture for want of a better, when I saw, at the top of the slope, two soldiers carrying a caldron between them on a pole. They were only a few paces off. It was impossible for us to re-embark without being seen. I therefore signed to my grenadiers to hide themselves again, and as soon as the two Austrians stooped to fill their vessel, powerful arms seized them from behind and plunged their heads under water. We had to stupefy them a little, since they had their swords, and I feared that they might resist. Then they were picked up in turn, their mouths covered with a handkerchief full of sand, and sword-points against their breasts constrained them to follow us. They were shipped as the servant had been, and my men and I got on board again.

So far, all had gone well. I made the sailors get up and take their oars, and ordered the corporal to cast loose the rope which held us to the bank. It was, however, so wet, and the knot had been drawn so tight by the force of the stream, that it was impossible to unfasten. We had to saw the rope, which took us some minutes. Meanwhile, the rope, shaking with our efforts, imparted its movement to the branches of the willow round which it was wrapped, and the rustling became loud enough to attract the notice of the sentry. He drew near, unable to see the boat, but perceiving that the agitation of the branches increased, he called out, "Who goes there?" No answer. Further challenge from the sentry. We held our tongues and worked away. I was in deadly fear; after facing so many dangers, it would have been too cruel if we were wrecked in sight of port. At last the rope was cut, and the boat pushed off. But hardly was it clear of the overhanging willows than the light of the bivouac fires made it visible to the sentry, who, shouting "To arms!" fired at us. No one was hit; but at the sound the whole camp was astir in a moment, and the gunners, whose pieces were ready loaded and trained on the river, honored my boat with some cannon-shots. At the report my heart leaped for joy, for I knew that the emperor and marshal would hear it. I turned my eyes toward the convent, with its lighted windows, of which I had, in spite of the distance, never lost sight. Probably all were open at this moment, but in one only could I perceive any increase of brilliancy; it was the great balcony window, which was as large as the doorway of a church, and sent from afar a flood of light over the stream. Evidently, it had just been opened at the thunder of the cannon, and I said to myself, "The emperor and the marshals are doubtless on the balcony; they know that I have reached the enemy's camp, and are making vows for my safe return." This thought raised my courage, and I heeded the cannon-balls not a bit. Indeed, they were not very dangerous, for the stream swept us along at such a pace that the gunners could not aim with any accuracy, and we must have been very unlucky to get hit. One shot would have done for us, but all fell harmless into the Danube. Soon I was out of range, and could reckon a successful issue to my enterprise. Still, all danger was not yet at an end. We had still to cross among the floating pine-stems, and more than once we struck on submerged islands, and were delayed by the branches of the poplars. At last we reached the right bank, more than two leagues below Mölk, and a new terror assailed me. I could see bivouac fires, and had no means of learning whether they belonged to a French regiment. The enemy had troops on both banks, and I knew that on the right bank Marshal Lannes's outposts were not far from Mölk, facing an Austrian corps, posted at Saint-Pölten.

Our army would doubtless go forward at daybreak, but was it already occupying this place? And were the fires that I saw those of friends or enemies? I was afraid that the current had taken me too far down, but the problem was solved by French cavalry trumpets sounding the reveillé. Our uncertainty being at an end, we rowed with all our strength to the shore, where in the dawning light we could see a village. As we drew near, the report of a carbine was heard, and bullet whistled by our ears. It was evident that the French sentries took us for a hostile crew. I had not foreseen this possibility, and hardly knew how we were to succeed in getting recognized, till the happy thought struck me of making my six grenadiers shout "Vive l'Empereur Napoléon!" This was, of course, no certain evidence that we were French, but it would attract the attention of the officers, who would have no fear of our small numbers, and would no doubt prevent the men from firing on us before they knew whether we were French or Austrians. A few moments later I came ashore, and I was received by Colonel Gautrin and the 9th Hussars, forming part of Lannes's division. If we had landed half a league lower down we should have tumbled into the enemy's pickets. The colonel lent me a horse, and gave me several wagons, in which I placed the grenadiers, the boatmen, and the prisoners, and the little cavalcade went off toward Mölk. As we went along, the corporal, at my orders, questioned the three Austrians, and I learned with satisfaction that the camp whence I had brought them away belonged to the very division, General Hiller's, the position of which the emperor was so anxious to learn. There was, therefore, no further doubt that that general had joined the archduke on the other side of the Danube. There was no longer any question of a battle on the road which we held, and Napoleon, having only the enemy's cavalry in front of him, could in perfect safety push his troops forward toward Vienna, from which we were but three easy marches distant. With this information I galloped forward, in order to bring it to the emperor with the least possible delay.

When I reached the gate of the monastery, it was broad day. I found the approach blocked by the whole population of the little town of Mölk, and heard among the crowd the cries of the wives, children, and friends of the sailors whom I had carried off. In a moment I was surrounded by them, and was able to calm their anxiety by saying, in very bad German, "Your friends are alive, and you will see them in a few moments." A great cry of joy went up from the crowd, bringing out the officer in

command of the guard at the gate. On seeing me
he ran off in pursuance of orders to warn the aides-
de-camp to let the emperor know of my return. In
an instant the whole palace was up. The good
Marshal Lannes came to me, embraced me cor-
dially, and carried me straight off to the emperor,
crying out, "Here he is, sir; I knew he would come
back. He has brought three prisoners from General Hiller's division." Napoleon received me
warmly, and though I was wet and muddy all over,
he laid his hand on my shoulder, and did not forget
to give his greatest sign of satisfaction by pinching
my ear. I leave you to imagine how I was questioned! The emperor wanted to know every incident of the adventure in detail, and when I had
finished my story said, "I am very well pleased with
you, 'Major' Marbot." These words were equivalent to a commission, and my joy was full. At that
moment, a chamberlain announced that breakfast
was served, and as I was calculating on having to
wait in the gallery until the emperor had finished,
he pointed with his finger toward the dining-room,
and said, "You will breakfast with me." As this
honor had never been paid to any officer of my
rank, I was the more flattered. During breakfast
I learned that the emperor and the marshal had not
been to bed all night, and that when they heard the
cannon on the opposite bank they had all rushed
onto the balcony. The emperor made me tell again
the way in which I had surprised the three prisoners, and laughed much at the fright and surprise
which they must have felt.

At last, the arrival of the wagons was announced,

but they had much difficulty in making their way
through the crowd, so eager were the people to see
the boatmen. Napoleon, thinking this very natural,
gave orders to open the gates, and let everybody
come into the court. Soon after, the grenadiers,
the boatmen, and the prisoners were led into the
gallery. The emperor, through his interpreter,
first questioned the three Austrian soldiers, and
learning with satisfaction that not only General
Hiller's corps, but the whole of the archduke's
army, were on the other bank, he told Berthier to
give the order for the troops to march at once on
Saint-Pölten. Then, calling up the corporal and
the five soldiers, he fastened the Cross on their
breast, appointed them knights of the empire, and
gave them an annuity of 1,200 francs apiece. All
the veterans wept for joy. Next came the boatmen's turn. The emperor told them that, as the
danger they had run was a good deal more than he
had expected, it was only fair that he should increase their reward; so instead of the 6,000 francs
promised, 12,000 in gold were given to them on
the spot. Nothing could express their delight; they
kissed the hands of the emperor and all present,
crying, "Now we are rich!" Napoleon laughingly
asked the leader if he would go the same journey
for the same price the next night. But the man
answered that, having escaped by miracle what
seemed certain death, he would not undertake such
a journey again even if his lordship, the abbot of
Mölk, would give him the monastery and all its
possessions. The boatmen withdrew, blessing the
generosity of the French emperor, and the grena-

diers, eager to show off their decoration before their comrades, were about to go off with their three prisoners, when Napoleon perceived that the Austrian servant was weeping bitterly. He reassured him as to his safety, but the poor lad replied, sobbing, that he knew the French treated their prisoners well, but that, as he had on him a belt containing nearly all his captain's money, he was afraid that the officer would accuse him of deserting in order to rob him, and he was heart-broken at the thought. Touched by the worthy fellow's distress, the emperor told him that he was free, and as soon as we were before Vienna he would be passed through the outposts, and be able to return to his master. Then, taking a rouleau of 1,000 francs, he put it in the man's hand, saying, "One must honor goodness wherever it is shown." Lastly, the emperor gave some pieces of gold to each of the other two prisoners, and ordered that they too should be sent back to the Austrian outposts, so that they might forget the fright which we had caused them.

A RESCUE FROM SHIPWRECK

By Arthur Quiller-Couch

ON the 13th of October, 1811, we were cruising in the *Endymion,* off the north of Ireland, on a fine clear day succeeding one in which it had almost blown a hurricane. The master had just taken his meridian observation, the officer of the watch had reported the latitude, the captain had ordered it to be made twelve o'clock, and the boatswain, catching a word from the lieutenant, was in the full swing of his "Pipe to dinner!" when the captain called out—

"Stop! stop! I meant to go about first."

"Pipe belay! Mr. King," smartly ejaculated the officer of the watch, addressing the boatswain; which words, being heard over the decks, caused a sudden cessation of the sounds peculiar to that hungry season. The cook stood with a huge six-pound piece of pork uplifted on his tormentors, his mate ceased to bale out the pea-soup, and the whole ship seemed paralyzed. The boatswain, having checked himself in the middle of his long-winded dinner-tune, drew a fresh inspiration, and dashed off into the opposite sharp, abrupt, cutting sound of the "Pipe belay!" the essence of which peculiar note is that its sounds should be understood and acted on with the utmost degree of promptitude.

There was now a dead pause of perfect silence all over the ship, in expectation of what was to come next. All eyes were turned to the chief.

"No; never mind, we'll wait," cried the good-natured captain, unwilling to interfere with the comforts of the men; "let them go to dinner; we shall tack at one o'clock, it will do just as well."

The boatswain, at a nod from the lieutenant of the watch, at once recommenced his merry "Pipe to dinner" notes; upon which a loud, joyous laugh rang from one end of the ship to the other. This hearty burst was not in the slightest degree disrespectful; on the contrary, it sounded like a grateful expression of glee at the prospect of the approaching good things which, by this time, were finding their speedy course down the hatchways.

Nothing was now heard but the cheerful chuckle of a well-fed company, the clatter of plates and knives, and the chit-chat of light hearts under the influence of temperate excitement.

When one o'clock came, the hands were called "About ship!" But as the helm was in the very act of going down, the look-out-man at the fore-top-mast head called out—

"I see something a little on the lee-bow, sir!"

"Something! What do you mean by 'something'?" cried the first lieutenant, making a motion to the quarter-master at the con to right the helm again.

"I don't know what it is, sir," cried the man; "it is black, however."

"Black! Is it like a whale?" asked the officer, playing a little with his duty.

"Yes, sir," cried the look-out-man, unconscious that Shakespeare had been before him, "very like a whale!"

The captain and the officer exchanged glances at the poor fellow aloft having fallen into the trap laid for him, and the temptation must have been great to have inquired whether it were not "like a weasel"; but this might have been stretching the jest too far; so the lieutenant merely called to the signal midshipman, and desired him to skull up to the mast-head with his glass, to see what he made of the look-out-man's whale.

"It looks like a small rock," cried young "Sky-

lark" as soon as he reached the top-gallant-yard
and had taken the glass from his shoulders, across
which he had slung it with a three-yarn fox.

"Stuff and nonsense!" replied the officers, "there
are no rocks hereabouts; we can but just see the
top of Muckish, behind Tory Island. Take another
spy at your object, youngster; the mast-head-man
and you will make it out to be something by-and-
by, between you, I dare say."

"It's a boat, sir!" roared out the boy. "It's a
boat adrift, two or three points on the lee-bow."

"Oh-ho!" said the officer, "that may be, sir,"
turning with an interrogative air to the captain,
who gave orders to keep the frigate away a little
that this strange-looking affair might be investi-
gated. Meanwhile, as the ship was not to be
tacked, the watch was called, and one half only of
the people remained on deck. The rest strolled,
sleepy, below; or disposed themselves in the sun on
the lee gangway, mending their clothes, or telling
long yarns.

A couple of fathoms of the fore and main sheets,
and a slight touch of the weather topsail and top-
gallant braces, with a check on the bow-lines, made
the swift-footed *Endymion* spring forward, like a
greyhound slipped from the leash. In a short time
we made out that the object we were in chase of
was, in fact, a boat. On approaching a little nearer,
some heads of people became visible, and then
several figures stood up, waving their hats to us.
We brought to, just to windward of them, and
sent a boat to see what was the matter.

It turned out as we supposed; they had belonged

to a ship which had foundered in the recent gale.
Although their vessel had become water-logged,
they had contrived to hoist their long-boat out, and
to stow in her twenty-one persons, some of them
seamen and some passengers; of these, two were
women, and three children. Their vessel, it appeared, had sprung a leak in middle of the gale,
and, in spite of all their pumping, the water gained
so fast upon them that they took to baling as a
more effectual method. After a time, when this
resource failed, the men, totally worn out and quite
dispirited, gave it up as a bad job, abandoned their
pumps, and actually lay down to sleep. In the
morning the gale broke; but the ship had filled in
the meantime, and was falling fast over her broadside. With some difficulty they disentangled the
long-boat from the wreck, and thought themselves
fortunate in being able to catch hold of a couple of
small oars, with a studding-sail-boom for a mast,
on which they hoisted a fragment of their main-
hatchway tarpaulin for a sail. One ham and three
gallons of water were all the provisions they were
able to secure; and in this fashion they were set
adrift on the wide sea. The master of the ship,
with two gentlemen who were passengers, preferred
to stick by the vessel while there was any part of
her above water.

This, at least, was the story told us by the people
we picked up.

The wind had been fair for the shore when the
long-boat left the wreck, and though their ragged
sail scarcely drove them along, their oars were only
just sufficient to keep the boat's head the right way.

A RESCUE FROM SHIPWRECK

Of course they made but slow progress; so that when they rose on the top of a swell, which was still very long and high in consequence of the gale, they could only just discover the distant land, Muckish, a remarkable flat-topped mountain on the north-west coast of Ireland, not very far from the promontory called the Bloody Foreland.

There appeared to have been little discipline among this forlorn crew, even when the breeze was in their favor; but when the wind chopped round, and blew off shore, they gave themselves up to despair, laid in their oars, let the sail flap to pieces, gobbled up all their provisions, and drank out their whole stock of water. Meanwhile the boat, which had been partially stove, in the confusion of clearing the ship, began to fill with water; and, as they all admitted afterwards, if it had not been for the courage and patience of the women under this sharp trial, they must have gone to the bottom.

As it was both cold and rainy, the poor children, who were too young to understand the nature of their situation, or the inutility of complaining, incessantly cried out for water, and begged that more clothes might be wrapped round them. Even after they came to us the little things were still crying, "Oh! do give us some water"—words which long sounded in our ears. None of these women were by any means strong—on the contrary, one of them seemed to be very delicate; yet they managed to rouse the men to a sense of their duty by a mixture of reproaches and entreaties, combined with the example of that singular fortitude which often gives more than masculine vigor to female minds in seasons of danger. How long this might have lasted I cannot say; but probably the strength of the men, however stimulated, must have given way before night, especially as the wind freshened, and the boat was driving further to sea. Had it not been for the accident of the officer of the forenoon watch on board the *Endymion* being unaware of the captain's intention to tack before dinner, these poor people, most probably, would all have perished.

The women, dripping wet, and scarcely capable of moving hand or foot, were lifted up the side, in a state almost of stupor; for they were confused by the hurry of the scene, and their fortitude had given way the moment all high motive to exertion was over. One of them, on reaching the quarter-deck, slipped through our hands, and falling on her knees, wept violently as she returned thanks for such a wonderful deliverance; but her thoughts were bewildered, and, fancying that her child was lost, she struck her hands together, and leaping again on her feet, screamed out, "Oh! where's my bairn—my wee bairn?"

At this instant a huge quarter-master, whose real name or nickname (I forget which) was Billy Magnus, appeared over the gangway hammocks, holding the missing urchin in his immense paw, where it squealed and twisted itself about, like Gulliver between the finger and thumb of the Brobdingnag farmer. The mother had just strength enough left to snatch her offspring from Billy, when she sank down flat on the deck, completely exhausted.

A RESCUE FROM SHIPWRECK

By means of a fine blazing fire, and plenty of hot tea, toast, and eggs, it was easy to remedy one class of these poor people's wants; but how to rig them out in dry clothes was a puzzle, till the captain bethought him of a resource which answered very well. He sent to several of the officers for their dressing-gowns; and these, together with supplies from his own wardrobe, made capital gowns and petticoats—at least, till the more fitting drapery of the ladies was dried. The children were tumbled into bed in the same compartment, close to the fire; and it would have done any one's heart good to have witnessed the style in which the provisions vanished from the board, while the women wept, prayed, and laughed, by turns.

The rugged seamen, when taken out of the boat, showed none of these symptoms of emotion, but running instinctively to the scuttle-butt, asked eagerly for a drop of water. As the most expeditious method of feeding and dressing them, they were distributed among the different messes, one to each, as far as they went. Thus they were all soon provided with dry clothing, and with as much to eat as they could stow away; for the doctor, when consulted, said they had not fasted so long as to make it dangerous to give them as much food as they were disposed to swallow. With the exception of the ham devoured in the boat, and which, after all, was but a mouthful apiece, they had tasted nothing for more than thirty hours; so that, I suppose, better justice was never done to his Majesty's beef, pork, bread, and other good things, with which our fellows insisted on stuffing the new-comers, till they fairly cried out for mercy and begged to be allowed a little sleep.

Possibly some of us were more disposed to sympathize with the distress of these people when adrift in their open boat on the wide sea, from having ourselves, about a month before, been pretty much in the same predicament. It always adds, as any one knows, greatly to our consideration for the difficulties and dangers of others, to have recently felt some touch of similar distress in our own persons. This maxim, though it is familiar enough, makes so little impression on our ordinary thoughts, that when circumstances occur to fix our attention closely upon it we are apt to arrive as suddenly at the perception of its truth as if it were a new discovery.

REBECCA THE DRUMMER

By Charles Barnard

IT was about nine o'clock in the morning when the ship first appeared. At once there was the greatest excitement in the village. It was a British warship. What would she do? Would she tack about in the bay to pick up stray coasters as prizes, or would she land soldiers to burn the town? In either case there would be trouble enough.

Those were sad days, those old war-times in 1812. The sight of a British warship in Boston Bay was not pleasant. We were poor then, and had no monitors to go out and sink the enemy or drive him off.

REBECCA THE DRUMMER

Our navy was small, and, though we afterwards had the victory and sent the troublesome ships away, never to return, at that time they often came near enough, and the good people in the little village of Scituate Harbor were in great distress over the strange ship that had appeared at the mouth of the harbor.

It was a fishing-place in those days, and the harbor was full of smacks and boats of all kinds. The soldiers could easily enter the harbor and burn up everything, and no one could prevent them. There were men enough to make a good fight, but they were poorly armed, and had nothing but fowling-pieces and shotguns, while the soldiers had muskets and cannon.

The tide was down during the morning, so that there was no danger for a few hours; and all the people went out on the cliffs and beaches to watch the ship and to see what would happen next.

On the end of the low, sandy spit that makes one side of the harbor, stood the little white tower known as Scituate Light. In the house behind the light lived the keeper's family, consisting of himself, wife, and several boys and girls. At the time the ship appeared, the keeper was away, and there was no one at home save Mrs. Bates, the eldest daughter, Rebecca, about fourteen years old, two of the little boys, and a young girl named Sarah Winsor, who was visiting Rebecca.

Rebecca had been the first to discover the ship, while she was up in the light-house tower polishing the reflector. She at once descended the steep stairs and sent off the boys to the village to give the alarm.

For an hour or two, the ship tacked and stood off to sea, then tacked again, and made for the shore. Men, women and children watched her with anxious interest. Then the tide turned and began to flow into the harbor. The boats aground on the flats floated, and those in deep water swung round at their moorings. Now the soldiers would probably land. If the people meant to save anything it was time to be stirring. Boats were hastily put out from the wharf, and such clothing, nets and other valuables as could be handled were brought ashore, loaded into hay carts, and carried away.

It was of no use to resist. The soldiers, of course, were well armed, and if the people made a stand among the houses, that would not prevent the enemy from destroying the shipping.

As the tide spread out over the sandy flats it filled the harbor so that, instead of a small channel, it became a wide and beautiful bay. The day was fine, and there was a gentle breeze rippling the water and making it sparkle in the sun. What a splendid day for fishing or sailing! Not much use to think of either while that warship crossed and recrossed before the harbor mouth.

About two o'clock the tide reached high water mark, and, to the dismay of the people, the ship let go her anchor, swung her yards round, and lay quiet about half-a-mile from the first cliff. They were going to land to burn the town. With their spy-glasses the people could see the boats lowered to take the soldiers ashore.

Ah! then there was confusion and uproar. Every horse in the village was put into some kind of team, and the women and children were hurried off to the woods behind the town. The men would stay and offer as brave a resistance as possible. Their guns were light and poor, but they could use the old fish-houses as a fort, and perhaps make a brave fight of it.

If worse came to worse, they could at least retreat and take to the shelter of the woods.

It was a splendid sight. Five large boats, manned by sailors, and filled with soldiers in gay red coats. How their guns glittered in the sun! The oars all moved together in regular order, and the officers in their fine uniforms stood up to direct the expedition. It was a courageous company come with a warship and cannon to fight helpless fisher-men.

So Rebecca Bates and Sarah Winsor thought, as they sat up in the light-house tower looking down on the procession of boats as it went past the point and entered the harbor.

"Oh! If I only were a man!" cried Rebecca.

"What could you do? See what a lot of them; and look at their guns!"

"I don't care. I'd fight. I'd use father's old shotgun—anything. Think of uncle's new boat and the sloop!"

"Yes; and all the boats."

"It's too bad; isn't it?"

"Yes; and to think we must sit here and see it all and not lift a finger to help."

"Do you think there will be a fight?"

"I don't know. Uncle and father are in the vil-lage, and they will do all they can."

"See how still it is in town. There's not a man to be seen."

"Oh, they are hiding till the soldiers get nearer. Then we'll hear the shots and the drum."

"The drum! How can they? It's here. Father brought it home to mend it last night."

"Did he? Oh! then let's——"

"See, the first boat has reached the sloop. Oh! oh! They are going to burn her."

"Isn't it mean?"

"It's too bad!—too——"

"Where is that drum?"

"It's in the kitchen."

"I've got a great mind to go down and beat it."

"What good would that do?"

"Scare 'em."

"They'd see it was only two girls, and they would laugh and go on burning just the same."

"No. We could hide behind the sand hills and the bushes. Come, let's——"

"Oh, look! look! The sloop's afire!"

"Come, I can't stay and see it any more. The cowardly Britishers to burn the boats! Why don't they go up to the town and fight like——"

"Come, let's get the drum. It'll do no harm; and perhaps——"

"Well, let's. There's the fife, too; we might take that with us."

"Yes; and we'll——"

No time for further talk. Down the steep stairs of the tower rushed these two young patriots, bent on doing what they could for their country. They burst into the kitchen like a whirlwind, with rosy cheeks and flying hair. Mrs. Bates sat sorrowfully gazing out of the window at the scene of destruction going on in the harbor, and praying for her country and that the dreadful war might soon be over. She could not help. Son and husband were shouldering their poor old guns in the town, and there was nothing to do but to watch and wait and pray.

Not so the two girls. They meant to do something, and, in a fever of excitement, they got the drum and took the cracked fife from the bureau drawer. Mrs. Bates, intent on the scene outside, did not heed them, and they slipped out by the back door, unnoticed.

They must be careful, or the soldiers would see them. They went round back of the house to the north and towards the outside beach, and then turned and plowed through the deep sand just above high water mark. They must keep out of sight of the boats, and of the ship, also. Luckily, she was anchored to the south of the light; and as the beach curved to the west, they soon left her out of sight. Then they took to the water side, and, with the drum between them, ran as fast as they could towards the mainland. Presently they reached the low heaps of sand that showed where the spit joined the fields and woods.

Panting and excited, they tightened up the drum and tried the fife softly.

"You take the fife, Sarah, and I'll drum."

"All right; but we mustn't stand still. We must march along the shore towards the light."

"Won't they see us?"

"No; we'll walk next the water on the outside beach."

"Oh, yes; and they'll think it's soldiers going down to the Point to head 'em off."

"Just so. Come, begin! One, two—one, two!"

Drum! drum!! drum!!!

Squeak! squeak!! squeak!!!

"For'ard—march!"

"Ha! ha!"

The fife stopped.

"Don't laugh. You'll spoil everything, and I can't pucker my lips."

Drum! drum!! drum!!!

Squeak! squeak!! squeak!!!

The men in the town heard it and were amazed beyond measure. Had the soldiers arrived from Boston? What did it mean? Who were coming?

Louder and louder on the breeze came the roll of a sturdy drum and the sound of a brave fife. The soldiers in the boats heard the noise and paused in their work of destruction. The officers ordered everybody into the boats in the greatest haste. The people were rising! They were coming down the Point with cannons, to head them off! They would all be captured, and perhaps hung by the dreadful Americans!

How the drum rolled! The fife changed its tune. It played "Yankee Doodle,"—that horrid tune! Hark! The men were cheering in the town! there were thousands of them in the woods along the shore!

In grim silence marched the two girls—plodding over the sharp stones, splashing through the pud-

432

dles—Rebecca beating the old drum with might and main; Sarah blowing the fife with shrill determination.

How the Britishers scrambled into their boats! One of the brave officers was nearly left behind on the burning sloop. Another fell overboard and wet his good clothes, in his haste to escape from the American army marching down the beach—a thousand strong! How the sailors pulled! No fancy rowing now, but desperate haste to get out of the place and escape to the ship.

How the people yelled and cheered on the shore! Fifty men or more jumped into the boats to prepare for the chase. Ringing shots began to crack over the water.

Louder and louder rolled the terrible drum. Sharp and clear rang out the cruel fife.

Nearly exhausted, half dead with fatigue, the girls toiled on—tearful, laughing, ready to drop on the wet sand, and still beating and blowing with fiery courage.

The boats swept swiftly out of the harbor on the outgoing tide. The fishermen came up with the burning boats. Part stopped to put out the fires, and the rest pursued the flying enemy with such shots as they could get at them. In the midst of it all, the sun went down.

The red-coats did not return a shot. They expected every minute to see a thousand men open on them at short range from the beach, and they reserved their powder.

Out of the harbor they went in confusion and dismay. The ship weighed anchor and ran out her big guns, but did not fire a shot. Darkness fell down on the scene as the boats reached the ship. Then she sent a round of shot towards the light. It fell short and threw a great fountain of white water into the air.

The girls saw it, and dropping their drum and fife, sat down on the beach and laughed till they cried.

That night the ship sailed away. The great American army of two had arrived, and she thought it wise to retreat in time!

Rebecca lived until old and feeble in body, but ever brave in spirit and strong in patriotism, she told this story herself to the writer. and it is true.

THE MESSENGER

By M. E. M. Davis

"THOSE reptiles of Americans, I say to you, Marcel—mark my words!—that they have it in their heads to betray Louisiana to the Spaniard. They are tr-r-raitors!" Old Galmiche rolled the word viciously on his French tongue.

"Yes," assented his young companion, absently. He quite agreed with Galmiche—the Americans were traitors, oh, of the blackest black! But the sky overhead was so blue, the wind blowing in from the Gulf and lifting the dark curls on his bared forehead was so moist and sweet, the scene under his eyes, although familiar, was so enchanting! He rose, the better to see it all once again.

THE MESSENGER

Grand Terre, the low-lying strip of an island upon which he stood, was at that time—September, 1814—the stronghold of Jean Lafitte, the famous freebooter, or, as he chose rather to call himself, privateer, and his band of smugglers and buccaneers.

The island, which lies across the mouth of Barataria Bay, with a narrow pass at each end opening into the Gulf of Mexico, had been well fortified. Lafitte's own bungalow-like house was protected on the Gulf side by an enclosing wall surmounted by small cannon. The rich furniture within the house—the pictures, books, Oriental draperies, silver and gold plate and rare crystal—attested equally—so declared his enemies—to the fastidious taste of the Lord of Barataria and to his lawlessness.

The landlocked bay holds in its arms many small islands.

These served Lafitte as places of deposit for smuggled or pirated goods. Water-craft of every description—more than one sloop or lugger decorated with gay lengths of silk or woolen cloth —rode at ease in the secure harbor. In a curve of the mainland a camp had been established for the negroes imported in defiance of United States law, from Africa, to be sold in Louisiana and elsewhere. The buccaneers themselves were quartered on the main island.

Marcel Lefort, the slender, dark-eyed creole *voyageur*, drew a deep sigh of delight as he resumed his seat on the grassy sward beside Galmiche. But he sprang again to his feet, for the tranquil morning air was suddenly disturbed by the reverberating boom of a cannon!

Island, bay and mainland were instantly in commotion. Lafitte himself appeared on the east end of his veranda, spy-glass in hand.

The noted outlaw was a tall, sinewy, graceful man, then a little past thirty, singularly handsome, with clear-cut features, dark hair and fierce gray eyes which could, upon occasion, soften to tenderness. The hands which lifted the spy-glass were white and delicate.

He lowered the glass.

"A British sloop of war in the offing," he remarked to his lieutenant, Dominique You, standing beside him. "She has sent off a pinnace with a flag of truce. I go to meet it. Order an answering salute."

A moment later he had stepped into his four-oared barge and was skimming lightly down the Great Pass toward the Gulf.

When he returned, two officers in the British uniform were seated in the barge with him. The freebooters, a formidable array of French, Italians, Portuguese and West Indians, with here and there a sunburned American, stared with bold and threatening eyes at the intruders as they passed through the whispering *chênaiè* (oak grove) to the house, to unfold their mission to the "Great Chief," and to share his princely hospitality.

Shortly after nightfall of the same day, on one of the little inner islands, Marcel Lefort stood leaning upon his long boat paddle, awaiting orders; his pirogue was drawn up among the reeds hard by.

He lifted his head, but hardly had his keen eye caught the shadowy outlines of a boat on the bay before its occupants had landed.

"The lad is too young," objected Dominique You, as the two men drew near.

"His father was a gunner in Kelerec's army at sixteen," returned Lafitte. "You are sure of the route, Marcel?" he continued, touching the *voyageur* on the shoulder.

"Yes, my captain. As the bird is of his flight through the air. This is not the first time," he added proudly, "that I have brought secret despatches from New Orleans to Barataria."

"True. Now listen. You will set out at once with this." He handed the lad a small packet wrapped in oil silk, which Marcel thrust into his bosom. "You will make all speed to the city," he continued. "There you will find Monsieur Pierre Lafitte, my brother—whether he be in prison, at the smithy, or at the Café Turpin—"

"Yes, my captain—"

"And give the packet into his own hand—"

"Yes, my captain."

"None but his, you understand. In case the packet should be lost or stolen by the way, you will all the same seek monsieur, my brother, and say to him that the British have this day offered to me, Jean Lafitte, Lord of Barataria, the sum of thirty thousand dollars, the rank of captain in the British navy, and a free pardon for my men, if I will assist them in their invasion of Louisiana. I am sure that monsieur, my brother, will not need to be told that Jean Lafitte spurns this insulting proposition.

But you will say to him that the governor must be warned at once. The British officers will be—detained—here until you are well on your way."

"Yes, my captain."

"You quite understand, Marcel? And you quite understand also that if you risk your life, it is for Louisiana?"

"For Louisiana!" echoed Marcel, solemnly. He touched his cap in the darkness, stepped warily into the pirogue, pushed off, and dropped his paddle into the water.

The needle-like boat threaded its way in and out among the islands, and leaped into the mouth of a sluggish gulfward-stealing bayou. Here a few strokes of the paddle swept pirogue and paddler into a strange and lonely world. The tall cypress-trees on each bank, draped with funeral moss, cast impenetrable shadows on the water; the deathlike silence was broken only by the occasional ominous hoot of an owl or the wheezy snort of an alligator; the clammy air breathed poison. But the stars overhead were bright, and Marcel's heart throbbed exultant.

"For Louisiana!" he murmured. "He might have chosen Galmiche, or José, or Nez Coupé; but it is I, Marcel Lefort, whom the Great Chief has sent with the warning. For Louisiana! For Louisiana!" His muscular arms thrilled to the finger-tips with the rhythmic sweep of his paddle to the words.

Turn after turn of the sinuous, ever-narrowing bayou slipped behind him as the night advanced. He kept a wary eye upon the black masses of foliage to right and left, knowing that a runaway negro, mutineer from Barataria, or a murderous Choctaw might lurk there in wait for the passing boatman; or an American spy—he quickened his strokes at the thought!—to wrest from him the precious despatch.

"Those vipers of Americans!" he breathed. "The Governor Claiborne, since the Great Chief trusts him, must have become a creole at his heart. But the rest have the heart of a cockatrice. And these British, as Galmiche says, are surely Americans in disguise."

The young creole's ideas were not strange, his upbringing considered. He had stood in 1803, a boy of eight, beside his father on the Place d'Armes of New Orleans and watched the French flag descend slowly from the tall staff, and the Stars and Stripes ascend proudly in its place. He had seen the impotent tears and heard the impotent groans of the French creoles when the new American governor, standing on the balcony of the *cabildo*, took possession, in the name of the United States, of the French province of Louisiana.

Daily since then, almost hourly, he had heard his father and his father's friends denounce the Americans as double-dyed traitors, who had bought Louisiana from France that they might hand it over to the still more detested Spaniards.

"Vipers of Americans!" he repeated, humming under his breath a refrain much in vogue:

> "Americain coquin,
> 'Billé en nanquin,
> Voleur du pain."

439

("American rogue, dressed in nankeen, bread-stealer.")

"It will soon be morning." He glanced up at the open sky, for he was breasting the surface of a small lake. "Good!" The pirogue slipped into another bayou at the upper end of the lagoon. The shadows here seemed thicker than ever after the starlit lake.

"Ugh!" ejaculated Marcel. An unseen log had lurched against the pirogue, upsetting it and throwing its occupant into the water. He sank, but rose in a flash and reached out, swimming, after pirogue and paddle.

But the log lurched forward again, snapping viciously, and before he could draw back, a huge alligator had seized his left forearm between his great jaws. The conical teeth sank deep in the flesh.

Marcel tugged under water at the knife in his belt. It seemed an eternity before he could draw it. A swift vision of the Great Chief's brooding eyes darted through his brain.

"For Louisiana!" The words burst involuntarily from his lips as the keen blade buried itself under the knotty scales deep in the monster's throat. The mighty jaws relaxed and dropped the limp and bloody arm.

Half an hour later the messenger stepped again into his recovered boat. A groan forced its way between his clenched teeth as he set his paddle to the dark waters of the bayou, but its rhythmic sweep did not slacken.

In the gray dawnlight of the second morning

THE MESSENGER

Lafitte's messenger came up from the Mississippi River at New Orleans, and walked swiftly across the Place d'Armes into Condé Street.

The nineteen-year-old lad looked twice his age; his lips were parched, his eyes were bloodshot, a red spot glowed in each livid cheek. One arm, wrapped in a bloody sleeve of his hunting-shirt, hung limply at his side. He paid no heed to the wondering questions of the few people he met, but sped like one in a dream to his goal.

In the great smithy of the Lafitte brothers, which served as a blind for their smuggling operations, the forges were already aglow, the army of black slaves at work, and Pierre Lafitte, who, although outlawed like his brother, knew himself secure in this citadel, was giving orders. At sight of Marcel he leaped forward. "Why, Marcel!" he cried. "Why, my poor lad, what—"

But Marcel had thrust the packet into his hand, and dropped as one dead at his feet.

"Those Americans, they are traitors, oh, of the blackest black!" The familiar phrase in his father's well-known voice fell upon Marcel's returning consciousness. He listened with closed eyes. "And that General An-drrew Jack-*son*, look you, Coulon, he has the liver of a Spaniard. He will betray Louisiana. That sees itself!"

"That sees itself," echoed old Coulon.

Marcel opened his eyes. "Who is General Andrew Jackson?" he demanded, surprised at the stiffness of his own tongue. And those hands, pale and inert, lying on the coverlet before him, could

they be his own? And why should he, Marcel, be
in his bed in broad daylight? Suddenly he remembered that yesterday he had fetched a despatch to
Monsieur Pierre from the Great Chief—

"Did M'sieu' Pierre—" he began, eagerly, trying
to rise on his elbow.

"Thank God!" ejaculated old Lefort, commonly
called "Piff-Paff," springing to the bedside. "The
boy is himself once more. But not so fast, my little
Marcel, not so fast!"

Many weeks, it appeared, had passed since Marcel had been borne in the strong arms of Pierre
Lafitte to Lefort's cottage near the smithy. Fever
and delirium had set in before the worn figure was
laid on the couch.

"But now," tears were streaming down the
weather-beaten face of the old gunner, "now, by
God's help, we shall get on our feet!"

"But *who* is General Andrew Jackson?" per-
sisted Marcel, querulously.

"General An-drrew Jack-*son*," replied Coulon,
seeing that the father's throat was choked with
sobs, "General An-drrew Jack-*son* is an American.
He arrives from day to day at New Orleans. He
is in league with those British who are Americans
in disguise. He comes to betray Louisiana to the
Spaniard."

"The monster!" said Marcel, drowsily.

His recovery thenceforth was rapid. Old Lefort's private forge was in his own court-yard.
Here, among the rustling bananas and the flower-
ing pomegranates, where he had played, a mother-
less infant, the slim, emaciated lad sat or walked

about in the November sunshine. And while Marcel hung about, the smith, hammering out the delicate Lefort wrought-iron work so prized in New Orleans to-day, anathematized indiscriminately General Jackson, the Spaniards, the British and the Americans.

Meanwhile strange sounds filtered into the courtyard from without—the beat of drums, the shrill concord of fifes, the measured tread of marching feet.

Marcel heard and wondered. He was not permitted to walk abroad, but what he saw from his window under the roof quickened his blood.

"Is it that Governor Claiborne has heeded the Great Chief's warning?" he asked of his father.

"The governor is an American," said Piff-Paff. "All Americans are perfidious. But the traitor of traitors is General An-drrew Jack-*son*. Be quiet, my son. Do you wish to die of fever?"

"When I do get out," Marcel was saying to himself one sunny day early in December, "I will slay the traitor with my own hand."

A steady tread came echoing down the corridor, and the Great Chief stepped into the court-yard.

"M'sieu' Jean!" cried Piff-Paff, running to meet him.

Lafitte pressed the old man's hands in his, and turned to Marcel.

"Aha, my little game-cock, there you are!" he said, catching the boy in his arms. "My faith, but you paddled well for Louisiana that time we know of! And the arm? Is it all there?" A winning tenderness softened the fierce eyes. "But I am pressed for time, my friends," he continued, stepping back.

As he spoke he unbuckled his belt, to which hung a short sword with jeweled cross-hilt. "Keep this, lad, in memory of Lafitte—and the alligator," he laughed, handing sword and belt to Marcel, who stood open-mouthed, unable for sheer ecstasy to utter a word.

"And look you, Marcel," his tones became grave, "I charge you henceforth to forget the road to Barataria. It leads to riches, yes, but it is a crooked and dishonest road. I would I had never myself set foot in such ways!" He paused a moment, his eyes bent on the ground. "Learn your father's honest trade. Live by it, an honest man and a good citizen."

"Yes, my captain," stammered Marcel.

"Swear!" said Lafitte, imperiously.

"I swear!" breathed Marcel, his hand on the cross-hilt of the sword. "By God's help!"

"Amen!" said Lafitte, reverently. He turned away.

"But where are you going, M'sieu' Jean?" cried Piff-Paff. "Do you not know that a reward of five hundred dollars is offered for your arrest?"

"I know." Lafitte shrugged his shoulders disdainfully. "I go to offer my services to General Jackson."

"*Gen-e-ral Jackson!*" echoed Piff-Paff. His jaws dropped. He stood like one suddenly turned to stone while the chief's retreating footsteps rang down the alleyway. "General Jack-*son!*" he repeated, mechanically. "But he shall not!"

With a roar of rage he leaped for the saber—his old saber which hung by the forge. "Myself, I will slay the traitor Jack-*son* before M'sieu' Jean dishonors himself! I, Blaise Lefort, will save him."

He dashed out. Marcel followed, buckling on his cross-hilted sword as he ran.

"Nevertheless it is I who will destroy the traitor!" he muttered. "I have already said it."

The narrow streets of the old town presented a unique spectacle. The tall dormer-window houses with their latticed balconies looked down upon hurrying crowds almost as motley as those of the carnival. But the faces of these men and women were earnest, grimly determined.

And soldiers, soldiers everywhere! United States soldiers in trim uniforms; Coffee's Tennesseans in brown shirts and slouched hats; Planché's gaily clad creole infantry; D'Aquin's freemen of color; Indians in blankets and leggings —all carrying guns, all stepping briskly to drumbeat and fife-call.

Pennons, guidons and banners tossed about in the orderly confusion; American and French flags waved together from balconies and windows.

"But, look!" exclaimed Marcel in pained astonishment, "our creoles are drilling with the Americans!"

"They are mad!" growled Piff-Paff. "This General Jack-*son* has poisoned their hearts."

In truth, the threatened attack on New Orleans by the British had united creoles and Americans. A few only of the former held aloof—like old

Lefort himself; these, honest in their convictions, were uncompromising.

Marcel set his teeth, gripping his sword. At the entrance to General Jackson's headquarters in Royal Street they were questioned by a sentry, who looked from the swarthy old man to the pale lad, and let them pass.

They hurried down the long, dim corridor, which opened upon a sunny court-yard hung with blossoming rose vines. Huge water-jars were ranged against the wall. A fountain played in the center, and round the pool beneath, some soldiers in uniform were lounging and gossiping. Marcel glanced curiously at these as he followed his father up the winding stair. The arched hall above, with its Spanish windows, opened into an anteroom.

Father and son paused instinctively here among the shadows. The large room beyond the folding doors, which were thrown open, was filled with the afternoon sunshine; a table strewn with maps and papers was placed near one of the long windows. Beyond it, in an armchair, was seated a man in an attitude of rigid attention. Several staff-officers were gathered about him.

The Great Chief stood directly in front of the seated figure. He had doubtless been speaking for some minutes. Now, holding out his sword, he concluded:

"And I offer my services and those of my Baratarians in this hour of my country's peril to General Jackson."

He spoke in English. Marcel, who was acquainted with the forbidden tongue, glanced sidewise at his father. He saw that the old man had also understood. Both father and son, as if moved by the same spring, made a step forward.

But both paused. General Jackson had risen from his seat. The light fell full upon his face as he reached out without a word and grasped Lafitte's hand.

At sight of the tall, martial figure, erect and commanding in the simple uniform of the United States army, the compelling face, with its crown of bristling silvered hair, the eyes that shone with a curious, soft fire, the firm mouth and masterful chin, Marcel Lefort's soul seemed drawn from his bosom as by an invisible hand. A mist gathered before his eyes, his throat clicked, a mysterious longing suddenly swept over him from head to foot.

Before he knew what he was about he had traversed the antechamber and entered the larger room, his footfalls on the bare polished floor disturbing the dramatic silence.

"My captain!" he cried, stopping short and lifting his eager, boyish face to the Great Chief. "My general!" He turned with outstretched sword to the greater chief beyond. He wished to say more, but the throbbing of his heart was too loud in his ears.

Suddenly Marcel heard a footstep sound behind him. His father! He had quite forgotten his father.

"He will slay me where I stand!" he groaned inwardly.

A hand whose touch thrilled him was slipped

under his arm. He felt himself drawn to his father's side.

"General An-drrew Jack-*son*"—the old gunner spoke with great dignity and feeling, although his English was queer—"we haf come, my son an' me, to hoffer ou' swo'de to dose United State'. Yes, my general. If dose United State' will make us the honah to haccep'."

"By the Eternal," cried General Jackson, surprised into his favorite oath, "with such a spirit in the air, I would storm all the powers of the world!"

In less than a month the memorable Battle of New Orleans was fought—January 8, 1815. The Baratarians, under command of Jean Lafitte, rendered distinguished service in the short but bloody and decisive engagement. The two batteries directed by Beluche and Dominique You were especially commended in the general's official reports. Piff-Paff and his son served side by side in Dominique You's battery.

When the battle was over, Marcel stood with his fellow gunners on the parapet of Rodriguez Canal and looked out across the field—smoke-hung under the cloudless morning sky. The British dead, in their scarlet uniforms, were lying row on row, one behind the other, like grain cut down by the mower's scythe. The boy's heart sickened. But a prolonged cheer came ringing along the parapet.

General Jackson was walking slowly down the line, stopping in front of each command to salute the men and to praise their coolness and courage. As he came up, the Baratarians broke into wild shouts. The great commander shook hands with Lafitte and his brother, who stood a little apart.

"Well done, Baratarians!" he said, stepping into the midst of the powder-grimed crew. His swift glance fell upon a lad whose luminous eyes were fixed upon him.

"Well done, my little creole!" he added, a rare smile flashing across his worn face.

"My general," said Marcel, saluting proudly, "me, I am an American!"

HUMPHRY DAVY AND THE SAFETY-LAMP

By George C. Towle

FEW boys have ever led a happier, busier or more varied existence than did Humphry Davy. He was the son of a poor wood-carver, who lived in the pretty seaside town of Penzance, in England, where Humphry was born in 1778. Lowly, however, as was his birth, in his earliest years Humphry gave many proofs that nature had endowed him with rare talents.

Some of the stories told of his childish brightness are hard to believe. They relate, for instance, that before he was two years old he could talk almost as plainly and clearly as a grown person; that he could repeat many passages of "Pilgrim's Progress," from having heard them, before he could read; and that at five years old he could read very rapidly, and remembered almost everything he read.

His father, the wood-carver, had died while Humphry was still very young, and had left his family poor. But by good-fortune a kind neighbor and friend, a Mr. Tonkine, took care of the widow and her children, and obtained a place for Humphry as an apprentice with an apothecary of the town. Humphry proved, indeed, a rather troublesome inmate of the apothecary's house. He set up a chemical laboratory in his little room upstairs, and there devoted himself to all sorts of experiments. Every now and then an explosion would be heard, which made the members of the apothecary's household quake with terror.

Humphry began to dream ambitious dreams. Not for him, he thought, was the drudgery of an apothecary store. He felt that he had in himself the making of a famous man, and he resolved that he would leave no science unexplored. He set to work with a will. His quick mind soon grasped the sciences not only of mathematics and chemistry, but of botany, anatomy, geology, and metaphysics. His means for the experiments he desired to make were very limited, but he did not allow any obstacle to prevent him from pursuing them.

He was especially fond of wandering along the seashore, and observing and examining the many curious and mysterious objects which he found on the crags and in the sand. One day his eye was struck with the bladders of seaweed, which he found full of air. The question was, how did the air get into them? This puzzled him, and he could find no answer to it, because he had no instruments to experiment with.

But on another day, soon after, as he strolled on the beach, what was his surprise and delight to find a case of surgical instruments, which had been flung up from some wreck on the coast! Armed with this, he hastened home, and managed to turn each one of the instruments to some useful account. He constructed an air-pump out of a surgeon's syringe, and made a great many experiments with it.

Fortunately for Humphry, he formed a friendship with a youth who could not only sympathize with him, but was of a great deal of use to him. This was Gregory Watt, a son of the great James Watt, the inventor of the steam-engine. Gregory Watt had gone to Penzance for his health, and had there fallen in with the ambitious son of the woodcarver. This new friend was able to give Humphry many new and valuable hints and encouraged him with hopeful words to go on with his studies and experiments.

Already Humphry was getting to be known as a scientific genius beyond the quiet neighborhood of Penzance. He had proposed a theory on heat and light which had attracted the attention of learned men; and at twenty-one he had discovered the peculiar properties of nitrous oxide—what we now call "laughing-gas"—though he nearly killed himself by inhaling too much of it. He had also made many experiments in galvanism, and had found silicious earth in the skin of reeds and grass.

So famous indeed had he already become, that

at the age of twenty-two—when most young men are only just leaving college—he was chosen lecturer on science at the great Royal Institution in London. There he amazed men by the eloquence and clearness with which he revealed the mysteries of science. He was so bright and attractive a young man, moreover, that the best London society gladly welcomed him to its drawing-rooms, and praises of him were in every mouth. His lecture-room was crowded whenever he spoke.

But he was not a bit spoiled by all this flattery and homage. He worked all the harder; resolved to achieve yet greater triumphs in science than he had yet done. An opportunity soon arose to turn his knowledge and inventive powers to account in a very important way. For a long time the English public had every now and then been horrified by the terrible explosions which took place in the coal mines. These explosions resulted often in an appalling loss of human life. Their cause was the filling of the mine by a deadly gas, called "fire-damp," which, when ignited by a lighted candle or lamp, exploded with fearful violence. One day an explosion of fire-damp occurred which killed over one hundred miners on the spot.

This event called universal attention to the subject, and Humphry Davy was besought to try and find some means of preventing, or at least lessening, similar calamities. He promptly undertook the task, and set about it with all his wonted energy. The problem before him was how to provide light in the mines in such a way that the miners might see to work by it, and at the same time be safe from the danger of fire-damp explosion. Many attempts had been made to achieve this, but they had all failed.

Davy began his experiments. He soon made several valuable discoveries. One was that explosions of inflammable gases could not pass through long narrow metallic tubes. Another was that when he held a piece of wire gauze over a lighted candle, the flame would not pass through it. As a result of his long and patient toil Davy was able at last to construct his now famous *Safety-Lamp,* which has undoubtedly saved the lives of thousands during the period which has elapsed since it was invented. He presented a model of his new lamp to the Royal Society, in whose rooms in London it is to be seen to this day.

It is a simple affair, being merely a lamp screwed on to a wire gauze cylinder, and fitted to it by a tight ring. His idea was to admit the fire-damp into the lamp gradually by narrow tubes, so that it would be consumed by combustion. The Safety-Lamp was in truth the greatest triumph of Humphry Davy's useful life.

"I value it," he said, "more than anything I ever did."

Honors of all kinds were showered upon him. Many medals were awarded to him, and the grateful miners subscribed from their scant wages enough to present him with a magnificent service of silver worth $12,000. His discovery was hailed from every part of Europe. The Czar Alexander of Russia sent him a beautiful vase, and he was chosen a member of the historic Institute of

France; while his own government conferred upon him the coveted title of baronet.

Sir Humphry Davy, as he was now called, died in the prime of life and in the fulness of honor and fame. Fond of travel, and continuing to the last his scientific studies, he went to the continent, and took up his abode at Geneva, on the borders of one of the loveliest of Swiss lakes. There he had a laboratory, where he could work at will, and could also indulge his passion for fishing and hunting.

But he was worn out before his time. He was attacked by palsy, and passed away at Geneva in 1829, in the fifty-first year of his age. There he was buried. A simple monument reveals where he lies in the foreign churchyard; while a tablet in Westminster Abbey keeps alive his memory in the hearts of his countrymen.

KIT CARSON'S DUEL

By Emerson Hough

"HOW much farther, François?" asked the leader of a little mountain cavalcade which wound its way down a broad river valley in the heart of the Rocky Mountains. "See, it is now noon, and the encampment is not yet in sight. Shall we not stop and rest?"

The speaker was a tall, thin man, whose face, browned by the sun of the plains and mountains, none the less bore a refinement almost approaching austerity. The man accosted was leaner and

browner than himself, and wore the full costume
of the Western *engagé* of the fur trade.

"M'sieu' Parker," he replied, "halways you hask
how far to ze hencampment. I do not know. In
ze mountain we do no hask how far. We push on
ze horse. Thass all."

"But the rendezvous—are you sure it is in this
valley of the Green?"

"It is establish for ze month of August in ze valley of ze Green. Those man of ze mountain, he
do not disappoint. This rendezvous of ze year
1835, it may be ze last one for ze trappaire. But
me, François Verrier, say to you that you shall see
ze rendezvous, also ze trappaire, and ze trader, and
ze Injin—hundreds of heem. My faith! Zay shall
see for ze first time ze missionaire to ze Injin!
M'sieu' Parker, you are not ze good father? *Eh
bien,* you shall make some little *prière* for those
sauvages."

The thin face of Samuel Parker brightened.
This land before his view, majestic, beautiful, was
as fabled and unknown as the continent of lost At-
lantis. It was a wild world, a new one. He, first to
answer that strange appeal from the wild North-
west—that appeal carried by the four Nez Percés
Indians, who travelled in ignorance and hope across
half a continent to ask that the Book might be sent
out to them by the white man—felt now exaltation
swell within his soul.

What a meeting must be this, which he had
pushed forward so eagerly to discover! It was a
gathering, as he had been well advised, not in the
name of religion or of politics, of art or science—

hardly even in the cause of commerce, although here the wild trappers and hunters, absent from one year's end to the other in the mountains, annually met, at some appointed spot in the Rockies, those bold merchants who brought out to them stores of goods to trade for furs. The trappers' rendezvous! He had heard of it a thousand tales distorted and unreal. Truly there was work ahead. He caught up the reins upon his horse's neck, forgot his weariness, and resumed his way.

His followers, a score or more of horsemen and pack-train drivers, among whom rode a short sturdy young man, the future martyr-missionary, Marcus Whitman, moved on, browned, gaunt, dust-begrimed, yet cheerful.

They had travelled for perhaps a mile or so down the valley when the guide, riding abreast of his employer, suddenly pulled up his horse and signed for his companion to pause.

"M'sieu'," said he, "you think I know little of zis land. Behol'! We are harrive' zis hour."

He pointed. There, against the sky-line, on a projecting range of the mountainside which sloped down to the edge of the valley, was the figure of a mountain man, motionless, and evidently on guard.

"*En avant!*" cried François, setting heels to his horse. "*V'la!* It is ze guard of ze encampment. Ride quick, *mes camarades!*"

The train, packhorses and all, pushed forward at a gallop, which soon broke into a wild run—the proper gait in trapper custom for all who arrived at the mountain rendezvous.

As they rounded the spur of rocks which had

made the watch-tower of the sentinel, the full scene
burst upon their eyes. There was a wide, sweet
space in the valley, made as if for the very purpose
of the great rendezvous. A flat of green cotton-
woods adjoined the river-bank. "Benches," or natural terraces, of sweet grass rose along the hillside
a half-mile away. Hundreds of horses, picketed or
hobbled, grazed here and there. Others, favorite
steeds of their masters, stood tied at the doors of
lodges, in front of which rose long, tufted spears,
in the heraldry of that land insignia of their owner's rank. Teepees, a hundred and twoscore, skin
tents of the savage tribes and homes also of the
whites, were grouped irregularly over a space of
more than half a mile. At the doors of many of
these, silent Indians sat and smoked. In the wide
interspaces of the village were many men, some of
them dressed in brown buckskins, others clad more
gaudily. These passed to and fro, some on foot,
others riding furiously. Animation was in all the
air.

Shouts, cries, a tumult formed of many factors
filled the air. Babel of speech rose from Frenchmen, Spaniards, Canadians, English, Scotch, Irish,
and American backwoodsmen, and Indians of half
a dozen tribes. Horses, dogs, black-haired and
blanketed women, and children of divers colors
moved about continually. The gathering was
heterogeneous, conglomerate, picturesque, savage.

Samuel Parker, missionary to the Oregon tribes,
and now come hither to the mountain market of
1835 as knight-errant of the Gospel, pulled up his
horse at the edge of the encampment and gazed in

sheer amazement. His party—except Whitman, who reined in his horse at his friend's side—passed on and joined the shouting throng. Apparently they conveyed certain news as they rode; for now out of the circling ranks of wild horsemen there swept toward the strangers a group of yelling riders.

Long ribbons and waving eagle feathers streamed from the manes and tails of their ponies. Some riders, even of the white men, wore the great war-bonnets of the northern tribes, the long crests of feathers sweeping back upon the croups of the rough-coated steeds they rode. Weapons were in the hands of all. Loud speech and many oaths were on their lips. They might well have disturbed bolder hearts than that of a peaceful missionary.

The leader of the approaching band was a man of gigantic stature, more than six inches above the six-feet mark. He was dark of hair and eye; a wide mustache swept back across his face, and his heavy, untrimmed beard, matted and sunburned at the edges, gave him an expression savage and forbidding.

Clad in the buckskin of a mountain trapper, none the less this personage affected a certain finery. A brilliant sash encircled his waist, his hat bore a wide plume. At his belt hung pistols, and in his hand was a long rifle. He pulled up his horse squatting, its nose high in air.

"How, friend!" he cried. "Or *be* you friend, who come thus without word to Bill Shunan's camp?"

"Sir," replied the missionary, "my name is Parker—Samuel Parker. I am from far New England, and am bound upon my way to Oregon. I have come aside from the Sublette Cutoff trail to be present at this rendezvous. Yourself I do not know."

"What! Not know Bill Shunan, the bully of the Rockies and the owner of this camp? Hark ye, stranger, ye're treading on dangerous ground. I've whipped half a dozen men to-day, and driven every fighter of the rendezvous back into his lodge. *They* know Bill Shunan, and they show him respect, as you shall yourself."

Samuel Parker made no reply, and found no way to move forward, even had he been sure that friends awaited him in the village. The giant went on:

"Now, what's your business, man? Ye look like no trapper nor good mountain man. As for more Yankee traders, we've enough of them now, and more than enough. Look ye at their packs, laid out there, half of them not opened! The traders are robbing us mountain men at this market. Two skins they ask for a pint of sugar, if one would please his squaw. As much goes for a knife; and three skins for coffee as much as you could put in a pint cup. Powder they hold as high as gold-dust, and a blanket is worth a pair of horses. It's robbery, and I'll have no more of it. If Jim Bridger and Bill Williams, and their half-black Beckwourth, and Gervais, and Fraeb, and their other offscourings of old Ashley, will not rebel against such doings, then, for one, Bill Shunan is not afraid. My people were French back in old Canada. It is the French who found the Rockies, and who ought to own them! These Americans—I whip them with switches! And so I'll whip you if ye come here as a trader and give us no better measure than these others! Now, I say, who are ye?"

The dark eye of the missionary lighted again with its hidden fire.

"I am a missionary," said he, "a man of the church, a minister of the Gospel, as I would have said to you. I have come to this encampment to hold divine services among you. Red men or white, we are brethren, and we are sinners in common." The close-shut mouth, the dull flush visible beneath the tan, the flash of the eye, all bespoke him a man not devoid of courage. Yet his speech brought only rage to the other.

"Minister!" he cried. "By all the saints, no unfrocked priest shall speak words in this camp of mine! Not even a good father of the French has been present at a rendezvous of the bully boys of the mountains; and who are you, to come intruding at the frolic of the trappers? I'll have no sniveling Protestant here. So get ye gone at once!"

"Sir," said the minister, "I have ridden far, and I am not of a mind to go back." He crowded his horse forward, the more so as he saw approaching another band of men from the encampment. He could only hope that they might be of a class not quite the same as this desperado. A moment later these riders joined the group of parleyers.

"How now, what is this?" cried out the tall man

who led these newcomers. "Who's the stranger?
Does he carry news from the States?"

"Back with ye, Bill Williams!" cried Shunan.
" 'Tis but a sniveling preacher from the East, and
I have told him he shall bring no psalms here."

The freshly arrived horsemen made small reply
to Shunan's speech, but bent a curious gaze upon
the stranger. The latter saw at a glance that these
were no allies of the bully. Therefore he glanced
toward them as if in appeal.

Without a word a half-score of them urged their
horses round him, and separated him from Shunan's party.

"What!" cried Shunan. "You dispute me? I
tell ye he will never see the sun again if he pushes
himself into this camp. What do ye mean, you
puny Yankees? Do ye want me to put ye on
your death-beds, as I have a couple of ye before
to-day? Back with ye! For I say this man shall
not come into camp!"

"Shunan," broke in a quiet voice, "who gives you
right to issue orders here?"

The speaker was a young man, still in his twen-
ties; and so far from equaling in stature the giant
whom he addressed, he was slight and small, not
over five feet six inches in height, although of good
shoulders and great depth of chest.

He sat a dark-brown horse, fully caparisoned in
the Spanish fashion. His garb was of buckskin,
but plain and devoid of ornamentation. A wide
hat swept over his well-tanned face, and from beneath its brim there shone the steely glance of gray-
blue eyes.

Shunan, dumfounded, whirled his horse toward the speaker.

"Shunan," repeated this man, in turn urging his own horse forward, "you've made trouble enough in the encampment. You shall no longer act the bully here. The stranger comes in peace, and he shall be heard here if he likes. What!" and the blue eyes flashed. "Would you issue orders at a meeting of the free men of the mountains—the very place in all the world where every man who comes in friendship is made welcome? This is our country. This is our encampment. The law of what is right shall govern here; and I take it upon myself to say this to you!"

Silence fell upon all who heard these words. The last speaker raised his hand as Parker would have spoken. The friends of the young man now pressed closer about him. He did not give back, but urged his mount still forward, until it breasted the cream-colored horse which Shunan rode. The bully, half-sobered from his potations by this stern situation, did not himself give back.

"Who are you?" he cried. "By what right do ye question Bill Shunan? Would ye be the next to be whipped with switches? There is but one end to this, boy! Are ye ready for it?"

"Have I ever been found unready?" asked the young man, quietly. "I say again, this land is free. The stranger shall have meat and robes at my lodge, and if he will speak, he shall have his say."

In a rage Shunan spurred forward, his hand uplifted; yet the brown horse and its rider receded not an inch. The issue was joined. There must now be combat!

"Not here!" cried old Bill Williams, suddenly. "Wait! Back to the camp with ye all, and there let it be decided proper!"

This speech met with sudden approval upon both sides. An instant later the missionary's horse was swept forward in a rush which carried both parties, intermingled, deep into the center of the tented village.

Well toward the middle of the encampment there was a large and irregular space left unoccupied, a sort of plaza, devoted to common use, and employed as meeting-ground in the trading operations of the market, or the jollifications, which occupied far more of the time. As the riders came into this open space Shunan and his party drew off to the right. His antagonist sought out his lodge upon the opposite side. He was followed here by several of his warmer friends, Williams, Bridger, Fraeb, other men of the mountains at one time known throughout the length and breadth of the West.

"Sir," said the young man, turning toward Samuel Parker, "get you down, and come within my house. Perhaps by this time you are used to such. We bid you welcome. I shall return to you soon, after I have settled this matter which has come up between me and yonder ruffian."

"I beseech you!" cried the missionary, reaching out an imploring hand. "What is it you would do? Surely you do not mean—you would not engage in combat with this man—you do not mean bloodshed? This—on my account—no, no! Let me go."

The quiet man whom he thus accosted made no answer at first, but pushed back the hat from his brow and gazed upon the newcomer with a kindly eye.

"There is but one way," said he. "Bill, see to it that our friend has good treatment here." The man addressed took Parker by the arm and thrust him gently within the lodge.

The young man now summoned another friend. "Gervais," he said, "go to yonder bully, and say to him that unless his threats and boasts cease, I shall be forced to kill him. Our bullets should be for our enemies, but Shunan has made trouble enough; and he must go to his lodge or meet me, man to man."

"Are ye ready for him, boy?" asked Gervais. "How is the shoulder where you caught the Blackfoot bullet last fall? Can you handle the rifle?"

"I'll not trust the shoulder," was the reply, "and will not risk the rifle." He drew a pistol from his belt and looked at the priming of the pan. "One shot," said he, "and it must do."

"But he'll use his rifle."

"Very well. Go to him and say that I shall come mounted, like himself, and he may be armed as he likes. No man is my superior on horse or with any weapon. Moreover, you shall see that I do not seek so much to kill him as to end his boasting, and to restore the law in this camp."

Gervais sprang upon his horse and was off, calling out to others, who drew near, the instructions which he had received. He approached Shunan, who was now urging his horse round and round the open space of the village, shouting defiance and uttering foul reproaches for his antagonist, whom he announced himself eager to meet. Gervais delivered his message.

The bully continued to crowd his horse back and forth, pulling it up so sharply that it was thrown upon its haunches now and again in mid-career. He waved his long rifle over his head, and issued a general challenge to all within reach of his voice.

At this moment there rode out from the farther side of the circle the champion of law and order. The horse which he bestrode came on strongly and lightly, its head up. The rider had stripped off all his accouterments, and rode a buckskin pad-saddle, Indian fashion. About his waist was a belt, which bore no weapons. His long rifle, at which weapon he had no master, did not rest upon the saddle front. His hat was gone, and a handkerchief bound back his long light hair. He rode forward lightly, easily, in confidence.

Shunan, yelling wildly, charged at once upon him.

The young man sat erect; but when Shunan was still a score of yards away, the brown horse leaped aside, its rider lying along its neck as an Indian might have done, and swept round and to the rear of Shunan.

The bully, fumbling with his piece, endeavored to follow. Then he saw the pistol barrel pointing under the neck of the brown horse, and cold terror smote his soul.

The two swept past again at full gallop, Shunan still not quite master of his horse and weapon at the same time, for the long-barreled, muzzle-loading rifle was difficult to manage from the back of a plunging horse. They wheeled and passed yet again; but this time, as they turned, they headed directly toward each other at a steady pace.

The spectators knew that in an instant the issue would be decided.

Shunan jerked up his horse and threw his rifle sharply to his face. His antagonist made no attempt to swerve, but instead spurred forward sharply. The brown horse sprang breast to breast with the cream-colored mustang. The two men were within arm's length. At this minute there rang out two reports, almost at the same instant. The horses sprang apart.

The slighter man was still sitting erect. He swept his hand hastily across his temple, where he felt a stinging burn. Shunan, dazed, sat his horse for an instant, but his rifle dropped to the ground; and as his horse sprang forward, he himself fell, and so lay, one arm hanging limp and the other raised in the sign of surrender.

The duel was over. The late friends of Shunan joined the riders who now crowded into the open space from the opposite sides of the arena.

"Did he touch ye, boy?" cried old Bill Williams.

"No, though he meant it well enough. See, there's a twist of hair gone from the side of my head."

"He got your bullet through the hand and wrist," said Williams, as they turned away. "His right arm's done for, for a while. You were a bit the first with your fire, my son."

"I know it, and I knew I had need to be. I fired at his hand, and knew I must be a shade the first. I knew if I held true, his aim would be thrown out."

As he spoke, he dismounted at the door of his own lodge. There Samuel Parker met him, and cried, "Is it over? Is any one hurt? Has there been murder done?"

"There, there, friend," said old Bill Williams, gently, "you bring here still your Yankee way of speech. Besides, 'tis no murder unless some one is killed, and yonder bully Shunan will only have a sore hand for a month or so. 'Twas a lesson that was well needed for him. See now, the camp is quiet already. Men and women may venture out-of-doors in peace and comfort. 'Tis but the law of the mountains you have seen, man."

"And as for the law of the Gospel," interrupted Gervais, "they shall have that this night round the fire, if you wish to speak."

The minister gazed from one to the other with emotions new to him.

"And you, sir," he said, extending his hand to the young man who had thus stoutly championed him, "who are you? Whom shall I thank for this strange act—for this strange justice of the mountains, as you call it?"

The bronzed men who stood or sat their horses near at hand gazed from one to another, smiling. At last old Bill Williams broke out into a laugh.

"Man," cried he, " 'tis easily seen you're fresh from the States! What, not know the best man in all the Rockies? There is but one could have done this deed so well. We have few courts here, but whenever we've needed a sheriff of our own we've had one, and here he is. So you did not know Kit Carson!"

THE STORY OF GRACE DARLING

Anonymous

ON the evening of Wednesday, September 5, the steamship *Forfarshire* left Hull for Dundee, carrying a cargo of iron, and having some forty passengers on board. The ship was only eight years old; the master, John Humble, was an experienced seaman; and the crew, including firemen and engineers, was complete. But even before the vessel left the dock one passenger at least had felt uneasily that something was wrong—that there was an unusual commotion among officials and sailors. Still, no alarm was given, and at dusk the vessel steamed prosperously down the Humber River.

The next day (Thursday, the 6th) the weather changed, the wind blowing N.N.W., and increasing toward midnight to a perfect gale. On the morning of Friday, the 7th, a sloop from Montrose, making for South Shields, saw a small boat laboring hard in the trough of the sea. The Montrose vessel bore down on it, and in spite of the state of the weather managed to get the boat's crew on board. They were nine men in all, the sole survivors, as they believed themselves to be, of the crew and passengers of the *Forfarshire,* which was then lying a total wreck on Longstone, one of the outermost of the Farne Islands.

It was a wretched story they had to tell of lives thrown away through carelessness and negligence, unredeemed, as far as their story went, by any heroism or unselfish courage.

While still in the Humber, and not twenty miles from Hull, it was found that one of the boilers leaked, but the captain refused to put about. The pumps were set to work to fill the boiler, and the vessel kept on her way, though slowly, not passing between the Farne Islands and the mainland till Thursday evening. It was eight o'clock when they entered Berwick Bay; the wind freshened and was soon blowing hard from N.N.W. The motion of the vessel increased the leakage, and it was now found that there were holes in all the three boilers. Two men were set to work the pumps, one or two of the passengers also assisting, but as fast as the water was pumped into the boilers it poured out again. The bilge was so full of steam and boiling water that the firemen could not get to the fires. Still the steamer struggled on, laboring heavily, for the sea was running very high. At midnight they were off St. Abbs Head, when the engineers reported that the case was hopeless; the engines had entirely ceased to work. The ship rolled helplessly in the waves, and the rocky coast was at no great distance. They ran up the sails fore and aft to try and keep her off the rocks, and put her round so that she might run before the wind, and as the tide was setting southward she drifted fast with wind and tide. Torrents of rain were falling, and in spite of the wind there was a thick fog. Some of the passengers were below, others were on deck with crew and captain, knowing well their danger.

About three the noise of breakers was distinctly heard a little way ahead, and at the same time a light was seen away to the left, glimmering faintly through the darkness. It came home to the anxious crew with sickening certainty that they were being driven on the Farne Islands. These islands form a group of desolate rocks lying off the Northumbrian coast. They are twenty in number, some only uncovered at low tide, and all offering a rugged iron wall to any ill-fated boat that may be driven upon them.

Even in calm weather and by daylight seamen are glad to give them a wide berth.

The master of the *Forfarshire* in this desperate strait attempted to make for the channel which runs between the Islands and the mainland. It was at best a forlorn chance; it was hopeless here; the vessel refused to answer her helm! On she drove in the darkness, nearer and nearer came the sound of the breakers; the passengers and crew on board the boat became frantic. Women wailed and shrieked; the captain's wife clung to him, weeping; the crew lost all instinct of discipline, and thought of nothing but saving their skins.

Between three and four the shock came—a hideous grinding noise, a strain and shiver of the whole ship, and she struck violently against a great rock. In the awful moment which followed, five of the crew succeeded in lowering the larboard quarter-boat and pushed off in her. The mate swung himself over the side, and also reached her; and a passenger rushing at this moment up from the cabin and seeing the boat already three yards from the ship, cleared the space with a bound and landed safely in her, though nearly upsetting her by his weight. She righted, and the crew pulled off with the desperate energy of men rowing for their lives. The sight of agonized faces, the shrieks of the drowning, were lost in the darkness and in the howling winds, and the boat with the seven men on board was swept along by the rapidly-flowing tide.

Such was the story the exhausted boat's crew told next morning to their rescuers on board the Montrose sloop. And the rest of the ship's company—what of them? Had they all gone down by the island crag with never a hand stretched out to help them?

Hardly had the boat escaped from the stranded vessel when a great wave struck her on the quarter, lifted her up bodily, and dashed her back on the rock. She struck midships on the sharp edge and broke at once into two pieces. The after part was washed clean away with about twenty passengers clinging to it, the captain and his wife being among them. A group of people, about nine in number, were huddled together near the bow; they, with the whole forepart of the ship, were lifted right on to the rock. In the fore cabin was a poor woman, Mrs. Dawson, with a child on each arm. When the vessel was stranded on the rock the waves rushed into the exposed cabin, but she managed to keep her position, cowering in a corner. First one and then the other child died from cold and exhaustion, and falling from the fainting mother were swept from her sight by the waves, but the poor soul herself survived all the horrors of the night.

It was now four o'clock; the storm was raging with unabated violence, and it was still two hours to daybreak. About a mile from Longstone, the island on which the vessel struck, lies Brownsman, the outermost of the Farne Islands, on which stands the lighthouse. At this time the keeper of the lighthouse was a man of the name of William Darling. He was an elderly, almost an old man, and the only other inmates of the lighthouse were his wife and daughter Grace, a girl of twenty-two. On this Friday night she was awake, and through the raging of the storm heard shrieks more persistent and despairing than those of the wildest seabirds. In great trouble she rose and awakened her father. The cries continued, but in the darkness they could do nothing. Even after day broke it was difficult to make out distant objects, for a mist was still hanging over the sea. At length, with a glass they could discern the wreck on Longstone, and figures moving about on it. Between the two islands lay a mile of yeasty sea, and the tide was running hard between them. The only boat on the lighthouse was a clumsily built jolly-boat, heavy enough to tax the strength of two strong men in ordinary weather, and here there was but an old man and a young girl to face a raging sea and a tide running dead against them. Darling hesitated to undertake anything so dangerous, but his daughter woula hear of no delay. On the other side of that rough mile of sea men were perishing, and she *could* not stay where she was and see them die.

So off they set in the heavy coble, the old man with one oar, the girl with the other, rowing with straining breath and beating hearts. Any moment they might be whelmed in the sea or dashed against the rocks. Even if they got the crew off it would be doubtful if they could row them to the lighthouse; the tide was about to turn, and would be against them on their homeward journey; death seemed to face them on every side.

When close to the rock there was imminent danger of their being dashed to pieces against it. Steadying the boat an instant, Darling managed to jump on to the rock, while Grace rapidly rowed out a little and kept the boat from going on the rocks by rowing continually. It is difficult to imagine how the nine shipwrecked people, exhausted and wearied as they were, were got into the boat in such a sea, especially as the poor woman, Mrs. Dawson, was in an almost fainting condition; but finally they were all gotten on board. Fortunately, one or two of the rescued crew were able to assist in the heavy task of rowing the boat back to Brownsman.

The storm continued to rage for several days after, and the whole party had to remain in the lighthouse. Moreover, a boatload which had come to their rescue from North Shields was also storm-stayed.

It is told of this admirable girl that she was the tenderest and gentlest of nurses and hostesses, as she was certainly one of the most singularly courageous of women.

She could never be brought to look upon her exploit as in any way remarkable, and when by-and-by honors and distinctions were showered upon her, and people came from long distances to see her, she kept through it all the dignity of perfect simplicity and modesty.

Close to Bamborough, on a windy hill, lie a little gray church and a quiet churchyard. At all seasons high winds from the North Sea blow over the graves and fret and eat away the soft gray sandstone of which the plain headstones are made. So great is the wear and tear of these winds that comparatively recent monuments look like those which have stood for centuries. On one of these stones lies a recumbent figure, with what looks not unlike a lance clasped in the hand and laid across the breast. Involuntarily one thinks of the stone crusaders, who lie in their armor, clasping their half-drawn swords, awaiting the Resurrection morning. It is the monument of Grace Darling, who here lies at rest with her oar still clasped in her strong right hand.

THE STRUGGLES OF CHARLES GOODYEAR

By George C. Towle

NEVER did any man work harder, suffer more keenly, or remain more steadfast to one great purpose of life, than did Charles Goodyear. The story of his life—for the most part mournful —teems with touching interest. No inventor ever struggled against greater or more often returning obstacles, or against repeated failures more overwhelming. Goodyear is often compared, as a martyr and hero of invention, to Bernard Palissy the potter. He is sometimes called "the Palissy of the nineteenth century." But his sufferings were more various, more bitter, and more long enduring than ever were even those of Palissy; while the result of his long, unceasing labors was infinitely more precious to the world. For if Palissy restored the art of enamelling so as to produce beautiful works of art, Goodyear perfected a substance which gives comfort and secures health to millions of human beings.

Charles Goodyear was born at New Haven, Connecticut, in 1801. He was the eldest of the six children of a leading hardware merchant of that place, a man both of piety and of inventive talent. When Charles was a boy, his father began the manufacture of hardware articles, and at the same time carried on a farm. He often required his son's assistance, so that Charles's schooling was limited. He was very fond of books, however, from an early age, and instead of playing with his mates, devoted most of his leisure time to reading.

It was even while he was a schoolboy that his attention was first turned to the material, the improvement of which for common uses became afterwards his life-work. "He happened to take up a thin scale of India-rubber," says his biographer, "peeled from a bottle, and it was suggested to his mind that it would be a very useful fabric if it could be made uniformly so thin, and could be so prepared as to prevent its melting and sticking together in a solid mass." Often afterward he had a vivid presentiment that he was destined by Providence to achieve these results.

The years of his youth and early manhood were spent in the hardware trade in Philadelphia and then in Connecticut; and at twenty-four he was married to a heroic young wife, who shared his trials, and was ever to him a comforting and encouraging spirit. From boyhood he was always devout and pure in habits. On one occasion, soon after his marriage, he wrote to his wife while absent from her: "I have quit smoking, chewing, and drinking all in one day. You cannot form an idea of the extent of this last evil in this city [New York] among the young men."

Charles Goodyear's misfortunes began early in his career. He failed in business, his health broke down, and through life thereafter he suffered from almost continual attacks of dyspepsia. He was, moreover, a small, frail man, with a weak constitution. He was imprisoned for debt after his failure; nor was this the only time that he found himself within the walls of a jail. That was almost a frequent experience with him in after life.

It was under discouragements like these that Goodyear began his long series of experiments in India-rubber. Already this peculiar substance— a gum that exudes from a certain kind of very tall tree, which is chiefly found in South America— had been manufactured into various articles, but it had not been made enduring, and the uses to which it could be put were very limited.

There is no space here to follow Goodyear's experiments in detail. He entered upon them with the ardor of a fanatic and the faith of a devotee. But he very soon found that the difficulties in his way were great and many. He was bankrupt, in bad health, with a growing family dependent on him, and no means of support. Yet he persevered, through years of wretchedness, to the very end. It is a striking fact that his very first experiment was made in a prison cell.

During the long period occupied by his repeated trials of invention he passed through almost every calamity to which human flesh is heir. Again and again he was thrown into prison. Repeatedly he saw starvation staring him and his gentle wife and his poor little children in the face. He was reduced many times to the very last extreme of penury. His friends sneered at him, deserted him, called him mad. He was forced many times to beg the loan of a few dollars, with no prospect of repayment. One of his children died in the dead of winter, when there was no fuel in the cheerless house. A gentleman was once asked what sort of a looking man Goodyear was. "If you meet a man," was the reply, "who wears an India-rubber coat, cap, stock, vest, and shoes, with an India-rubber money purse without a cent in it, that is Charles Goodyear."

Once, while in the extremity of want, when he was living at Greenwich, near New York, he met his brother-in-law, and said, "Give me ten dollars, brother; I have pawned my last silver spoon to pay my fare to the city."

"You must not go on so; you cannot live in this way," said the other.

"I am going to do better," replied Goodyear cheerily.

It was by accident at last that he hit upon the secret of how to make India-rubber durable. He was talking one day to several visitors, and in his ardor making rapid gestures, when a piece of rubber which he was holding in his hand accidentally hit against a hot stove. To his amazement, instead of melting, the gum remained stiff and charred, like leather. He again applied great heat to a piece of rubber, and then nailed it outside the door, where it was very cold. The next morning he found that it was perfectly flexible; and this was the discovery which led to that successful invention which he had struggled through so many years to perfect. The main value of the discovery lay in this, that while the gum would dissolve in a moderate heat, it both remained hard and continued to be flexible when submitted to an extreme heat. This came to be known as the "vulcanization" of India-rubber.

Two years were still to elapse, however, before Goodyear could make practical use of his great discovery. He had tired everybody out by his previous frequent assertions that his invention had been perfected, when it had until now always proved a failure. Many a time he had gone to his friends, declaring that he had succeeded, so that when he really had made the discovery nobody believed in it.

He was still desperately poor and in wretched health. Yet he moved to Woburn, in Massachusetts, resolutely continuing his experiments there. He had no money, and so baked his India-rubber in his wife's oven and saucepans, or hung it before the nose of her tea-kettle. Sometimes he begged the use of the factory ovens in the neighborhood after the day's work was over, and sold his children's very school-books in order to supply himself with the necessary gum. At this time he lived almost exclusively on money gifts from pitying friends, who shook their heads in their doubts of his sanity. Often his house had neither food nor fuel in it; his family were forced to go out into the woods to get wood to burn. "They dug their potatoes before they were half-grown, for the sake of having something to eat."

Goodyear was terribly afraid that he should die before he could make the world perceive the great uses to which his discovery might be applied. What he was toiling for was neither fame nor fortune, but only to confer a vast benefit on his fellow-men.

At last, after infinite struggles, the absorbing purpose of his life was attained. India-rubber was

introduced under his patents, and soon proved to
have all the value he had, in his wildest moments,
claimed for it. Success thus crowned his noble
efforts, which had continued unceasingly through
ten years of self-imposed privation. India-rubber
was now seen to be capable of being adapted to at
least five hundred uses. It could be made "as pli-
able as kid, tougher than ox-hide, as elastic as
whalebone, or as rigid as flint." But, as too often
happens, his great discovery enriched neither Goodyear nor his family. It soon gave employment to
sixty thousand artisans, and annually produced articles in this country alone worth eight millions of
dollars.

Happily the later years of the noble, self-denying
inventor were spent at least free from the grinding
penury and privations of his years of uncertainty
and toil. He died in his sixtieth year (1860),
happy in the thought of the magnificent boon he
had given to mankind.

OLD JOHNNY APPLESEED

By Elizabeth Harrison

MANY years ago on the sparsely settled
prairies of America there lived an old man
who was known by the queer name of "Johnny
Appleseed." His wife had died long ago and his
children had grown up and scattered to the corners
of the earth. He had not even a home that he
could call his own, but wandered about from place

to place, with only a few friends and little or no money. His face was wrinkled, his hair was thin and gray, and his shoulders stooped. His clothes were old and ragged and his hat was old and shabby. Yet inside of him was a heart that was brave and true, and he felt that even he, old and poor as he was, could be of use in the world, because he loved his fellow-men, and love always finds something to do.

As he trudged along the lonely road from town to town, or made for himself a path through the unbroken forest, he often thought of the good God, and of how all men were children of the One Father. Sometimes he would burst out singing the words of a song which he had learned when he was a young man.

> "Millions loving, I embrace you,
> All the world this kiss I send!
> Brothers, o'er yon starry tent
> Dwells a God whose love is true!"

These words, by the way, are a part of a great poem you may some day read. And they once so stirred the heart of a great musician that he set them to the finest music the world has ever heard. And now the great thought of a loving God and the great music of a loving man comforted the lonely traveller.

The old man wandered about from village to village, which in those days were scattered far apart, with miles and miles of prairie land stretching between them, and sometimes woodland and rivers, too, separated one village from the next.

OLD JOHNNY APPLESEED

At night he usually earned his crust of bread and lodgings by mending the teakettle or wash-boiler of some farmer's wife, or by soldering on the handle of her tin cup or the knob to her tea-pot, as he always carried in one of his coat pockets a small charcoal stove and a bit of solder. He always carried under his arm or over his shoulder a green baize bag, and when the mending was done he would oftentimes draw out of this green bag an old violin and begin to play, and the farmer, as well as his wife and the children, would gather around him and listen to his strange music.

Sometimes it was gay and sometimes it was sad, but always sweet. Sometimes he sang words that he himself had written, and sometimes the songs which had been written by the great masters. But mending broken tinware and playing an old violin were not the only things he did to help the world along. As he wandered from place to place he often noticed how rich the soil was, and he would say to himself, "Some day this will be a great country with thousands of people living on this land, and though I shall never see them, they may never read my verses or hear my name, still I can help them, and add some things to their lives."

So whenever a farmer's wife gave him an apple to eat he carefully saved every seed that lay hidden in the heart of the apple, and next day as he trudged along he would stoop down every now and then and plant a few of the seeds and then carefully cover them with the rich black soil of the prairie. Then he would look up reverently to the sky and say, "I can but plant the seed, dear Lord, and Thy clouds may water them, but Thou alone can give the increase. Thou only can cause this tiny seed to grow into a tree whose fruit shall feed my fellow-men." Then the God-like love that would fill his heart at such a thought would cause his face to look young again, and his eyes to shine as an angel's eyes must shine, and oftentimes he would sing in clear rich tones—

> "Millions loving, I embrace you,
> All the world this kiss I send!
> Brothers, o'er yon starry tent
> Dwells a God whose love is true!"

And he knew that God dwelt in his heart as well as in the blue sky above.

When the cold winters came and the ground was frozen too hard for him to plant his apple seeds, he still saved them, and would often have a small bag full of them by the time that spring returned again. And this is how he came to be called "Old Johnny Appleseed."

Though nobody took very much notice of what he was doing, he still continued each day to plant apple seeds and each evening to play on his violin.

By-and-by his step grew slower and his shoulders drooped lower until at last his soul, which had always been strong and beautiful, passed out of his worn old body into the life beyond, and the cast-off body was buried by some villagers who felt kindly towards the old man, but who never dreamed that he had ever done any real service for them or their children. And soon his very name was forgotten. But the tiny apple seeds took root and began to grow, and each summer the young saplings grew taller and each winter they grew stronger, until at last they were young trees, and then they were old enough to bear apples. As people moved from the east out to the wild western prairies they naturally enough selected sites for building their homes near the fruitful apple trees, and in the springtime the young men gathered the blossoms for the young maidens to wear in their hair, and in the autumn the fathers gathered the ripe red and yellow apples to store away in their cellars for winter use, and the mothers made apple sauce and apple pies and apple dumplings of them, and all the year round the little children played under the shade of the apple trees, but none of them ever once thought of the old man who had planted for people he did not know, and who could never even thank him for his loving services.

Each apple that ripened bore in it's heart a number of new seeds, some of which were planted and grew into fine orchards from which were gathered many barrels of apples. These were shipped farther west, until the Rocky Mountains were reached. In the center of each apple shipped were more seeds, from which grew more apple trees, which bore the same kind of apples that the wrinkled old man in the shabby old clothes had planted long years before. So that many thousands of people have already been benefited by what the poor old man in the shabby old coat did, and thousands yet to come will enjoy the fruits of his labor.

It is true he never wore the armor of a great

knight and never held the title of a great general. He never discovered a new world, nor helped his favorite to sit on the throne of a king. But perhaps after all, though ragged and poor, he was a hero, because in his heart he really and truly sang, as well as with his lips:

> "Millions loving, I embrace you,
> All the world this kiss I send!
> Brothers, o'er yon starry tent
> Dwells a God whose love is true!"

For the greatest of all victories is to learn to love others even when they do not know it. This is to be God-like, and to be God-like is to be the greatest of heroes.

THE LITTLE POST-BOY

By Bayard Taylor

VERY few foreigners travel in Sweden in the winter, on account of the intense cold. As you go northward from Stockholm, the capital, the country becomes ruder and wilder, and the climate more severe. In the sheltered valleys along the Gulf of Bothnia and the rivers which empty into it, there are farms and villages for a distance of seven or eight hundred miles, after which fruit-trees disappear, and nothing will grow in the short, cold summers, except potatoes and a little barley. Farther inland, there are great forests and lakes, and ranges of mountains where bears, wolves, and herds of wild reindeer make their home. No people could live in such a country unless they were very industrious and thrifty.

I made my journey in the winter, because I was on my way to Lapland, where it is easier to travel when the swamps and rivers are frozen, and the reindeer-sleds can fly along over the smooth snow. It was very cold indeed, the greater part of the time; the days were short and dark, and if I had not found the people so kind, so cheerful, and so honest, I should have felt inclined to turn back, more than once. But I do not think there are better people in the world than those who live in Norrland, which is a Swedish province, commencing about two hundred miles north of Stockholm.

They are a hale, strong race, with yellow hair and bright blue eyes, and the handsomest teeth I ever saw. They live plainly, but very comfortably, in snug wooden houses, with double windows and doors to keep out the cold; and since they cannot do much out-door work, they spin and weave and mend their farming implements in the large family room, thus enjoying the winter in spite of its severity. They are very happy and contented, and few of them would be willing to leave that cold country and make their homes in a warmer climate.

Here there are neither railroads nor stages, but the government has established post-stations at distances varying from ten to twenty miles. At each station a number of horses, and sometimes vehicles, are kept, but generally the traveller has his own sled, and simply hires the horses from one station to another. These horses are either furnished by the keeper of the station or some of the neighboring farmers, and when they are wanted a man or boy goes along with the traveller to bring them back. It would be quite an independent and convenient way of travelling, if the horses were always ready; but sometimes you must wait an hour or more before they can be furnished.

I had my own little sled, filled with hay and covered with reindeer-skins to keep me warm. So long as the weather was not too cold, it was very pleasant to speed along through the dark forests, over the frozen rivers, or past farm after farm in the sheltered valleys up hill and down, until long after the stars came out, and then to get a warm supper in some dark-red post cottage, while the cheerful people sang or told stories around the fire. The cold increased a little every day, to be sure, but I became gradually accustomed to it, and soon began to fancy that the Arctic climate was not so difficult to endure as I had supposed. At first the thermometer fell to zero; then it went down ten degrees below; then twenty, and finally thirty. Being dressed in thick furs from head to foot, I did not suffer greatly; but I was very glad when the people assured me that such extreme cold never lasted more than two or three days. Boys of twelve or fourteen very often went with me to bring back their father's horses, and so long as those lively, red-cheeked fellows could face the weather, it would not do for me to be afraid.

One night there was a wonderful aurora in the sky. The streamers of red and blue light darted hither and thither, chasing each other up the zenith and down again to the northern horizon with a rapidity and a brilliance which I had never seen before. "There will be a storm, soon," said my post-boy; "one always comes, after these lights."

Next morning the sky was overcast, and the short day was as dark as our twilight. But it was not quite so cold, and I travelled onward as fast as possible. There was a long tract of wild and thinly-settled country before me, and I wished to get through it before stopping for the night. Unfortunately it happened that two lumber-merchants were travelling the same way, and had taken the horses; so I was obliged to wait at the stations until other horses were brought from the neighboring farms. This delayed me so much that at seven o'clock in the evening I had still one more station of three Swedish miles before reaching the village where I intended to spend the night. Now a Swedish mile is nearly equal to seven English, so that the station was at least twenty miles long.

I decided to take supper while the horse was eating his feed. They had not expected any more travellers at the station, and were not prepared. The keeper had gone on with the two lumber-merchants; but his wife — a friendly, rosy-faced woman — prepared me some excellent coffee, potatoes, and stewed reindeer-meat, upon which I made an excellent meal. The house was on the border of a large, dark forest, and the roar of the icy northern wind in the trees seemed to increase while I waited in the warm room. I did not feel inclined to go forth into the wintry storm, but, having set my mind on reaching the village that night, I was loath to turn back.

THE LITTLE POST-BOY

"It is a bad night," said the woman, "and my husband will certainly stay at Umea until morning. His name is Neils Petersen, and I think you will find him at the post-office when you get there. Lars will take you, and they can come back together."

"Who is Lars?" I asked.

"My son," said she. "He is getting the horse ready. There is nobody else about the house tonight."

Just then the door opened, and in came Lars. He was about twelve years old; but his face was so rosy, his eyes so clear and round and blue, and his golden hair was blown back from his face in such silky curls, that he appeared to be even younger. I was surprised that his mother should be willing to send him twenty miles through the dark woods on such a night.

"Come here, Lars," I said. Then I took him by the hand, and asked, "Are you not afraid to go so far to-night?"

He looked at me with wondering eyes, and smiled; and his mother made haste to say: "You need have no fear, sir. Lars is young; but he'll take you safe enough. If the storm don't get worse, you'll be at Umea by eleven o'clock."

I was again on the point of remaining; but while I was deliberating with myself, the boy had put on his overcoat of sheep-skin, tied the lappets of his fur cap under his chin, and a thick woolen scarf around his nose and mouth, so that only the round blue eyes were visible; and then his mother took down the mittens of hare's fur from the stove

489

where they had been hung to dry. He put them on, took a short leather whip, and was ready.

I wrapped myself in my furs, and we went out together. The driving snow cut me in the face like needles, but Lars did not mind it in the least. He jumped into the sled, which he had filled with fresh, soft hay, tucked in the reindeer-skins at the sides, and we cuddled together on the narrow seat, making everything close and warm before we set out. I could not see at all, when the door of the house was shut, and the horse started on the journey. The night was dark, the snow blew incessantly, and the dark fir-trees roared all around us. Lars, however, knew the way, and somehow or other we kept the beaten track. He talked to the horse so constantly and so cheerfully, that after a while my own spirits began to rise, and the way seemed neither so long nor so disagreeable.

"Ho there, Axel!" he would say. "Keep to the road—not too far to the left. Well done. Here's a level; now trot a bit."

So we went on—sometimes up hill, sometimes down hill—for a long time, as it seemed. I began to grow chilly, and even Lars handed me the reins, while he swung and beat his arms to keep the blood in circulation. He no longer sang little songs and fragments of hymns, as when we first set out; but he was not in the least alarmed, or even impatient. Whenever I asked (as I did about every five minutes), "Are we nearly there?" he always answered, "A little farther."

Suddenly the wind seemed to increase.

"Ah," said he, "now I know where we are; it's

one mile more." But one mile, you must remember, meant *seven*.

Lars checked the horse, and peered anxiously from side to side in the darkness. I looked also, but could see nothing.

"What is the matter?" I finally asked.

"We have got past the hills, on the left," he said. "The country is open to the wind, and here the snow drifts worse than anywhere else on the road. If there have been no ploughs out to-night we'll have trouble."

You must know that the farmers along the road are obliged to turn out with their horses and oxen, and plough down the drifts, whenever the road is blocked up by a storm.

In less than a quarter of an hour we could see that the horse was sinking in the deep snow. He plunged bravely forward, but made scarcely any headway, and presently became so exhausted that he stood quite still. Lars and I arose from the seat and looked around. For my part, I saw nothing except some very indistinct shapes of trees; there was no sign of an opening through them. In a few minutes the horse started again, and with great labor carried us a few yards farther.

"Shall we get out and try to find the road?" said I.

"It's no use," Lars answered. "In these drifts we would sink to the waist. Wait a little, and we shall get through this one."

It was as he said. Another pull brought us through the deep part of the drift, and we reached a place where the snow was quite shallow. But it was not the hard, smooth surface of the road: we could feel that the ground was uneven, and covered with roots and bushes. Bidding Axel stand still, Lars jumped out of the sled, and began wading around among the trees. Then I got out on the other side, but had not proceeded ten steps before I began to sink so deeply into the loose snow that I was glad to extricate myself and return. It was a desperate situation, and I wondered how we should ever get out of it.

I shouted to Lars, in order to guide him, and it was not long before he also came back to the sled. "If I knew where the road is," said he, "I could get into it again. But I don't know; and I think we must stay here all night."

"We shall freeze to death in an hour!" I cried. I was already chilled to the bone. The wind had made me very drowsy, and I knew that if I slept I should soon be frozen.

"Oh, no!" exclaimed Lars cheerfully. "I am a Norrlander, and Norrlanders never freeze. I went with the men to the bear-hunt last winter, up on the mountains, and we were several nights in the snow. Besides, I know what my father did with a gentleman from Stockholm on this very road, and we'll do it to-night."

"What was it?"

"Let me take care of Axel first," said Lars. "We can spare him some hay and one reindeer-skin."

It was a slow and difficult task to unharness the horse, but we accomplished it at last. Lars then led him under the drooping branches of a fir-tree, tied him to one of them, gave him an armful of hay, and fastened the reindeer-skin upon his back. Axel began to eat, as if perfectly satisfied with the arrangement. The Norrland horses are so accustomed to cold that they seem comfortable in a temperature where one of ours would freeze.

When this was done, Lars spread the remaining hay evenly over the bottom of the sled and covered it with the skins, which he tucked in very firmly on the side toward the wind. Then, lifting them up on the other side, he said: "Now take off your fur coat, quick, lay it over the hay, and then creep under it."

I obeyed as rapidly as possible. For an instant I shuddered in the icy air; but the next moment I lay stretched in the bottom of the sled, sheltered from the storm. I held up the ends of the reindeer-skins while Lars took off his coat and crept in beside me. Then he drew the skins down and pressed the hay against them. When the wind seemed to be entirely excluded Lars said we must pull off our boots, untie our scarfs, and so loosen our clothes that they would not feel tight upon any part of the body. When this was done, and we lay close together, warming each other, I found that the chill gradually passed out of my blood. My hands and feet were no longer numb; a delightful feeling of comfort crept over me; and I lay as snugly as in the best bed. I was surprised to find that, although my head was covered, I did not feel stifled. Enough air came in under the skins to prevent us from feeling oppressed. There was barely room for the two of us to lie, with no chance of turning over or rolling about

In five minutes, I think, we were asleep, and I dreamed of gathering peaches on a warm August day, at home. In fact, I did not wake up thoroughly during the night; neither did Lars, though it seemed to me that we both talked in our sleep. But as I must have talked English and he Swedish, there could have been no connection between our remarks. I remember that his warm, soft hair pressed against my chin, and that his feet reached no farther than my knees. Just as I was beginning to feel a little cramped and stiff from lying so still I was suddenly aroused by the cold wind on my face. Lars had risen up on his elbow, and was peeping out from under the skins.

"I think it must be near six o'clock," he said. "The sky is clear, and I can see the big star. We can start in another hour."

I felt so much refreshed that I was for setting out immediately; but Lars remarked very sensibly that it was not yet possible to find the road. While we were talking, Axel neighed.

"There they are!" cried Lars, and immediately began to put on his boots, his scarf, and heavy coat. I did the same, and by the time we were ready we heard shouts and the crack of whips. We harnessed Axel to the sled, and proceeded slowly in the direction of the sound, which came, as we presently saw, from a company of farmers, out thus early to plough the road. They had six pairs of horses geared to a wooden frame, something like the bow of a ship, pointed in front and spreading out to a breadth of ten or twelve feet. This machine not only cut through the drifts but packed the snow, leaving a good, solid road behind it. After it had passed, we sped along merrily in the cold morning twilight, and in a little more than an hour reached the post-house at Umea, where we found Lars' father prepared to return home. He waited, nevertheless, until Lars had eaten a good warm breakfast, when I said good-bye to both, and went on towards Lapland.

Some weeks afterwards, on my return to Stockholm, I stopped at the same little station. This time the weather was mild and bright, and the father would have gone with me to the next post-house; but I preferred to take my little bed-fellow and sled-fellow. He was so quiet and cheerful and fearless, that although I had been nearly all over the world, and he had never been away from home —although I was a man and he a young boy—I felt that I had learned a lesson from him, and might probably learn many more if I should know him better. We had a merry trip of two or three hours, and then I took leave of Lars forever.

HOW JUNE FOUND MASSA LINKUM

By Elizabeth Stuart Phelps

JUNE laid down her knives upon the scrubbing-board, and stole softly out into the yard. Madame Joilet was taking a nap upstairs, and, for a few minutes at least, the coast seemed to be quite clear.

JUNE AND MASSA LINKUM

Who was June? and who was Madame Joilet?

June was a little girl who had lived in Richmond ever since she could remember, who had never been outside of the city's boundaries, and who had a vague idea that the North lay just above the Chickahominy River and the Gulf of Mexico about a mile below the James. She could not tell A from Z, nor the figure 1 from 40; and whenever Madame Joilet made those funny little curves and dots and blots with pen and ink, in drawing up her bills to send to the lodgers upstairs, June considered that she was moved thereto by witches. Her authority for this theory lay in a charming old woman across the way, who had one tooth, and wore a yellow cap, and used to tell her ghost stories sometimes in the evening.

Somebody asked June once how old she was.

" 'Spect I's a hundred—dunno," she said gravely. Exactly how old she was nobody knew. She was not tall enough to be more than seven, but her face was like the face of a little old woman. It was a queer little face, with thick lips and low forehead, and great mournful eyes. There was something strange about those eyes. Whenever they looked at one, they seemed to cry right out, as if they had a voice. But no one in Richmond cared about that. Nobody cared about June at all. When she was unhappy, no one asked what was the matter; when she was hungry, or cold, or frightened, Madame Joilet laughed at her, and when she was sick she beat her. If she broke a teacup or spilled a mug of coffee, she had her ears boxed, or was shut up in a terrible dark cellar, where the rats were as large as kittens. If she tried to sing a little, in her sorrowful, smothered way, over her work, Madame Joilet shook her for making so much noise. When she stopped, she scolded her for being sulky. Nothing that she could do ever happened to be right; everything was sure to be wrong. She had not half enough to eat, nor half enough to wear. What was worse than that, she had nobody to kiss, and nobody to kiss her; nobody to love her and pet her; nobody in all the wide world to care whether she lived or died, except a half-starved kitten that lived in the wood-shed. For June was black, and a slave; and this Frenchwoman, Madame Joilet, was her mistress.

Exactly what was the use of living under such circumstances June never could clearly see. She cherished a secret notion that, if she could find a little grave all dug out somewhere in a clover-field, she would creep in and hide there. Madame Joilet could not find her then. People who lived in graves were not supposed to be hungry; and, if it were ever so cold, they never shivered. That they could not be beaten was a natural consequence, because there was so much earth between, that you wouldn't feel the stick. The only objection would be leaving Hungry. Hungry was the kitten. June had named it so because it was black. She had an idea that everything black was hungry.

That there had been a war, June gathered from old Creline, who told her the ghost stories. What it was all about, she did not know. Madame Joilet said some terrible giants, called Yankees, were coming down to eat up all the little black girls in

Richmond. Creline said that the Yankees were the Messiah's people, and were coming to set the negroes free. Who the Messiah was, June did not know; but she had heard vague stories from Creline of old-time African princes, who lived in great free forests, and sailed on sparkling rivers in boats of painted bark, and she thought that he must be one of them.

Now, this morning, Creline had whispered mysteriously to June, as she went up the street to sell some eggs for Madame Joilet, that Massa Linkum was coming that very day. June knew nothing about Massa Linkum, and nothing about those grand, immortal words of his which had made every slave in Richmond free; it had never entered Madame Joilet's plan that she should know. No one can tell, reasoned Madame, what notions the little nigger will get if she finds it out. She might even ask for wages, or take a notion to learn to read, or run away, or something. June saw no one; she kept her prudently in the house. Tell her? *No, no, impossible!*

But June had heard the beautiful news this morning, like all the rest; and June was glad, though she had not the slightest idea why. So, while her mistress was safely asleep upstairs, she had stolen out to watch for the wonderful sight— the mysterious sight that every one was waiting to see. She was standing there on tiptoe on the fence, in her little ragged dress, with the black kitten in her arms, when a great crowd turned a corner, and tossed up a cloud of dust, and swept up the street. There were armed soldiers with glittering uniforms, and there were flags flying, and merry voices shouting, and huzzas and blessings distinct upon the air. There were long lines of dusky faces upturned, and wet with happy tears. There were angry faces, too, scowling from windows, and lurking in dark corners.

It swept on, and it swept up, and June stood still, and held her breath to look, and saw, in the midst of it all, a tall man dressed in black. He had a thin, white face, sad-eyed and kindly and quiet, and he was bowing and smiling to the people on either side.

"God bress yer, Massa Linkum, God bress yer!" shouted the happy voices; and then there was a chorus of wild hurrahs, and June laughed outright for glee, and lifted up her little thin voice and cried, "Bress yer, Massa Linkum!" with the rest, and knew no more than the kitty what she did it for.

The great man turned, and saw June standing alone in the sunlight, the fresh wind blowing her ragged dress, her little black shoulders just reaching to the top of the fence, her wide-open, mournful eyes, and the kitten squeezed in her arms. And he looked right at her, oh, so kindly! and gave her a smile all to herself—one of his rare smiles, with a bit of a quiver in it—and bowed, and was gone.

"Take me 'long wid yer, Massa Linkum, Massa Linkum!" called poor June faintly. But no one heard her; and the crowd swept on, and June's voice broke into a cry, and the hot tears came, and she laid her face down on Hungry to hide them. You see, in all her life, no one had ever looked so at June before.

"June, June, come here!" called a sharp voice from the house. But June was sobbing so hard she did not hear.

"*Venez ici—vite, vite!* June! *Voila!* The little nigger will be the death of me. She tears my heart. June, *vite*, I say!"

June started, and jumped down from the fence, and ran into the house with great frightened eyes.

"I just didn't mean to, noways, missus. I want to see Massa Linkum, an' he look at me, an' I done forget eberyting. O missus, don't beat me dis yere time, an' I'll neber—"

But Madame Joilet interrupted her with a box on the ear, and dragged her upstairs. There was a terrible look on Madame's face. Just what happened upstairs, I have not the heart to tell you.

That night, June was crouched, sobbing and bruised, behind the kitchen stove, when Creline came in on an errand for her mistress. Madame Joilet was obliged to leave the room for a few minutes, and the two were alone together. June crawled out from behind the stove. "I see him—I see Massa Linkum, Creline."

"De Lord bress him foreber'n eber. Amen!" exclaimed Creline fervently, throwing up her old thin hands.

June crept a little nearer, and looked all around the room to see if the doors were shut.

"Creline, what's he done gone come down here fur? Am he de Messiah?"

"Bress yer soul, chile! don' ye know better'n *dat* ar?"

"Don' know nuffin," said June sullenly. "Neber

knows nuffin; 'spects I neber's gwine to. Can' go out in de road to find out—she beat me. Can' ask nuffin—she jest gib me a push down cellar. O Creline, der's *sech* rats down dar now—dar is!"

"Yer poor critter!" said Creline, with great contempt for her ignorance. "Why, Massa Linkum, eberybody knows 'bout he. He's done gone made we free—whole heap on we."

"Free!" echoed June, with puzzled eyes.

"Laws, yes, chile; 'pears like yer's drefful stupid. Yer don' b'long—" Creline lowered her voice to a mysterious whisper, and looked carefully at the closed door—"yer don' b'long to Missus Jolly no more dan she b'long to you, an' dat's de trufe now, 'case Massa Linkum say so—God bress him!"

Just then Madame Joilet came back.

"What's that you're talking about?" she said sharply.

"June was jes' sayin' what a heap she tink ob you, missus," said Creline with a grave face.

June lay awake a long time that night, thinking about Massa Linkum, and the wonderful news Creline had brought, and wondering when Madame Joilet would tell her that she was free.

But many days passed, and Madame said nothing about it. Creline's son had left his master and gone North. Creline herself had asked and obtained scanty wages for her work. A little black boy across the street had been sentenced to receive twenty-five lashes for some trifling fault, and they had just begun to whip him in the yard, when a Union officer stepped up and stopped them. A little girl, not a quarter of a mile away, whose name June had often heard, had just found her father, who had been sold away from her years ago, and had come into Richmond with the Yankee soldiers. But nothing had happened to June. Everything went on as in the old days before Master Linkum came. She washed dishes, and scrubbed knives, and carried baskets of wood, so heavy that she tottered under their weight, and was scolded if she dropped so much as a shaving on the floor. She swept the rooms with a broom three times as tall as she was, and had her ears boxed because she could not get the dust up with such tiny hands. She worked and scrubbed and ran on errands from morning to night, till her feet ached so she cried out with the pain. She was whipped and scolded and threatened and frightened and shaken, just as she had been ever since she could remember. She was kept shut up like a prisoner in the house, with Madame Joilet's cold gray eyes forever on her, and her sharp voice forever in her ear. And still not a word was said about Massa Linkum and the beautiful freedom he had given to all such as little June, and not a word did June dare to say.

But June *thought!* Madame Joilet could not help that. If Madame had known just what June was thinking, she would have tried hard to help it.

Well, so the days passed, and the weeks, and still Madame said not a word; and still she whipped and scolded and shook, and June worked and cried, and nothing happened. But June had not done all her thinking for nothing.

One night Creline was going by the house,

when June called to her softly through the fence: "Creline!"

"What's de matter?" said Creline, who was in a great hurry. "I's gwine to fine Massa Linkum—don' yer tell nobody." "Law's a massy, what a young un dat ar chile is!" said Creline, thinking that June had just waked up from a dream, and forthwith forgetting all about her.

Madame Joilet always locked June in her room, which was nothing but a closet with a window in it, and a heap of rags for a bed. On this particular night she turned the key as usual, and then went to her own room at the other end of the house, where she was soon soundly asleep.

About eleven o'clock, when all the house was still, the window of June's closet softly opened. There was a roofed doorway just underneath it, with an old grapevine trellis running up one side of it. A little dark figure stepped out timidly on the narrow, steep roof, clinging with its hands to keep its balance, and then down upon the trellis, which it began to crawl slowly down. The old wood creaked and groaned and trembled, and the little figure trembled and stood still. If it should give way, and fall crashing to the ground!

She stood a minute looking down; then she took a slow, careful step; then another and another, hand under hand upon the bars. The trellis creaked and shook and cracked, but it held on, and June held on, and dropped softly down, gasping and terrified at what she had done, all in a little heap on the grass below.

She lay there a moment perfectly still. She

could not catch her breath at first, and she trembled so that she could not move.

Then she crept along on tiptoe to the wood-shed. She ran a great risk in opening the wood-shed door, for the hinges were rusty, and it creaked with a terrible noise. But Hungry was in there. She could not go without Hungry. She went in, and called in a faint whisper. The kitten knew her, dark as it was, and ran out from the wood-pile with a joyful mew, to rub itself against her dress.

"We's gwine to fine Massa Linkum, you an' me, bof two togeder," said June.

"Pur! pur-r-r!" said Hungry, as if she were quite content; and June took her up in her arms, and laughed softly. How happy they would be, she and Hungry! and how Massa Linkum would smile and wonder when he saw them coming in! and how Madame Joilet would hunt and scold!

She went out of the wood-shed and out of the yard, hushing the soft laugh on her lips, and holding her breath as she passed under her mistress's window. She had heard Creline say that Massa Linkum had gone back to the North; so she walked up the street a little way, and then she turned aside into the vacant squares and unpaved roads, and so out into the fields where no one could see her.

It was very still and very dark. The great trees stood up like giants against the sky, and the wind howled hoarsely through them. It made June think of the bloodhounds that she had seen rushing with horrible yells to the swamps, where hunted slaves were hiding.

"I reckon 'tain't on'y little ways, Hungry," she

said with a shiver; "we'll git dar 'fore long. Don'
be 'fraid."

"Pur! pur-r-r!" said Hungry, nestling her head
in warmly under June's arm.

" 'Spect *you* lub me, Hungry—'spect you does!"

And then June laughed softly once more. What
would Massa Linkum say to the kitty? Had he
ever seen such a kitty in all his life?

So she folded her arms tightly over Hungry's
soft fur, and trudged away into the woods. She
began to sing a little as she walked, in that sorrowful, smothered way, that made Madame Joilet
angry. Ah, that was all over now! There would
be no more scolding and beating, no more tired
days, no more terrible nights spent in the dark and
lonely cellar, no more going to bed without her
supper, and crying herself to sleep. Massa Linkum would never treat her so. She never once
doubted, in that foolish little trusting heart of hers,
that he would be glad to see her, and Hungry too.
Why should she? Was there anyone in all the
world who had looked so at poor June?

So on and away, deep into the woods and
swamps, she trudged cheerily; and she sang low to
Hungry, and Hungry purred to her. The night
passed on and the stars grew pale, the woods deepened and thickened, the swamps were cold and wet,
the brambles scratched her hands and feet.

"It's jes' ober here little ways, Hungry," trying
to laugh. "We'll fine him purty soon. I's terrible
tired an'—sleepy, Hungry."

She sat down there on a heap of leaves to rest,
and laid her head down upon her arm, and Hungry

mewed a little, and curled up in her neck. The
next she knew, the sun was shining. She jumped
up frightened and puzzled, and then she remembered where she was, and began to think of breakfast. But there were no berries but the poisonous
dog-wood, and nothing else to be seen but leaves
and grass and bushes. Hungry snapped up a few
grasshoppers, and looked longingly at an unat-
tainable squirrel, who was flying from tree-top to
tree-top; then they went slowly on.

About noon they came to a bit of a brook. June
scooped up the water in her hands, and Hungry
lapped it with her pink tongue. But there was no
dinner to be found, and no sign of Massa Linkum;
the sun was like a great ball of fire above the tree-
tops, and the child grew faint and weak.

"I didn't 'spect it was so fur," groaned poor
June. "But don't yer be 'feared now, Hungry.
'Pears like we'll fine him bery soon."

The sun went down, and the twilight came. No
supper, and no sign of Massa Linkum. Nothing but the great forest and the swamps and the
darkening shadows and the long, hungry night.
June lay down once more on the damp ground
where the poisonous snakes hid in the bushes, and
hugged Hungry with her weak little arms, and
tried to speak out bravely: "We'll fine him, Hungry, sure, to-morrer. He'll jes' open de door an'
let us right in, he will; an' he'll hab breakfas' all
ready an' waitin'; 'pears like he'll hab a dish ob
milk up in de corner for you now—tink o' dat ar,
Hungry!" and then the poor little voice that tried
to be so brave broke down into a great sob. "Ef

I on'y jes' had one little mouthful now, Hungry!—
on'y one!"

So another night passed, and another morning
came. A faint noise woke June from her uneasy
sleep, when the sun was hardly up. It was Hungry, purring loudly at her ear. A plump young
robin lay quivering between her paws. She was
tossing it to and fro with curves and springs of delight. She laid the poor creature down by June's
face, looking proudly from June to it, saying as
plainly as words could say, "Here's a fine breakfast. I got it on purpose for you. Why don't you
eat, for pity's sake? There are plenty more where
this came from!"

But June turned away her eyes and moaned; and
Hungry, in great perplexity, made away with the
robin herself.

Presently June crawled feebly to her feet, and
pushed on through the brambles. The kitten,
purring in her arms, looked so happy and contented with her breakfast that the child cried out at
the sight of it in sudden pain.

"O, I tought we'd git dar 'fore now, an' I tought
he'd jes' be so glad to see us!"—and then presently,
"He jes' look so kinder smilin' right out ob his eyes,
Hungry!"

A bitter wind blew from the east that day, and
before noon the rain was falling, dreary and chilly
and sharp. It soaked June's feet and ragged dress,
and pelted in her face. The wind blew against her,
and whirled about her, and tossed her to and fro—
she was such a little thing, and so weak now and
faint.

507

Just as the early twilight fell from the leaden sky, and the shadows began to skulk behind the bushes, and the birds gathered to their nests with sleepy twitter, she tripped over a little stone, fell weakly to the ground, and lay still. She had not the strength to get to her feet again.

But somehow June felt neither troubled nor afraid. She lay there with her face upturned to the pelting rain, watching it patter from leaf to leaf, listening to the chirp of the birds in the nests, listening to the crying of the wind. She liked the sound. She had a dim notion that it was like an old camp-meeting hymn that she had heard Creline sing sometimes. She never understood the words, but the music came back like a dream. She wondered if Massa Linkum ever heard it. She thought he *looked like it*. She should like to lie there all night and listen to it; and then in the morning they would go on and find him—in the morning; it would come very soon.

The twilight deepened, and the night came on. The rain fell faster, and the sharp wind cried aloud. "It's bery cold," said June sleepily, and turned her face over to hide it on the kitten's warm, soft fur. "Goo' night, Hungry. We'll git dar to-morrer. We's mos' dar, Hungry."

Hungry curled up close to her cold, wet cheek —Hungry did not care how black it was—with a happy answering mew; but June said nothing more.

The rain fell faster, and the sharp wind cried aloud. The kitten woke from a nap, and purred for her to stir and speak; but June said nothing more.

Still the rain fell, and the wind cried; and the long night and the storm and the darkness passed, and the morning came.

Hungry stirred under June's arm, and licked her face, and mewed piteously at her ear. But June's arm lay still, and June said no word.

Somewhere, in a land where there was never slave and never mistress, where there were no more hungry days and frightened nights, little June was laughing softly, and had found some one to love her at last. And so she did not find Massa Linkum after all? Ah!—who would have guessed it? To that place where June had gone, where there are no masters and no slaves, he had gone before her.

And don't I suppose his was the first face she saw, as she passed through the storm and the night to that waiting, beautiful place? And don't I suppose he smiled as he had smiled before, and led her gently to that other Face, of which poor little June had known nothing in all her life? Of course I do.

THE STORY OF A FOREST FIRE

By Raymond S. Spears

FOR more than six weeks no rain had fallen along the southwest side of the Adirondacks. The ground was parched. In every direction from Seaberry Settlement fires had been burning through the forest, but as yet the valley of the West Canada had escaped.

But one night a careless man threw a burning match into a brush-heap. When morning came the west wind, blowing up the valley, was ash-laden and warm with the fire that was coming eastward toward the settlement in a line a mile wide.

Soon after daybreak Lem Lawson met the fire on his way to Noblesborough, and warned the settlement of its danger. One man hastened to Noblesborough for the fire-warden, two went up the West Canada to the lumber-camps. The rest of the male population, including boys, hastened down the main road to an old log trail.

It was hoped the fire might be stopped at the open the road afforded.

With hoes and shovels the men dug a trench through the loam to the sand, scattering the dirt over the leaves toward the fire. When the first flames came along, they redoubled their efforts amid the flying sparks and suffocating smoke, but without avail. The sparks and great pieces of flaming birch curls carried the flames over the road into the woods beyond the men, fairly surrounding them with fire.

The men could only go before it, pausing now and then to throw dirt on a spark. Those who lived in the settlement glanced from side to side, wondering if the fire would cross the brook, where they now determined to make another and the last possible stand.

The settlement was built along the brink of a steep side-hill. The bed of the stream was only a few feet wide—chiefly sand-bar and dry boulders at this time—and beyond it, toward the fire, was a flat, or bottom, sixty rods wide, averaging not two feet above the bed of the brook.

Should the fire cross the brook, it would climb the hill and burn the buildings. Then it would sweep across the narrow fields of grass, or go round the ends of the settlement clearing, into the "big woods."

One of the fire-fighters was Will Borson, son of the man who had thrown the match, and as he fought with his hoe along the road he heard the men on each side of him cursing his father by name for his carelessness. More than once these men turned on Will, and told him he ought to put that fire out, since his father was to blame for it.

Will did his best. Sparks burned holes in his shirt; a flare of sheet fire from a brush-heap singed his eyelashes and the hair over his forehead. When old Ike Frazier cried out, "It's no use here any more, boys!" Will was the last one to duck his head and run for the road up the creek to the settlement.

Half a dozen men were detailed to go to the houses and help the women carry the furniture and other household goods out in the fields to the watering-troughs; the rest hastened to the brook and scattered along it, and threw water on the brush at the edge, hoping the flames would be deadened when they came.

Among them worked Will Borson, thinking with all his might and looking up and down the creek as if the dry gray boulders, with the scant thread of water oozing down among them, would give him some inspiration. The width of the stream was only a few feet on an average, and twenty feet at the widest pools, over which the flame and sparks would quickly jump.

The fire reached the flat at the foot of the ridge and came toward the brook in jumps. The men worked faster than ever with their ten-quart pails. Old Ike Frazier glanced up the stream, and saw Will leaning on his hoe-handle, doing nothing.

"Hi there!" yelled the man. "Get to work!"

"You tell the men they want to be looking out!" Will called back. "Something'll happen pretty quick!" With that he dropped his hoe and went climbing up the side-hill toward his home at the top. Mrs. Borson was just piling the last of her bedding on the wagon when she saw Will coming toward her. He unhitched the horse from the wagon, and had the harness scattered on the ground before his mother could control herself enough to cry:

"Those things'll be burned here! What are you taking the horse for—we—we—"

Then she sank to the ground and cried, while Will's younger brothers and sisters joined in.

Will did not stop to say anything, but leaped to the back of the horse, and away he went up the road, to the amazement of those who were taking their goods from the houses. But he was soon in the woods above the settlement and out of sight of every one.

He was headed for the dam. He had thought to open the little sluice at the bottom of it, which would add to the volume of the water in the stream —raise it a foot, perhaps.

He reached the dam, and prying at the gate, opened the way. A stream of water two feet square shot from the bottom of the dam and went sloshing down among the rocks.

"That water'll help a lot," he thought. Then he heard the roar of the fire down the brook, and saw a huge dull, brick-colored flash as a big hemlock went up in flame. The amount of water gushing from the gate of the dam seemed suddenly small and useless. It would not fill the brookbed. In a little shanty a hundred yards away were the quarrying tools used in getting out the stone for the Cardin house. To this Will ran with all his speed.

With an old ax that was behind the shanty he broke down the door. Inside he picked up a full twelve-pound box of dynamite, and bored a hole the size of his finger into one side. Then with a fuse and cap in one hand and the box under his arm, he hurried back to the dam.

He climbed down the ladder to the bottom of the dam, and fixing the fuse to the cap, ran it into the hole he had bored till it was well among the sawdust and sticks of dynamite. He cut the fuse to two minutes' length, and carried the box back among the big key logs that held the dam. He was soon ready. He jammed the box under water among beams where it would stick. A match started the fuse going, and then Will climbed the ladder and ran for safety.

In a few moments the explosion came. Will heard the beams in the gorge tumbling as the dam gave way, and the water behind was freed. Away it went, washing and pounding down the narrow ravine, toward the low bottom.

The fire-fighters heard the explosion and paused, wondering, to listen. The next instant the roar of the water came to their ears, and the tremble caused by logs and boulders rolling with the flood was felt. Then every man understood what was done, for they had been log-drivers all their lives, and knew the signs of a loosed sluice-gate or of a broken jam.

They climbed the steep bank toward the buildings, to be above the flood-line, yelling warnings that were half-cheers.

In a few moments the water was below the mouth of the gorge, and then it rushed over the low west bank of the brook and spread out on the wide flat where the fire was raging. For a minute clouds of steam and loud hissing marked the progress of the wave, and then the brush-heaps from edge to edge of the valley bottom were covered and the fire was drowned.

The fires left in the trees above the high-water mark and the flames back on the ridge still thrust and flared, but were unable to cross the wide, wet flood-belt. The settlement and the "big woods" beyond were saved.

Sol Cardin reached the settlement on the following day, and heard the story of the fire. In response to an offer from Will, he replied:

"No, my boy, you needn't pay for the dam by working or anything else. I'm in debt to you for saving my timber above the settlement, instead." Then he added, in a quiet way characteristic of him, "It seems a pity if wit like yours doesn't get its full growth."